The aircraft carriers *Victorious*, *Ark Royal* and *Hermes* steaming in line ahead

B.R. 1938

NAVAL RATINGS
HANDBOOK

Revised 1964

(*Supersedes B.R. 1938 dated 1958*)

Reprinted 1972

(*N/CT 41/71*)

January 1965   *By Command of the Defence Council*

MINISTRY OF DEFENCE
Naval Training Department

T.402/63

CHANGES

Change No.	Authority	Date of Insertion in this Copy	Initials

FOREWORD

This book has been written for the benefit of all men in all Branches of the Royal Navy and is issued to each rating when he joins. It contains brief descriptions of the organization and administration of the Service, its Branches and Reserves, the routine and organization of a ship, and other matters which all ratings should know. Many of the subjects included are set forth in general and elementary terms only, and in order to obtain a thorough knowledge of any particular subject the relevant books and publications must be consulted. Some of the more important of these are quoted at the beginning of the chapters concerned.

All ratings should be sailors, no matter to which Branch they belong, and no warship has room for passengers who are indifferent to what is going on around them. A sailor should not only know his own job, but he should understand what is going on all about him. This book is designed to give a rating sufficient information to enable him to:

be safe at sea,

lend a hand in an emergency,

take an intelligent interest, and play his full part, in all the activities of a ship's daily life,

understand how life in the Service is organized.

Just as the driver of a motor vehicle must develop road sense and be continuously alert, so must a sailor develop a sea sense, conduct himself in a seamanlike manner and be always ready to act at any time to avoid injury to his ship, his messmates or himself.

Read and study this book so that you may know better how to live in a warship and will therefore be prepared to meet the many calls that will be made upon you. In doing so you will improve your general knowledge of the Service to which you belong—and you will become a more useful shipmate.

CONTENTS

CONTENTS

CHAPTER 1

The Royal Navy and its Administration

THE ROLE OF THE NAVY

From early times England has been a maritime power. As the centuries have gone by she has extended her maritime affairs all round the world, and until the advent of air travel the sea was our only link with the Commonwealth. Even today, despite the aeroplane, our survival as a nation depends upon keeping open the sea routes for our trade and our food. The Royal Navy has long been the symbol of our maritime power. This is still true today, even though we have fewer ships in service and fewer overseas bases. The Royal Navy must not only be a fighting force, but also one capable of meeting with speed and efficiency any emergency in any part of the world where Great Britain has interests.

The role of the Navy is considered under the wider aspects of the country's defence policy. This policy, together with the Defence Estimates, is brought before Parliament annually. Both are published in Government White Papers.

The Royal Navy must adapt itself to both peace and war, two roles which, though related, can be defined separately as follows:

In peacetime. In peacetime the Navy must be available to help carry out the Government's policy, which may involve:

Small-scale internal security operations,

Support of allies against aggression,

Working with our allies in NATO, CENTO and SEATO,

Assisting Commonwealth countries which are the victims of external aggression,

Providing a fighting force at sea in an emergency; or an amphibious group, which might include a commando ship, an assault ship, landing ships and escorts,

Policing the high seas and friendly coastal waters; performing anti-piracy patrols and Fishery Protection patrol duties,

Assisting ships in difficulty at sea and authorities ashore in, for example, a national disaster, such as an earthquake,

Visiting foreign ports where, by its presence, the Navy can spread the principles in which we believe and by which we live,

The custody of the Deterrent.

In wartime. In wartime the Navy will have the role of executing the Government's policy, both nationally and in conjunction with our allies. This may involve:

The destruction of enemy sea-borne forces and the total disruption of enemy submarine effort,

The support of our land army and air forces, especially in the event of an amphibious assault,

The protection of merchant shipping and its ports, and the provision of safe channels for its use,

The deployment of the Deterrent.

I

A*

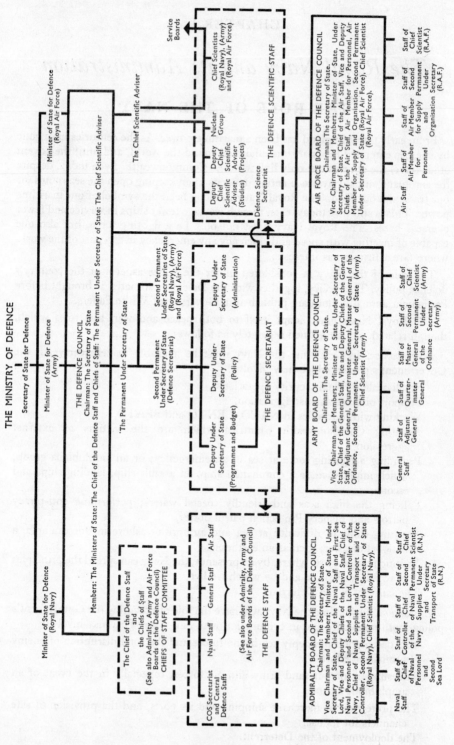

FIG. I-I. The Ministry of Defence

THE ADMINISTRATION OF THE NAVY

The administration of the Royal Navy is necessarily complicated, but its general principles should be understood by all members of the Service.

The Cabinet, Parliament and the nation

The nation elects its representatives to Parliament at a General Election, and from the members of the party in power a Government is formed. At the head of the Government is the Cabinet, which consists of the Prime Minister and other Cabinet Ministers, including the Secretary of State for Defence. Under the latter, and housed in one building, is the unified Ministry of Defence, the organisation of which is shown in Fig. 1-1. This Ministry is organised on a Service basis, i.e. each of the three Services has a Board of Council, with its own junior Minister and Chief of Staff. The Secretary of State for Defence is the chairman of each Board, though normally he asks each Minister of Defence for the individual Service to act for him.

The Admiralty Board of the Defence Council

In the 16th century the control of the Royal Navy was entrusted to a personage called the Lord High Admiral. This office was for a long time carried out by the Board of Admiralty. The Sovereign now holds this office, but the actual management of the Royal Navy is carried out by the Admiralty Board of the Defence Council. This Board is directly responsible to the Sovereign and—through the Secretary of State for Defence, the Cabinet and Parliament—to the nation for the administration of the Royal Navy. The members of the Board are:

The Minister of Defence for the Royal Navy, who is a member of Parliament. He is responsible, through the Secretary of State for Defence, to the Cabinet and Parliament for the administration of the Navy.

The Sea Lords and the Naval Members of the Admiralty Board of the Defence Council, who are all senior officers of Flag rank (Admiral of the Fleet, Admiral or Vice-Admiral) appointed to assist the Minister of State for the Navy on all professional matters. Each member is allotted certain spheres of responsibility in the general administration of the Navy.

The Chief of the Naval Staff and First Sea Lord, who is the principal naval adviser to Her Majesty's Government and is responsible for the general policy and conduct of naval affairs. He has two assistants—the Vice-Chief of the Naval Staff and the Deputy Chief of the Naval Staff.

The Vice-Chief of the Naval Staff, who is responsible to the Chief of the Naval Staff for operational policy, planning and direction; general policy, strategy and operational plans; naval defence of ports and bases; disposition of ships; protection of trade and merchant shipping.

The Deputy Chief of the Naval Staff, who is responsible for advising the Chief of the Naval Staff on tactics, technical policy and fighting efficiency, and Naval Air matters.

The Chief of Naval Personnel and Second Sea Lord, who is responsible for the recruiting and administration of officers, ratings, Royal Marines, and members of the Women's Royal Naval Service, including the Reserve forces, and all matters relating to them, e.g. manning, training, welfare, etc.

The Controller of the Navy, who is responsible for the requirements of the Royal Navy, the provision of ships, aircraft, weapons, dockyards, machinery, facilities, and associated research and development. As his title implies, he controls the spending of the money allocated for the provision of the above items.

The Chief of Naval Supplies and Vice-Controller, who assists the Controller and is responsible for seeing that the Navy is fed, and is supplied with the ammunition and technical stores to enable it to fight. He controls the transport of personnel and materials.

The Parliamentary Under-Secretary of State for Defence for the Royal Navy, who is also a member of Parliament in the same way as is the Minister of Defence for the Navy. As deputy to the Minister of Defence for the Navy, he is responsible for general Parliamentary duties. He is also Chairman of the Naval Finance Committee and the Naval Industrial Council.

The Chief Scientist (Royal Navy), who is responsible for all aspects of naval defence which are affected by scientific advance and, in particular, defence research and weapon development.

The Second Permanent Under-Secretary of State (Royal Navy), who is a civilian and a high-ranking officer in the Civil Service. He is responsible for the arrangement of the business of the Board. He is also responsible for the provision and administration of the Civil Staff. As 'Accounting Officer of Navy Votes' he is responsible for the proper expenditure of the monies voted for the upkeep of the Navy.

The Defence Estimates

The cost of the country's defence is paid from the revenues of the country, which are derived by direct and indirect taxation. The passing of the Defence Estimates (part of which is allocated for the upkeep of the Navy) by Parliament each year determines the number of officers, men, ships and shore establishments, pay and allowances for the Navy for the following twelve months.

Naval departments

The administration of the Royal Navy is carried out through Departments and Divisions, each of which is under the Directorship of a senior naval officer or senior Civil Servant, who is responsible to one of the members of the Admiralty Board of the Defence Council for the work of his Department or Division. Departments or Divisions do not hold any command or jurisdiction over the Fleet. They advise and assist in the general operation and administration of the Navy.

The Fleet

All the remainder of the Navy, consisting of officers and men serving in ships and most shore establishments, is known broadly by the general term 'the Fleet'. The high seas are divided into various spheres of jurisdiction and administration, each under the overall command of a Commander-in-Chief, who is responsible to the Admiralty Board of the Defence Council for all under his sphere of command. These spheres comprise all the Home Ports and all Fleets and Stations at home and abroad. H.M. Dockyards and Civil Establishments all come within a Command, though not regarded as part of 'the Fleet'.

Fleets, stations and squadrons. Each squadron, dockyard and shore establishment is under the command of its respective Flag or Senior Officer, who is responsible to his Commander-in-Chief for the squadron or establishment which he commands.

The ship. Finally, there is the ship, which is under the command of her Captain. He is responsible to his Flag or Senior Officer for his ship and the conduct of all who serve in her.

ADMINISTRATION AND REGULATIONS

The administration of the Royal Navy is carried out by regulations and instructions issued at intervals. These must apply to a ship and her company no matter where she goes in the world, and must allow for the different situations in which they find themselves. They must therefore comply with both the law of this country and International Law. Naval Regulations cover the general administration of the Navy. They apply to all persons of the Royal Navy and to anyone who embarks in one of H.M. ships or who serve in places ashore, at home and abroad which come under the jurisdiction of the Admiralty Board of the Defence Council, e.g. dockyards, naval canteens, etc.

The Naval Discipline Act

This is an Act of Parliament which lays down the general rules for the conduct and discipline of officers and men of the Royal Navy. The first part consists of the *Articles of War*, which specify the various punishable offences and their respective penalties. A copy of these articles is displayed in a prominent position in all ships and shore establishments. The remainder of the Act deals with the regulations for enforcing the details of the Articles of War.

The Queen's Regulations and Admiralty Instructions (Q.R. & A.I.)

These supplement the Naval Discipline Act and include all the various orders and instructions on a multitude of matters concerning every detail in the general government of the Royal Navy. They are available for study in the reference libraries of every ship or shore establishment.

The Navy List

This shows all ships, shore establishments, dockyards, etc. under the Admiralty Board of the Defence Council's control and the names of all officers of the Royal Navy and the Royal Naval Reserves, whether on the Active List or retired. The Appendix to the Navy List gives details of pay, pensions, gratuities, honours, decorations, medals, uniform regulations, etc. The Navy List and its Appendix are also available in all ships' libraries.

Defence Council Instructions (Royal Navy)

Defence Council Instructions (Royal Navy) are published weekly in pamphlet form and are issued to all ships and shore establishments. They provide the means for the rapid circulation of instructions concerning current administration and technical equipment of the Royal Navy. A special Notice Board edition draws the attention of the ship's company to orders of general interest.

Customs of the Service

It would not be practicable to lay down exact and detailed instructions covering every method of interpreting all the various regulations, but these methods have been regularised by custom, which has been built up from the experience gained through the centuries in which the Royal Navy has been in existence. These customs strike the balance between respect for individuality, authority, and consideration for others. Thus they enable officers and men of varying degrees of responsibility and of many professions and trades to live happily together on board a ship while at the same time maintaining the requisite degree of discipline towards each other.

RANK AND COMMAND

Command

This is the term used to indicate the authority exercised by all officers and ratings, according to their rank and seniority, over their subordinates in order to maintain good order and naval discipline in any normal activity, work or undertaking. Officers and ratings take command in the order of their rank or seniority. In the case of equal seniority, this is in the following order:

General List
Royal Marines (except R.M. Band Service)
Special Duties List
Supplementary List
Royal Naval Reserve

Seagoing command is exercised by officers entitled to command seagoing ships of the Royal Navy.

Military command is exercised by officers entitled to command all non-seagoing ships, establishments, units, boats and aircraft.

THE CHAIN OF COMMAND

In seagoing ships this descends through those officers entitled to seagoing command. In naval establishments the chain of command descends from the Captain to the Executive Officer, except for Naval Air Stations, where it descends to either the Executive Officer or the Commander (Air), whichever is the senior. It then descends to other officers entitled to exercise military command.

Flag Officer. This is an officer of the rank of Rear-Admiral and above exercising command and authorised by the Admiralty Board of the Defence Council to fly a flag.

Precedence of Services

This is in the order—Royal Navy, Army, Royal Air Force. The relative ranks in each are shown in Plate 1, together with the distinguishing badges and lace worn by the officers who hold these ranks.

CHAPTER 2

Branches, Specialisations, Rank and Badges

See *The Queen's Regulations and Admiralty Instructions*

BRANCHES AND SPECIALISATIONS

The prime object of a ship is to fight, and to do this she must be in good working order, be properly maintained, well supplied, and provided with good information. She therefore needs men to man and fight her weapons and others to steam, maintain and supply her. Neither group would serve any purpose without the other. The man at the weapon needs food and clothing, and the weapon itself must work properly and be supplied with ammunition: both must be carried to and from the scene of action. The members of a ship's company depend upon one another to achieve success in any action or undertaking.

In a busy household every member has to lend a hand with the day-to-day tasks which make up the running of a home. In a ship the same thing applies: domestic and communal duties are shared by everybody on board, for there is no room for a 'hotel staff' in a ship. Each section of a ship is the responsibility of a department, and where departments share a section they share responsibility for it. Likewise, general duties throughout the ship are shared by all departments.

The efficiency of a ship depends upon the efficiency of the individual departments and co-operation between them. Certain aspects of naval life are the concern of everybody, but it is also vital that each man should appreciate the work done outside his department. The following paragraphs give a brief outline of the various branches and specialisations in the Royal Navy and the purposes they fulfil.

OFFICERS

General List (G.L.)

General List officers are trained as cadets at Britannia Royal Naval College, Dartmouth, having entered direct from school or as specially selected ratings called 'Upper Yardmen'. Both groups are selected for their powers of leadership, character, ability and educational standard (see also Chapter 4).

The General List officers are selected to specialise as Seamen, Engineers or Supply and Secretariat specialists, and sub-specialise where applicable, as shown below.

On promotion to commander some seaman specialist officers are further selected for the Post List, from which operational appointments and appointments to seagoing command are made; other officers may, when appointed for 'seaman duties', fill operational appointments and exercise seagoing command.

SUB-SPECIALISATION

For seamen
  Torpedo and Anti-Submarine Warfare
  Navigation and Direction
  Gunnery
  Communications
  Submarines
  Pilots, Observers and Air Traffic Controllers

For marine engineers
Air Engineers
Mechanical Engineers
Weapons and Radio Engineers
Submarines

The Supply and Secretariat specialisation has no sub-specialisation for General List officers, but some officers qualify in legal matters as barristers.

Supplementary List (S.L.)

Supplementary List officers are entered on short-service engagements in branches that have a special requirement for junior officers, e.g. Seaman, Electrical and the Fleet Air Arm. The Seaman and Air Crew Supplementary Lists are open to ratings with the necessary qualifications.

Special Duties List (S.D.)

Ratings who show exceptional powers of leadership, character and technical ability may be selected for promotion to the Special Duties List. They carry out duties similar to those carried out by General List officers, but in general they are employed in appointments where their specialist skill and experience are most useful.

SPECIAL DUTIES SPECIALISATIONS AND SUB-SPECIALISATIONS

Air Electrical	Direction	Radio
Air Ordnance	Electrical	Regulating
Air Radio	Gunnery	Shipwright
Aviation	Hydrography	Stores
Boatswain	Mechanical Engineering	Torpedo and Anti-Submarine
Catering	Navigation	Warfare
Clearance Diver	Ordnance	Weapons and Radio
Communications	Physical Training	Writers
Cookery	Radar and Direction (P.R.)	

RATINGS

Ratings are selected for branches (Seamen, Engineers, Supply and Secretariat, Medical, Fleet Air Arm, etc.) upon entering the Royal Navy. They qualify further by specialising within their branches, and again by sub-specialising within those specialisations; for example, a rating may belong to the Seaman branch, specialise in Torpedo and Anti-Submarine Warfare and sub-specialise as an underwater control rating.

In general, it will be seen that branches, specialisations and sub-specialisations of officers and ratings correspond as shown below, and for the purposes of this chapter the ratings system will be followed.

OFFICERS

Specialisation	*Sub-specialisation*
Seaman	G, T.A.S., N, etc.
Engineering	
Supply and Secretariat	
Medical, etc.	

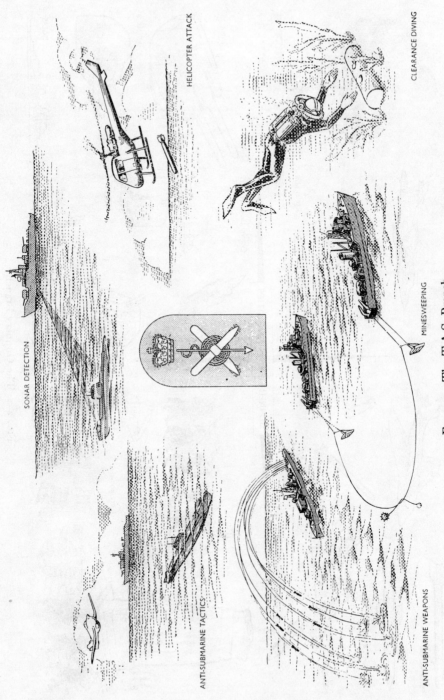

HELICOPTER ATTACK

CLEARANCE DIVING

SONAR DETECTION

MINESWEEPING

ANTI-SUBMARINE TACTICS

ANTI-SUBMARINE WEAPONS

Fig. 2-1. The T.A.S. Branch

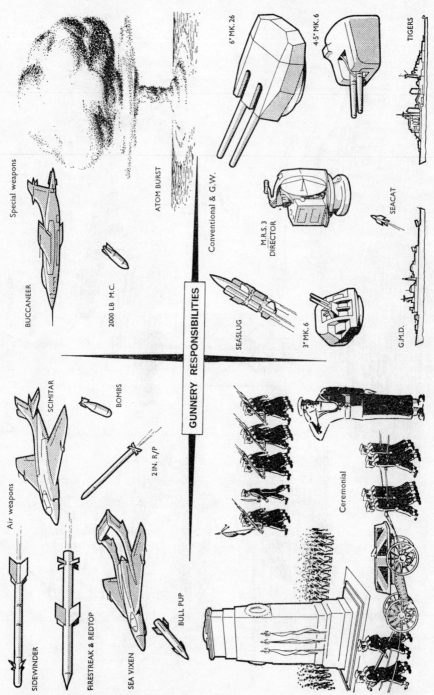

Fig. 2-2. The Gunnery Branch

RATINGS

Branch	Specialisation	Sub-specialisation
Seaman	T.A.S.	U.C., U.W., etc.
	G	G.L., G.A., etc.
	etc.	etc.

Engineers
Supply and Secretariat
Medical, etc.

Ratings' New Entry training is divided into two parts:

Part I. The basic naval training required by all new entries of all branches.

Part II. The basic professional training in the branch or specialisation for which they have been entered or selected.

Seaman Branch

Although seamen have specialisations (which will be described later), their collective employment is concerned with the work on the upper deck of a ship. This includes the use, care and maintenance of the upper deck structure, its equipment and fittings. They are the experts in seamanship drills in harbour and at sea, the handling of boats, rigging, ropes, anchors and cables and replenishment at sea, as well as the manning of the ship's armament. They also specialise in the various types of weapon and weapon control systems in the ship.

Torpedo and Anti-Submarine Warfare (T.A.S.)

The T.A.S. specialisation is responsible for all forms of underwater warfare. This includes:

(a) The operation of anti-submarine weapons, anti-submarine weapon control equipment and torpedoes. Some of the weapons and associated equipment are carried in helicopters.

(b) Anti-submarine warfare tactics, offensive and defensive. This involves the use of ships' aircraft and submarines.

(c) Minelaying and mine-countermeasures, which include all forms of dealing with mines (detection, sweeping, destruction and rendering them safe).

(d) Diving in all its aspects, both shallow and deep diving. The training and employment of underwater swimmers.

(e) The provision of T.A.S. ratings for naval anti-submarine helicopters.

Gunnery (G)

Gunnery in the Royal Navy covers all weapons designed to strike the enemy in the air, on the ground and above the waterline. There are five major responsibilities of the Gunnery specialisation:

Air weapons. These are used by fighter aircraft to shoot down attacking bombers and by strike aircraft against enemy ships and shore targets.

Nuclear weapons.

Guided weapons. Both long- and short-range guided missiles fired by our ships at enemy targets, ships and aircraft.

Guns. All guns and gun systems in the Service.

Training in aid to the civil power, and ceremonial. This includes everything from riot-quelling in remote trouble-spots throughout the world to parading for the Queen in the Guard at the Royal Tournament.

Radar Plot (R.P.)

Ratings in the Radar Plot specialisation man the Action Information Organization of ships at sea. The captain of a ship relies upon this organization to enable him to appreciate the tactical situation and to assist in the control of aircraft and weapons. Information is passed to the Action Information Organization from many sources, such as radar contacts, wireless signals, sonar contacts, visual sightings, etc. The A.I.O. ensures that this information is quickly and clearly displayed for the benefit of the Command. The ships of the future will contain many advances in design and equipment and the Action Information Organization will become even more important.

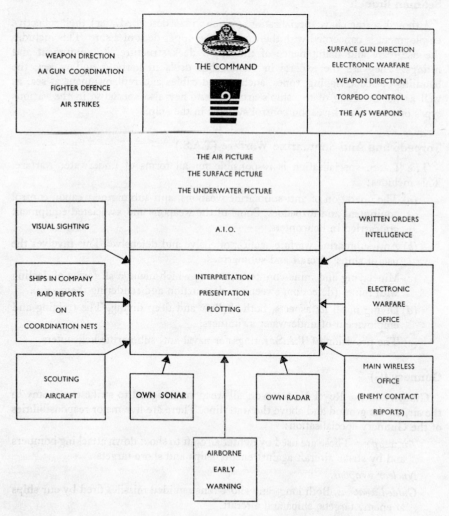

FIG. 2-3. The Action Information Organization

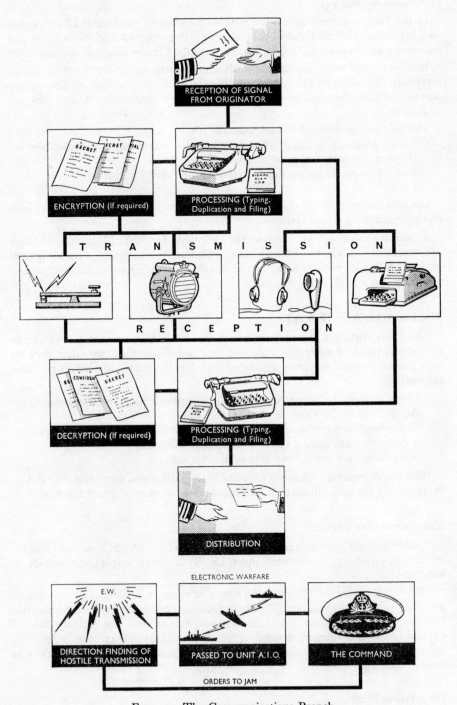

FIG. 2-4. The Communications Branch

Communications (C)

In the Navy communications are vital to the efficient conduct of all operations and exercises. The responsibility of ensuring that communications achieve and maintain a high standard of efficiency rests with the Communications specialisation.

Ratings of the Communications specialisation are responsible for the transmission, reception, processing and distribution of signals, from the time they are first written out to the time they are finally received by the authorities to whom they are addressed.

The primary methods of communications are:

Visual means, i.e. flashing light, and to a lesser extent flags and semaphore
Wireless telegraph, using the morse code
Radio teletype, including the operation of high-speed teleprinters
Voice.

Communications ratings also encrypt and decrypt classified messages, using both machine and book crypto systems.

A certain number of ratings are selected for the Electronic Warfare sub-specialisation, which operates all electronic warfare equipment. This equipment enables radar and wireless signals to be detected, a bearing to be obtained and, if necessary, the signals to be jammed.

The Fleet Air Arm (F.A.A.)

The Fleet Air Arm provides air power in areas which are out of effective or economical range of shore-based aircraft, or it reinforces the latter when they are only present in small numbers. Equipped with highly versatile aircraft, it performs the tasks of:

Close air support for the Army and Commandos in an amphibious assault
Air defence of the Fleet
Long-range reconnaisance and strike (The modern naval strike aircraft are capable of attacking a target with nuclear weapons.)
Anti-submarine patrols and anti-submarine warfare.

With the decreasing number of overseas bases available to our forces, the F.A.A. is frequently the only effective air striking force in support of ground forces.

The Submarine Service

The Submarine Service is manned by volunteers from certain specified branches of the Royal Navy. Volunteers must be fit in every respect for service in submarines.

This Service mans and maintains the navy's submarines, nuclear and conventional, and they will also man nuclear 'Polaris' submarines operating in the deterrent role (see also page 39). Apart from the 'Polaris' submarines, the primary role of submarines is anti-submarine warfare. Their operations also include minelaying, offensives against enemy shipping and warships, and special operations close to enemy territory.

Regulating Branch

The Regulating staff are carried in a ship to assist all personnel on board. Just as one might say in London 'Ask a policeman', so one might say 'Ask the Regulating

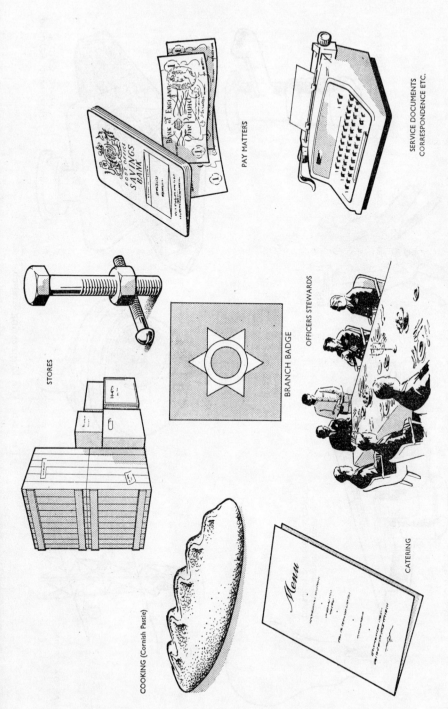

PAY MATTERS

SERVICE DOCUMENTS CORRESPONDENCE ETC.

STORES

BRANCH BADGE

OFFICERS STEWARDS

COOKING (Cornish Pastie)

CATERING

FIG. 2-5. The Supply and Secretariat Branch

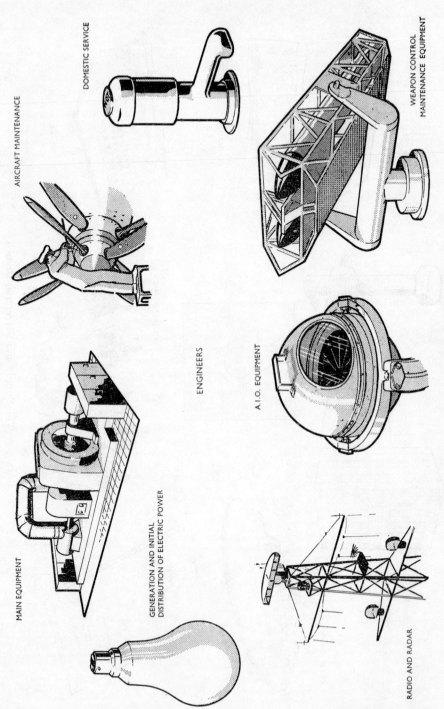

DOMESTIC SERVICE

AIRCRAFT MAINTENANCE

WEAPON CONTROL
MAINTENANCE EQUIPMENT

ENGINEERS

A.I.O. EQUIPMENT

MAIN EQUIPMENT

GENERATION AND INITIAL
DISTRIBUTION OF ELECTRIC POWER

RADIO AND RADAR

FIG. 2-6. The Engineering Branch

staff' in a ship. Their members are recruited from selected volunteers from all branches. Their work includes dealing with and making arrangements for:

Requestmen and defaulters
Leave
Movements of personnel to and from a ship (victualling and checking)
Handling of baggage
Mail
Shore patrols.

They also co-operate with the civilian police and H.M. Customs in the observance of the law and the customs regulations in the Service.

Supply and Secretariat Branch (S. and S.)

The work of this Branch covers many different aspects, all of which contribute to the overall efficiency of the ship. It includes:

Supply, preparation and cooking of all food
Supply and distribution of all stores (except armament stores) used to maintain ships and aircraft
Catering in officers' messes and attendance on officers
The 'office work' in a ship
Running of pay accounts for the ship's company.

In action these men carry out a variety of duties, including those of damage control parties, first aid teams, and communication and supply parties below decks.

Engineers (Eng.)

Engineer officers sub-specialise as follows:

Marine engineering, concerned with the general working of the ship's machinery;
Weapon and radio engineering, concerned with the working of the ship's armament (including radar) and its associated equipment;
Air engineering (Eng.(M) and Eng.(L)), concerned with the maintenance of the Fleet Air Arm's aircraft and supporting equipment and the maintenance of such airfield services as radar, navigational aids and communications.

MARINE ENGINEERS (ENG.M(ME) AND ENG.L(ME))

The Marine Engineers are responsible for the main propulsion units (steam, diesel, gas turbine or nuclear) of a ship, and for propulsion and hull electrical equipment. All domestic services are their responsibility, such as:

Ventilation and air conditioning plants
Refrigeration and distillation plants
Galley equipment
Internal communications connected with the Engineering department and Nuclear, Biological and Chemical Defence (NBCD).

They check, store and distribute all liquid fuel within the ship. The hull and ship's structure is the responsibility of the Marine Engineer, even though in some ships he may delegate this to a shipwright officer or a shipwright. The Marine Engineering branch man the main machinery compartments, and their members also form the pumping, flooding and fire parties in the ship's NBCD organization. Selected officers, after training, undertake these duties in submarines.

WEAPONS AND RADIO ENGINEERS (ENG.M(WR) OR ENG.L(WR))

The Weapon and Radio Engineers maintain all the ship's fighting equipment, navigational aids and communications equipment. Most of this machinery is driven by electricity and its upkeep depends upon a high degree of electrical knowledge. Their responsibilities include:

Generation and distribution of electrical power
All weapons and associated equipment
Gyros
Ship's logs
Plotting tables
Signalling equipment
Radio and radar equipment
Broadcasts and intercommunication equipment within the ship, except those
which are the responsibility of the Marine Engineer
Lighting and heating.

Here again selected officers, after training, undertake these duties in submarines.

AIR ENGINEERS (Eng.M AND Eng.L)

The Air Engineers maintain and repair complicated strike, fighter, anti-submarine and Airborne Early Warning aircraft of the Fleet Air Arm, ashore and afloat, and many types of training and communications aircraft ashore. In support of these aircraft there is a mass of equipment and weapons (including guided missiles) which the air engineers must maintain—anything from components in the aircraft to larger services such as fuel installations, airfield radar, navigational aids and communications, and aircraft salvage.

Some Eng.(M)(AE) officers qualify as pilots and some Eng.(L) officers as observers.

Shipwright Branch

The Shipwrights are responsible for the structure of the ship and its fittings. This includes the ship's plumbing systems. They are the experts in ship construction, hull maintenance and damage repair and they form an essential part of the ship's NBCD organization.

ROYAL MARINES, WOMEN'S NAVAL SERVICES AND NAVAL RESERVES

The Royal Marines

Many years ago soldiers embarked in ships to fight them, while sailors sailed the ships wherever the soldiers directed. Later the sailors sailed and fought their own ships; but when occasion arose for the use of trained riflemen for assault or landing parties regular soldiers were embarked for the purpose.

This was not an ideal state of affairs, as the soldiers were not trained for life at sea; and eventually, in 1664, the Duke of Albany's Maritime Regiment of Foot was raised and paid for out of Admiralty funds. Since that time the Royal Marines have been part and parcel of the Royal Navy.

The Corps of Royal Marines provides the following:

Commando units for amphibious assault and operations ashore,

FIG. 2-7. Royal Marines embarking in helicopters for an airborne assault exercise

Detachments for service at sea which, whilst capable of manning their share
of the armament, are specially trained to undertake operations ashore,
Personnel for minor landing craft and special boat sections, as authorised by
the Admiralty Board of the Defence Council,
Units of the assault force which operate on land with the Army beach
organization,
Bands for Naval Commanders-in-Chief and for certain naval vessels and R.N.
and R.M. shore establishments.

Women's Royal Naval Service

Although not subject to the Naval Discipline Act, the W.R.N.S. is an integral
part of the Royal Navy, with its own disciplinary code. Its members, who enter
on an initial four-year engagement, serve alongside their naval counterparts in
shore establishments in the United Kingdom and certain overseas stations in the
following categories:

Air Mechanic	Writer (Pay)
Radio Electrical (Air)	Writer (Shorthand)
Radar Plotter	Stores (S) and (V)
Range Assessor	Cook
Meteorological	Steward
Cinema Operator	Dental Surgery Attendant
Motor Transport Driver	Regulating
Radio Operator	Quarters
Switchboard Operator	Education
Writer (General)	Welfare Worker

New entries undergo Part I training in H.M.S. *Dauntless* and thereafter are drafted to the appropriate Training Establishment for Part II training—in many cases receiving instruction with their naval counterparts.

The ranks of officers are Commandant, Superintendent, Chief Officer, First Officer, Second Officer and Third Officer; they correspond with the ranks of Commodore to Sub-Lieutenant (inclusive).

The rates consist of Chief Wren, Petty Officer Wren, Leading Wren, Wren, corresponding with the naval rates from Chief Petty Officer to Able Seaman.

Queen Alexandra's Royal Naval Nursing Service

The Q.A.R.N.N.S. was formed in 1902 under the patronage of Queen Alexandra, although Sisters had been nursing in naval hospitals for many years before that time. Members of the Q.A.R.N.N.S. served at home and abroad during the two World Wars, staffing hospitals and hospital ships. In more recent years they have served wherever an emergency has arisen, and there are many serving personnel who owe them a debt for their well-being.

Officer members join with the qualification of State Registered Nurse and hold the following ranks, which are equivalent to the ranks of Commodore to Sub-Lieutenant: Matron-in-Chief, Principal Matron, Matron, Superintending Sister, Senior Nursing Sister, Nursing Sister.

More recently the Naval Nursing Auxiliary Section has been formed. Members join without the qualification of S.R.N. and may be trained and obtain this qualification in the naval hospitals. Members of the Q.A.R.N.N.S. Auxiliary Section are of non-officer status, with the ranks of: Head Naval Nursing Auxiliary, Assistant Head Naval Nursing Auxiliary, Senior Naval Nursing Auxiliary, Naval Nursing Auxiliary, Probationary Naval Nursing Auxiliary.

RESERVES

The Royal Naval Reserve

In 1957 a unified Reserve was formed of the former R.N.R., R.N.V.R., R.N.V.(P.)R., and W.R.N.V.R. The main aim of the Reserve is to provide officers and ratings (men and women) who, in an emergency, will be required to complete ships to war complement, to commission a large number of small ships from reserve, e.g. minesweepers, and to fill staff billets, base organizations and maritime headquarters.

The Reserve can be divided into three groups:

Group A (*General Service Reserve*). Professional sailors and fishermen, and volunteers from life ashore who are training for branches and sub-specialisations and who in an emergency can be employed both afloat and ashore.

Group B (*Special Categories of Reserve*). Volunteers from civil life who are training for appointments and billets, mainly ashore, which do not necessarily require experience at sea (e.g. Intelligence and postal duties).

Group C (*Headquarters*). Personnel who are training to fill specific billets ashore in an emergency within easy reach of their homes (e.g. maritime headquarters).

FIG. 2-8. A member of the W.R.N.S.

Members of Group A will carry out training in H.M. ships and establishments and also at Reserve Sea Training Centres at eleven ports in the British Isles, and, in the case of radio operators, at Wireless Districts elsewhere. At Sea Training Centres training is divided between formal instruction on drill nights and cruises of up to 14 days' duration in coastal minesweepers attached to the Centres. Members of other groups will carry out training mainly of a specialised nature, depending upon their experience and the billets they would be required to fill in an emergency.

The Reserves play an integral part in the large-scale NATO and national exercises which are held from time to time, mostly in billets which they may expect to occupy at the outset of a national emergency.

The Royal Marine Forces Volunteer Reserve

The R.M.F.V.R. is constitutionally similar to the R.N.R. and has five centres (City of London, Bristol, Merseyside, Tyne and Scotland) as well as a number of detachments in other towns in England and Scotland. Ranks are trained for commando, special boat service, minor landing craft and sea-service duties.

FIG. 2-9. Members of the R.N.X.S.

Women's Reserves

Women's Royal Naval Reserve. Units of the W.R.N.R. are attached to all R.N.R. Divisions. Officers and ratings carry out the same training obligations as their male counterparts, except that they go to naval shore establishments for their 14 days' continuous training.

Queen Alexandra's Royal Naval Nursing Service Reserve. The Q.A.R.N.N.S.(R.) is a reserve of nursing sisters to supplement the Q.A.R.N.N.S. in the event of a war or a national emergency.

Other Reserves

Royal Fleet Reserve (R.F.R.). Ratings. Personnel completing the reserve part of their Special Service engagement.

Royal Naval Volunteer Supplementary Reserve (R.N.V.S.R.). Officers. Personnel who have experience of the sea.

Emergency List and Retired Officers. Officers released for private reasons from active service.

Royal Naval Special Reserve. Ex-National Servicemen carrying out their part-time reserve period.

Royal Naval Special Reserve (Special List). Naval Reservists under the age of 45 who have completed National Service (full and part-time).

The last two types of Reserve will soon cease to exist.

The Royal Naval Auxiliary Service (R.N.X.S.)

The R.N.X.S. is a uniformed civilian volunteer organization, administered, trained and operated by the Royal Navy. It originated from the former Royal Naval Minewatching Service. Its task in time of war is:

To fulfil the minewatching commitments in our coastal waters,

To provide basic support staffs in commercial ports in the United Kingdom,

To man to the greatest possible extent the naval organization required in this country to control the movements of merchant shipping.

The Service is open to men and women over the age of 21 who have no other Reserve liabilities. Training is on a voluntary part-time basis in peacetime. In war, service would be full-time paid service.

Cadet organizations

The Admiralty Board of the Defence Council lends its support to certain youth movements and organizations that aim to cultivate a boy's interests in the sea services and teach him leadership based on such things as discipline, self-reliance and service. It co-operates with the Army Board and the Air Force Board in the management of the Combined Cadet Force and is wholly responsible for the administration and training of the Royal Naval sections of the C.C.F. Besides being responsible for the naval training of the Sea Cadet Corps, the Admiralty Board of the Defence Council assists the Boy Scouts and Girl Guides Associations by granting special qualifications to selected Sea Scout troops and Sea Ranger crews.

MARKS OF RANK AND DISTINGUISHING BADGES

Officers' marks of rank

Sleeve stripes. The rank of officers is indicated by stripes of gold lace on the cuff of each sleeve of the coat. For Surgeons and Dental Officers a coloured cloth is worn between the stripes, red for Surgeons and orange for Dental Officers.

Shoulder straps are worn with white uniform and greatcoats. Officers of Flag rank and Commodores wear the special badges shown in Plate 1. All other officers wear their distinguishing rank stripes (and colours if applicable) on their shoulder straps. Midshipmen and naval cadets do not wear shoulder straps.

Aiguillettes. Officers serving on the personal staff of Flag Officers or Commodores wear aiguillettes (ropes of gold lace) hung from the left shoulder. Aides-de-camp to the Sovereign, equerries to members of the Royal Family, Admirals of the Fleet and Honorary Physicians and Surgeons to the Sovereign wear aiguillettes on the right shoulder.

Ratings' distinguishing badges

Petty officers and junior ratings, whether dressed as seamen or not, wear the badges denoting rating and conduct on the left arm and the badges denoting branch or specialist qualification on the right arm. Certain special skill badges, e.g. marksman's badge, are worn on the right cuff.

Chief petty officers wear three large gilt buttons across each cuff and no arm badges. They wear the badges denoting their branch or specialist qualification on the collar of their jackets. Artificer chief petty officers wear no collar badges.

Cap ribbons. In peace, men dressed as seamen wear cap ribbons with the name of their ship on them in gilt letters; in wartime the cap ribbons bear the letters H.M.S. only. Cap badges for men not dressed as seamen, and also arm badges, are illustrated in Plate 2.

CHAPTER 3

General Sea Terms and Types of Ship

See B.R. 67(1), *Admiralty Manual of Seamanship*, Vol. I

GENERAL SEA TERMS

The language of the seaman

Every profession and trade uses its own technical terms to describe the more specialised parts of its work; this is particularly true of seamen. Because our small island kingdom has depended so long on the sea for its existence and prosperity, and many of its people have been born and bred near the sea, many of the terms used by British seamen have become part of our daily language. The main qualities of seafaring speech are simplicity, pithiness and accuracy of description. Orders must be simple, short and accurate, so that they can be obeyed instantly and exactly. The young sailor must first learn the language of his profession; in this chapter, therefore, some elementary terms are explained.

PARTS OF A SHIP

The hull

The main body of a ship is called the hull. It is divided into three parts—the *fore* part, the *midship* part and the *after* part. The fore part ends in the *stem* and the after part in the *stern*. The stem is the upright or inclined (*raked*) continuation of the *keel* at the fore end of the ship, and the word is seldom used at sea. It is more usual to speak of the *bow*.

FIG. 3-1. The hull

When standing anywhere inside the hull a man is facing *forward* when facing the stem and facing *aft* when facing the stern. Any line which runs lengthways in the ship is said to run *fore-and-aft*, and the line joining the middle of the stem and the middle of the stern is called the *fore-and-aft centre line* ('middle line' or 'centre line' in a ship's plans or drawings).

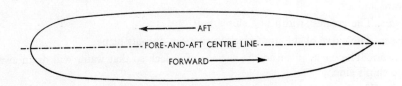

FIG. 3-2. Direction fore and aft

25

The vertical plane through the fore-and-aft centre line divides the ship into two halves. When facing forward the *starboard* side is on the right-hand side and the *port* side is on the left. It is customary to give equipment, such as ship's boats, odd numbers on the starboard side and even numbers on the port side.

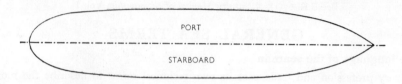

FIG. 3-3. Division athwartships

Hull surfaces

The port and starboard sides of the hull meet underneath in the keel. The curved surface of the fore part is known as the *bow* (port or starboard) and the curved surface of the after part is known as the *quarter* (port or starboard); the centre part is referred to as *amidships*.

When a ship is *afloat* or waterborne, the *waterline* divides the sides into *ship's side* above the waterline and *bottom* below it. These terms are used in a general sense—for example, 'painting the ship's side' or 'scraping the ship's bottom'. A more precise definition of an area can be achieved by referring to the side, the part and the waterline, e.g. 'the ship was holed on the starboard bow, four feet below the waterline'.

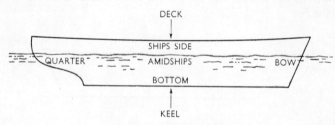

FIG. 3-4. Hull surfaces

Hull terms

Freeboard. The height of the highest continuous watertight deck above the waterline.

Draught. The depth of the keel below the waterline.

Draught marks. Numbers showing the draught in feet, placed on the hull both forward and aft.

Beam. The greatest width of a ship's hull.

Sheer. The curve of the upperdeck in the fore-and-aft plane.

Camber. The curve given to the surface of a deck so that water will drain away to the ship's side.

Bilge. The nearly flat part of the bottom of the hull, both inside and out. The foul water that collects inside the bottom of the hull is also known as 'bilge'.

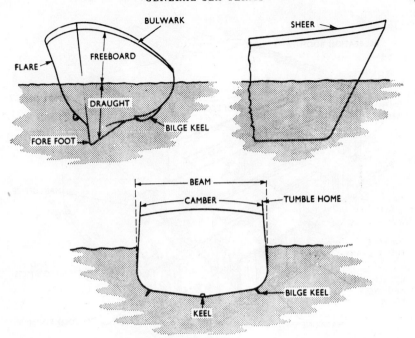

FIG. 3-5. Hull terms

Tumble home. The sides are said to 'tumble home' if they slope inwards above the waterline.

Flare. When a ship's sides curve outwards above the waterline they are said to be flared.

Flush-decked. A ship is said to be flush-decked when the uppermost deck of her hull runs continuously from stem to stern, unbroken by any raised or sunken portion (except for upperworks or superstructure).

Decks

The continuous horizontal surfaces of a ship are called *decks*; if exposed, they are called *weather decks*. All the decks in a modern man-of-war are now numbered in sequence from the uppermost weather deck downwards (1, 2, 3, etc.) and in the superstructure upwards (01, 02, 03, etc.). Formerly decks were known only by their names. The numbering method of identifying decks is shown in Fig. 3-6.

The highest complete deck (except in aircraft carriers) is known as the *upper deck*, the lowest the *hold*. In a carrier the *hangar deck* corresponds to the upper deck, but the numbering of decks starts from the *flight deck*, which is the weather deck (number 1).

Parts of decks have special names. A *flat* is a platform or part of a deck, below the upper deck, that does not run the full length or breadth of a ship. A *lobby* is a space giving access to one or more compartments.

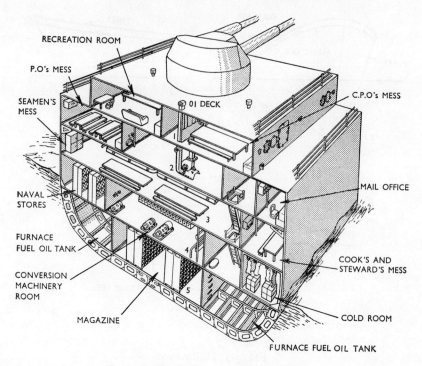

RECREATION ROOM

P.O's MESS

SEAMEN'S
MESS

01 DECK

C.P.O's MESS

NAVAL
STORES

MAIL OFFICE

FURNACE
FUEL OIL TANK

CONVERSION
MACHINERY
ROOM

COOK'S AND
STEWARD'S MESS

MAGAZINE

COLD ROOM

FURNACE FUEL OIL TANK

FIG. 3-6. Typical cross-section of a ship

The afterpart of the upper deck is the *quarterdeck*, while the forepart is the *forecastle* and the midships part extending both to starboard and port is the *waist*.

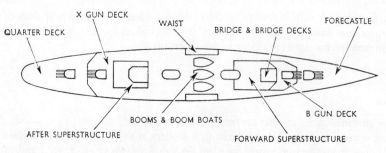

X GUN DECK

WAIST

FORECASTLE

QUARTER DECK

BRIDGE & BRIDGE DECKS

BOOMS & BOOM BOATS

B GUN DECK

AFTER SUPERSTRUCTURE

FORWARD SUPERSTRUCTURE

FIG. 3-7. General layout of the upper deck of a cruiser

TERMS DESCRIBING POSITION AND DIRECTION IN A SHIP

Position in general

Just as a landsman lives *in* a house, so does a seaman speak of living *in* a ship—not *on* a ship. Let us now describe the movements of a seaman who is returning to his ship, the ship in which he is *borne*. If he arrives by boat he goes up an *accommodation ladder*, which is secured *outboard* ('board' is the old name for the ship's side); he comes

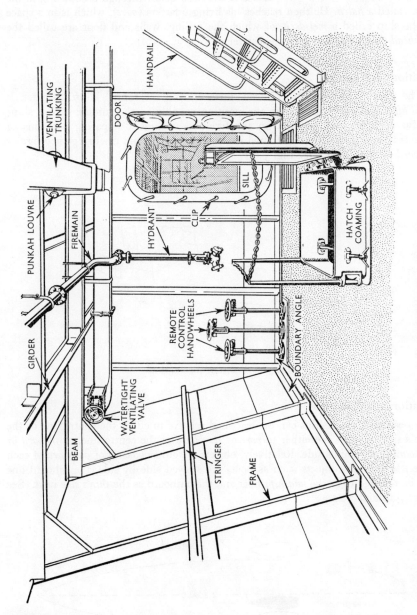

FIG. 3 8. A typical compartment

over the side and is then *on board*. If the ship is lying alongside the dock wall and the seaman crosses the *brow* from the dock to come on board, he steps *on deck*; or, if the brow leads below the weather deck, he steps *between decks*. In either case he is *inboard* once he comes over the side. Having reported his return, he goes below by a *ladder* which gives access to the deck below through an opening in the deck called a *hatch*. He then reaches his living quarters (*mess*), which is in a space in the ship called a *messdeck*, of which the ceiling, walls and floor are called the *deckhead*, *bulkheads* and *deck* respectively.

Position fore and aft

The mast is *forward* (pronounced 'forrard') and the funnel is *aft*. A hatch is *amidships*. Amidships describes the position roughly in the middle of the ship; it also describes any position on the fore-and-aft line. Comparing positions of objects with one another, the funnel is *abaft* the bridge, and the bridge is *before* or *forward* of the funnel. (See Fig. 3-9.)

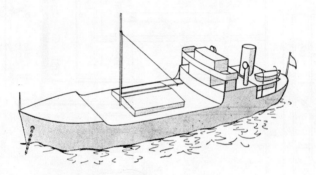

FIG. 3-9. Position fore and aft

Position athwartships

A position athwartships can be described relative to either the centre line or the ship's side. Objects are either to *port* or *starboard* of the centre line, or *inboard* or *outboard* of the ship's side. Relatively, objects are either *inboard* or *outboard* of each other. Where two objects such as boats are stowed side by side, the inboard one can be referred to as the *midships* boat and the outboard as the *ship's side* boat. (See Figs. 3-10 and 3-11.)

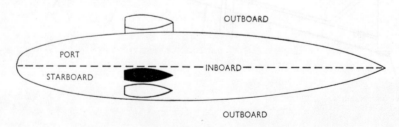

FIG. 3-10. Position athwartships

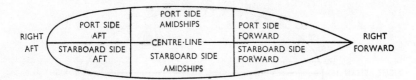

FIG. 3-11. How positions are described

Movement of objects on board

A seaman speaks of going forward, aft, below, on deck, aloft (anywhere in the rigging of a mast). He uses the same expressions for shifting an object; thus he may shift something further aft, or take it forward.

To *launch* is to drag or heave an object along. To *lift and launch* is to lift an object, then to launch it. To *fleet* is to shift an object a short distance. To *ship* is to place an object in its proper position. To *unship* is to remove an object from its proper position.

TERMS DEFINING POSITION AND DIRECTION OUTSIDE A SHIP

Relative bearings

Ahead, *astern* and *abeam* are relative bearings. In addition, when an object is midway between ahead and abeam it is said to bear on the *bow*, and when it is midway between abeam and astern it is said to bear on the *quarter*. The expression *fine* and *broad* may be used relative to ahead and astern, e.g. an object may be *fine* on the port bow or *broad* on the port quarter. (See Fig. 3-12.)

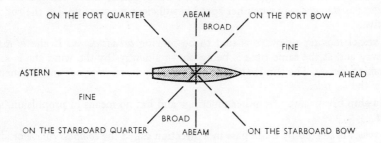

FIG. 3-12. Relative positions outside the ship

A greater degree of accuracy in relative bearings is obtained by expressing them in degrees from ahead on each side of the ship. The horizon is divided into degrees from zero (right ahead) to 180 (right astern); those on the starboard side are called *green* and those on the port side *red*. In Fig. 3-13 the sailing vessel bears 'red 40' and the steamship bears 'green 130'.

Compass bearings

The gyro-compass indicates true north, and other directions are indicated by three-figure numbers, the entire horizon, from true north clockwise through east,

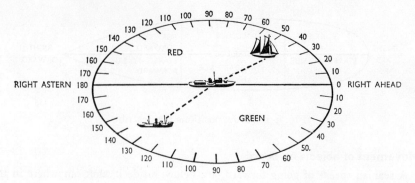

FIG. 3-13. Relative positions by colour and bearing

south and west and back to north being divided into 360°. Thus true east is 090°. The magnetic compass indicates magnetic north and the magnetic compass card is similarly divided into 360° round the horizon. Magnetic east is likely to be a different direction from true east, however, and is distinguished from it by being called '090 degrees magnetic', or 'magnetic east', and the same applies to all other magnetic directions (see Chapter 12). Thus the *bearing* (direction) of an object from the ship may be given either as a true bearing or as a magnetic-compass bearing.

TERMS DEFINING MOVEMENT OF A SHIP

A vessel is *under way* when she is neither anchored nor secured to a buoy, nor made fast to the shore, nor aground. When actually moving through the water she has *way* on her. When moving ahead, she is said to be *going ahead* or *making headway*. When moving astern she is said to be *going astern*, or *making sternway* or *a stern board*. A vessel *gathers way* when she begins to move through the water and she has *steerage way* when her speed is sufficient for steering, i.e. the rudder is effective.

A vessel moving sideways is said to be moving *broadside on*. If she is making headway and at the same time is being blown sideways by the wind she is said to be making *leeway*. The windward side of a vessel is the *weather side* and the sheltered side is the *lee side*.

If a ship breaks away from her moorings and has no means of propulsion, she is *adrift*.

A vessel is steered by a compass in a direction called the *compass course* or simply the *course*. The question 'How is the ship's head?' means 'In what direction by the compass is she heading (pointing)?'

LOCATION MARKINGS

See B.R. 2170, *Ship NBCD Manual, Vol. I*

Compartments

It is necessary for many reasons to have a standard system for the marking and identification of a compartment in a ship. This system supplements the naming of compartments, which is done according to the compartment's function; for example the Wardroom Mess is so called, but in addition it can be identified as, let us say, 2D.

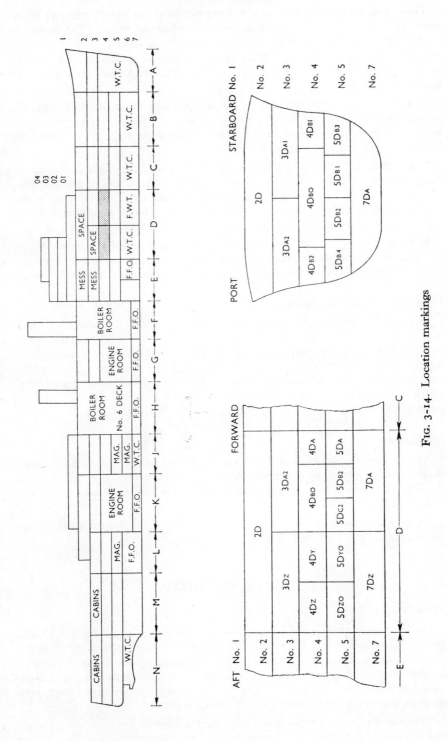

FIG. 3-14. Location markings

The system divides the ship up and down by *decks*, and from forward to aft by main transverse watertight bulkheads, between which lie *sections*. The decks are numbered as already described, while the sections are lettered A, B, C, etc. in sequence from forward, I and O being omitted in large ships. Thus in the example above, the Wardroom Mess is on 2 deck and occupies the whole of that part of D section on that deck. (See Fig. 3-14.)

If a section is further divided by an athwartships watertight bulkhead, the compartments within the section that lie before the bulkhead are given small suffixes, A, B, C, etc., starting from forward; while those abaft the bulkhead are lettered Z, Y, X, etc., starting from aft.

If a section is divided by a fore-and-aft (longitudinal) watertight bulkhead, the compartments to starboard of the centre line are given suffixes of small figures, I, 3, 5, etc., after the main section identification; and those to port 2, 4, 6, etc. In both cases numbering begins from the centre-line. Thus a compartment in the forward port corner of 3D could be, for example, 3DA2 as shown in Fig. 3-14.

It is convenient and practical always to refer to equipment, compartments, etc. by the deck number and section letter where they may be found, thus helping everybody to find their way about the ship—thus '4K, 70-ton pump' or '2D, Wardroom Mess'.

Watertight doors and hatches

In general, watertight doors bear the markings of the compartment to which they give access. When two or more doors give access to the same compartment they are distinguished by the words PORT (or STARBOARD) and/or FORWARD (or AFT) written in abbreviated form after the marking. A hatch bears the number of the deck in which it is cut followed by the letters (and number) of the compartment to which it gives access, e.g. Hatch 2DA1 is cut in 2 deck and gives access to compartment 3DA1.

Markings

NBCD markings are embossed and secured to the part of the ship's structure to which they apply. In an emergency they may play a small but vital part in saving the ship; therefore they must never be obscured, prised off or defaced in any way and are to be kept painted properly.

Some other special markings and further details of the system generally are given in B.R. 2170, *Ship NBCD Manual, Vol. I.*

TYPES OF SHIP

Features

Different kinds of ships can be recognised by certain distinctive features in their general appearance, because the design of a ship depends mainly on the work she is required to perform. For example, the chief considerations in the design of a freighter are maximum carrying capacity, easy handling of cargo and low running costs, whereas speed, manoeuvrability and armament govern the design of a warship, and so they differ widely in appearance.

In this section various types of warship, Fleet auxiliaries and craft are described and a glossary of the more common terms applied to the structure and equipment of a ship is included, in order to assist the young seaman in recognising the general features of a ship. Many of these terms are applicable to several types of ship, *and they should therefore not be read as referring only to the particular type of ship illustrated.*

Warships can be classified broadly under type and class.

Type. This term is used to distinguish between ships built for different purposes, e.g. aircraft carriers and frigates.

Class. This term is used to distinguish different ships of the same type, e.g. Leopard-class frigates.

Aircraft carrier

Aircraft carriers provide offensive power at very long ranges by using their aircraft to strike enemy targets with guided weapons, bombs, rockets and mines. Their aircraft intercept and destroy enemy strike and reconnaissance aircraft and provide long-range reconnaissance for their own Fleet. Carriers have defensive armament, but rely principally on other types of ship and anti-submarine warfare (ASW) helicopters for close protection against submarines. They are recognised by the flat-top flight deck. They displace between 20,000 and 80,000 tons, and are from 700 to 1000 ft in length.

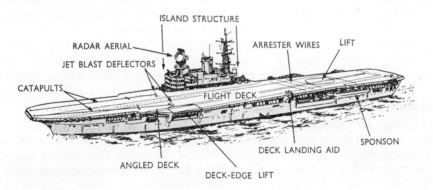

FIG. 3-15. Aircraft carrier

Flight deck. Long, flush uppermost deck used by aircraft for assembly, take-off (catapult) and landing. The modern carrier flight deck is angled for safer landing operations and to avoid interfering with the ranging of serviced aircraft and their catapult take-off.

Island superstructure. Compact structure which includes funnel, radar masts, aerials, bridges and operations room, situated on the starboard side of the flight deck.

Sponson. A platform projecting from the ship's side on which guns and other equipment are mounted.

Aircraft lifts. Power-operated platforms for carrying aircraft from the flight deck to the hangar below. Some aircraft carriers have both centre-line mounted and deck-edge mounted lifts.

Hangar. Storage space for aircraft below the flight deck where maintenance is carried out.

B* 2

Catapults. Most modern aircraft require a longer length of deck for take-off than can be conveniently provided afloat. Therefore steam-operated catapults are fitted at the fore end of the flight deck for short, boosted take-off.

Jet blast deflectors. Hinged screens fitted abaft the catapults to protect the rest of the flight deck when jet aircraft are being catapulted.

Deck landing aid. Mirror or projector deck landing sights are fitted to enable the pilot of an incoming aircraft to fly on a predetermined path and into the arrester wires.

Arrester wires. Modern aircraft need long runways for landing. To overcome the comparatively short flight deck, arrester wires are fitted to the flight deck, which, when hooked by the landing aircraft, bring it to rest in a short distance.

Radar aerial. These are rotating directional aerials used with radar sets for the detection of air or surface targets.

Commando ship

The commando ship has a full-strength commando embarked, together with its equipment, stores and vehicles, and is able to carry a second commando for short periods. The commando is capable of mounting and carrying out the initial assault on any area by air from helicopters, or by sea in landing craft, which are themselves carried in the ship. Throughout its period ashore the commando can be supported continuously from the ship. If required, a carrier acting as a commando ship can be converted for anti-submarine warfare helicopter operations.

These versatile ships provide the Royal Navy with a highly mobile assault capability at long distance from fixed bases. They enable our military forces to be moved to any area where we have interests or an emergency exists or is anticipated.

Cruiser

Cruisers are general-purpose fighting ships whose main function is to provide close cover and anti-aircraft support to convoys or carrier task groups. They combine hitting power with speed, manoeuvrability and endurance. Their turrets mount medium-calibre guns capable of a high rate of fire and are automatically controlled. They can be recognized by their turrets and extensive superstructure. They displace from 12,000 to 14,500 tons and have an overall length of between 550 and 620 ft.

Jackstaff. The staff at which the Union Flag is worn by day by H.M. ships at anchor and when *dressed* at sea. The forward anchor light is shown from the top of this staff at night.

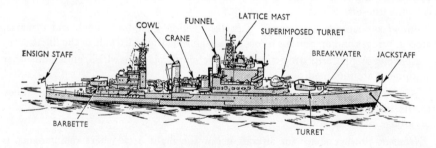

FIG. 3-16. Cruiser

Breakwater. A low, raked barrier across the forecastle to stop heavy seas from sweeping aft.

Turret. A revolving, box-like, armoured structure housing guns (usually two or three) and known as a twin or triple turret. A turret is *superimposed* when mounted above and behind another, over which it can fire.

Barbette. A circular armoured structure protecting the roller path and turret-turning gear beneath a turret.

Funnel. A streamlined casing containing the cylindrical duct which carries the exhaust gases from boilers and diesel engines above the superstructure. Generally fitted with a cowl top to help lift the gases clear of the ship.

Armour. Thick, special-quality steel plating fitted to the hull round the engines, magazines and steering gear, or used to construct turrets, barbettes and main electric cable trunks to protect these vital parts of a ship from enemy shells, bombs, etc.

Armament. Guns, guided weapons, anti-submarine mortars, torpedoes or other weapons carried by a warship.

Protective plating. Special-quality steel plating used in the construction of a ship to protect important radar, gun direction installations, etc. from bomb and shell splinters.

Crane. Lifting apparatus for handling boats, stores, etc.

Lattice mast. Steel pylons built to carry rotating radar aerials, fixed radio aerials and visual signalling arrangements. They are generally fitted with aerial spurs and pole topmasts.

Raked. Inclined to the vertical when viewed from the beam. The stem is usually raked, and so are occasionally the funnels and masts.

Ensign staff. Staff at which the White Ensign is worn in harbour. At sea it is usually shifted to the gaff (a short spar on the mainmast).

Guided-missile destroyer

These modern ships of the County class are equipped with guns, ship-to-air guided missiles and an ASW helicopter. They displace over 5000 tons, are 520 ft in length and have steam and gas-turbine engines.

FIG. 3-17. Guided-missile destroyer

Enclosed bridge. The modern warship's bridge is enclosed to give protection from radioactive fall-out. In the guided-missile destroyer the bridge is of a special type known as a 'turret' bridge.

Liferaft. This is the main lifesaving equipment in surface warships, where it is neither practical nor desirable to carry sufficient lifeboats for all the ship's company.

Whip aerials. These are the transmitting and receiving aerials for short- and medium-range radio communications.

Missile launchers. For close- and medium-range ship-to-air guided missiles.

Flagship. A ship of a fleet, task force, task group, squadron, etc., which flies an admiral's flag or the broad pendant of a commodore.

Squadron. A number of warships, usually of one type, grouped into one unit for operating or administrative purposes under one commander.

Frigates

There are four main types of frigate:

(*a*) the General-purpose frigate for anti-submarine warfare (ASW) and anti-aircraft (A/A) protection, and also capable of limited direction of aircraft;

(*b*) the A/S frigate, whose main function is the destruction of submarines;

(*c*) the A/A frigate, for the protection of convoys against aircraft;

(*d*) the Air Defence (A.D.) frigate for the direction of aircraft.

Both (*c*) and (*d*) and the larger A/S frigates have limited gunpower for offensive operations.

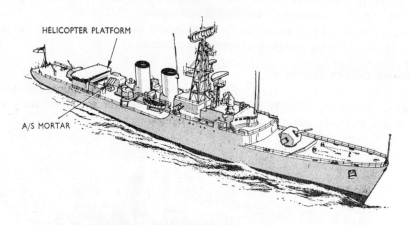

FIG. 3-18. General-purpose frigate

General-purpose frigates. These frigates, of the Tribal and Leander classes, are designed for the A/S and A/A protection of the Fleet, and have limited aircraft-direction facilities. The Tribal class displace 2300 tons, are 360 ft in length and are powered by combined steam and gas turbines. The Leander class are of similar displacement and dimensions, but are powered by steam turbines only.

A/S frigates. These include Rothesay and Whitby classes, of 2150 tons, converted destroyers of about 2200 tons, and Blackwood class frigates of 1020 tons.

A/A frigates. The A/A frigate of the Leopard class has a displacement of 2250 tons, is 340 ft in length and is powered by diesel engines.

A.D. frigates. These consist of the Salisbury-class frigate of 2080 tons, 340 ft in length and powered by diesel engines, and also converted Battle-class destroyers. They carry additional radar equipment for aircraft direction.

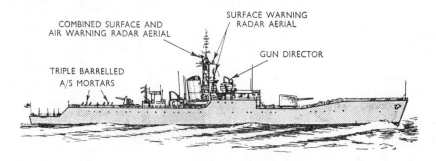

FIG. 3-19. Anti-submarine frigate

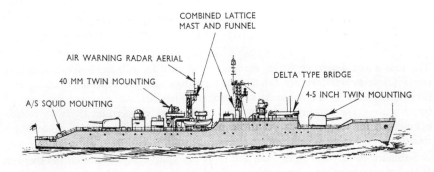

FIG. 3-20. Anti-aircraft frigate

Submarines

Submarines attack enemy submarines, surface warships and enemy supply ships. They usually patrol singly in enemy waters far in advance of the Fleet. Their main armament may consist of guided missiles and torpedoes, but they can also lay mines. Submarines rely on stealth to achieve success and emphasis is placed on quietness in their operation.

Nuclear-powered submarines are extremely versatile; they are designed to spend very long periods at sea completely submerged. Their speed is very high and their endurance practically unlimited.

Conventional submarines also have a long endurance compared with other types of warship, but they are not so fast as nuclear submarines. They can propel themselves by their diesel engines both on the surface and submerged, but in the latter case this has to be done by *snorting.* Their primary method of propulsion is by electric motor when submerged.

The 'Polaris', or fleet ballistic missile, submarine. This type of submarine is fitted with the 'Polaris' missile, which can be launched while the submarine is submerged.

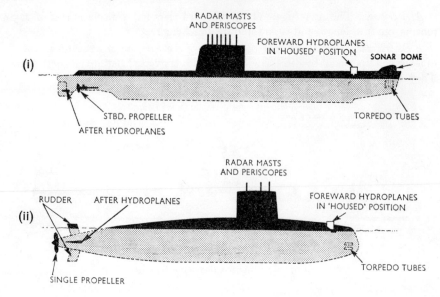

FIG. 3-21. Submarines: (i) conventional, (ii) nuclear

The role is as a deterrent, which eliminates the need for vulnerable fixed launching sites. These submarines are fitted with torpedoes and are capable of acting in a limited capacity as conventional submarines. They are nuclear-powered and are fitted with a very accurate navigational system which permits them to remain submerged for long periods yet to be positioned accurately prior to launching a missile.

Submarines vary in length from 250 to 350 ft. Conventional submarines displace from 1000 to 2000 tons, but nuclear ones displace considerably more.

Bridge fin. A prominent streamlined structure projecting above the main hull and embracing completely the surface directing position and the supports to the periscopes, snort, wireless and radar masts.

Periscope. A long, vertical tube which can be raised or lowered at will be means of a hydraulic hoist. It encloses a system of lenses and mirrors which enables an observer within the submarine to view over the surface of the sea. Usually two periscopes are fitted.

Pressure hull. The inner hull of a submarine, which is constructed to withstand the pressure of water at the greatest depth for which the submarine is designed.

Snort mast. A breathing tube, with automatic valve on top, which can be raised or lowered hydraulically. When the mast is raised a submarine can replenish air and run diesel engines whilst still submerged. The valve stops water entering the upper end of the tube if it happens to go under the surface.

Radio and radar masts. Long, vertical telescopic tubes on which are mounted the necessary radio and radar aerials and which can be raised and lowered to enable them to be used by a submerged submarine.

Conning tower. A narrow cylindrical extension of the pressure hull inside the fin which gives access to the bridge.

Main ballast tanks. Large blister-like tanks running along the sides of the pressure hull which are full of air when the submarine is on the surface and which can be filled with water to make the submarine dive.

Hydroplanes. Horizontal rudders at each end of the submarine which control the depth.

Casing. A light steel-aluminium framework external to the pressure hull, usually extending the length of the submarine, which provides a support for sonar installations, anchor and cable, bollards, etc., and is a working platform for personnel when the submarine is on the surface.

Coastal minesweepers

These small ships, displacing about 450 tons and 150 ft in length, are designed to sweep moored, magnetic and acoustic mines. They are constructed of wood, aluminium and a minimum amount of steel in order to reduce their magnetic properties. A number of coastal minesweepers have been converted into 'minehunters'. These ships are equipped to locate mines on the seabed, using divers from a rubber dinghy if necessary, and to destroy the mines.

FIG. 3-22. Coastal minesweeper

Landing ships and craft

These are specially designed ships and craft for landing assault troops, guns, tanks, equipment and stores on beaches.

Landing ship tank (L.S.T.). This displaces about 4000 tons and is designed to carry L.C.A.s (see page 42) at davits. On reaching the lowering position, the L.C.A.s are

FIG. 3-23. Landing ship tank

lowered and the assault troops embarked. The L.S.T. then opens hinged bow doors, beaches, and lowers her ramp, down which specially waterproofed track or wheeled vehicles can be driven on to the beach.

Landing craft tank (L.C.T.). Of about 800 tons, this is designed specially for carrying tanks when required in immediate support of infantry.

Landing craft assault (L.C.A.). This is the infantry assault craft of about 10 tons hoisted in assault ships, L.S.T.s and other specially designed ships.

Landing craft raiding (L.C.R.). A fast craft used for special landing operations.

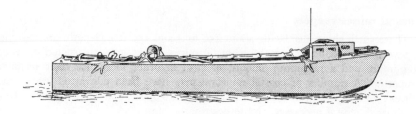

FIG. 3-24. Landing craft assault

Royal Fleet Auxiliaries

In ocean warfare the Fleet may remain for long periods at sea, working many thousands of miles from its main base. To enable a fleet to remain close to its operational area and to save time and fuel from being wasted in steaming to and from its bases, ships of the Royal Fleet Auxiliary Service replenish the fleet close to, but at a safe distance from, its operational area.

The Royal Fleet Auxiliary Service consists largely of tankers and store ships of various types equipped to supply the needs of the Fleet at sea when at advanced anchorages and bases, e.g.:

(a) Fleet replenishment tankers, Fleet replenishment ships, stores, air stores and armament stores support ships. These ships are specially fitted for replenishment at sea.

(b) Freighting tankers (which have a limited capability for underway replenishment by the astern method) and cargo ships.

(c) Harbour oilers and coastal store ships.

These ships can be distinguished by their grey colour, by the Blue Ensign defaced by a gold anchor, and in some cases by their special equipment and fittings. When a number of auxiliaries are collected together in support of a fleet they form 'the underway replenishment group'. The crews of R.F.A.s are employed by the Ministry of Defence (Navy Department) and are equivalent to the Merchant Navy counterparts in their professional qualifications.

STORE SUPPORT SHIP

Hull form. The type and shape of the hull.

Forecastle. The raised part of the hull at the fore end of the ship.

Aftercastle or poop. A raised part of the hull aft.

Derrick. A long spar, usually of tubular steel, hinged to the foot of the mast and used like the jib of a crane to load and discharge cargo.

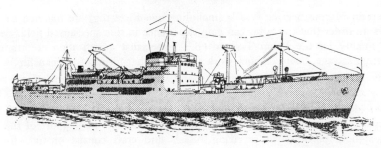

FIG. 3-25. Store ship

Hatches. Openings in the deck above the holds through which cargo is hoisted or lowered. They are usually covered at sea by hatch boards supported on steel beams and covered with tarpaulins. Modern ships have light, folding, quick-opening hatches of steel.

TANKER

Tankers are built to carry liquids such as fuel oils, gasoline and aviation spirit. They are easily recognised because their propulsion machinery and funnel are situated right aft.

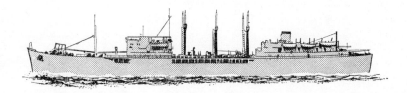

FIG. 3-26. Fleet tanker

Fore-and-aft bridge or catwalk. A raised gangway running fore-and-aft between forecastle, bridge and poop. Fitted in low freeboard ships for the safety of personnel.

Motor vessel. A vessel driven by internal combustion engines, usually diesel.

Marine services

Marine services include Marine Service vessels and Port Auxiliary Service vessels and craft, which are described below.

Marine Service vessels (which perform ancillary tasks for the Ministry of Defence (Navy Department) not performed by the Fleet) comprise:

(*a*) Ocean tugs, used for towing H.M. ships and vessels, and ocean and coastal salvage vessels, which are capable of being used anywhere in the world and are currently manned as Royal Fleet Auxiliaries.

(*b*) Boom Defence vessels, for laying anti-submarine and anti-torpedo net defences at ports and anchorages. Some of these are manned by the Royal Navy. Other B.D.V.s and a pair of dumb salvage lifting craft for work within the home trade limits are manned by civilians under a special agreement.

Certain Marine Service vessels (including one Fleet tug) are manned by naval crews, in order that the latter can gain experience in this specialised field. Seamen who qualify for the Boom Trained (B.T.) specialist qualification are trained in mooring, salvage, boom defence work and the higher forms of seamanship.

The civilian vessels are painted grey and wear the Blue Ensign defaced with a yellow anchor.

Port Auxiliary Service vessels and craft are used for the operation of H.M. dockyards and naval bases at home and abroad and for the support of the Fleet within these ports. Such servicing vessels and craft consist of tugs for ship movements within a harbour, mooring vessels, waterboats, self-propelled and dumb lighters and numerous small craft for ferry services. The crews of P.A.S. vessels and craft are civilians who live close to the port.

P.A.S. vessels and craft have black hulls and yellow upperworks and, when required, fly the same ensign as Marine Service vessels.

The local administration of Marine Service vessels and P.A.S. vessels and craft is carried out by the Captain of the Dockyard or Senior Naval Officer of the base where they operate.

CHAPTER 4

Drafting and Advancement

See B.R. 14, *Drafting Regulations*

DRAFTING

Drafting authorities and categories

There are three drafting authorities in the Royal Navy:

(a) The Commodore, Naval Drafting (C.N.D.), at Haslemere, for General Service ratings

(b) Flag Officer, Naval Air Command, for Fleet Air Arm ratings

(c) Flag Officer, Submarines, for General Service ratings allocated to him by the Commodore, Naval Drafting, for service in submarines.

These authorities are responsible for manning, in accordance with the schemes of complement laid down by the Ministry of Defence (Navy Department), the ships and establishments allocated to them.

For drafting purposes, service is divided into five categories:

Foreign Service ⎫
Local Foreign Service ⎬ Overseas Service
General Service ⎭

Home Sea Service ⎫ U.K.-based Service.
Port Service ⎭

Commissions

Continuous commission. A ship or establishment manned on a running commission basis which does not commission, pay off or recommission at pre-planned intervals.

Fixed commission. A ship which is normally commissioned for a pre-planned period, after which she pays off and recommissions.

Service

General service. A fixed commission of up to two and a half years in a ship operating from the U.K. and in a front-line air squadron. Normally not more than twelve months, including passage time, will be spent continuously overseas at any one time. Two periods will be spent overseas during a commission. The total time spent overseas, including passage time, will not normally exceed 18 months during one commission. Both the length of a commission and the time spent overseas may be varied to provide flexibility and to meet operational requirements.

Foreign service means service in ships commissioning (in either the U.K. or overseas) for a period of not more than 18 months overseas.

Local foreign service. Service in a ship permanently overseas, manned for a continuous commission, and operating in and around a specific base port; also in Naval establishments abroad, including Norway, but not including other countries in N. Europe. Unaccompanied service will be for 18 months, but accompanied men may be required to serve for up to 30 months.

45

Home sea service consists of one of the following:

(a) Service in specific seagoing ships on a continuous commission on the Home Station

(b) Service in the Royal Yacht

(c) Service in Northern Europe (excluding Norway) and the Orkneys

(d) Service for certain instructors in specified establishments in the United Kingdom.

Port service consists of one of the following:

(a) Service in a shore establishment in the United Kingdom manned for a continuous commission

(b) Service in certain ships operating from the United Kingdom

(c) Service in ships building, prior to commissioning or modernization, ships converting and ships in reserve

(d) Service in ships not on General Service, Foreign Service or Home Sea Service refitting.

These terms are purely for drafting purposes and have nothing to do with the term 'sea-going service' as used in the Advancement Regulations.

Drafting rosters

These are kept on a card index system to ensure that a man's whole service is spread fairly between the five categories shown on page 45 and that men are taken for overseas draft strictly in accordance with their position on the roster; this depends upon the amount of Overseas and Home Sea Service they have done. Separate rosters are kept for each rating and specialist qualification, e.g. there are separate rosters for Leading Seamen U.W.2, Leading Seamen R.P.2, and Leading Seamen G.A.2. The names of all men on Port Service appear on drafting rosters.

Roster dates

A man's position on the roster depends upon his roster date. On leaving the New Entry Training Establishment a man is normally drafted to sea at the first opportunity, but thereafter he is drafted strictly according to his roster date. On returning from Overseas or Home Sea Service a man is given a new roster date. This date depends upon the type of service he has just completed, i.e. Foreign Service, Local Foreign Service, General Service, or Home Sea Service.

The rules for calculating roster dates are laid down in the Drafting Regulations and are amended from time to time by current Defence Council Instructions (R.N.).

Volunteering

Any man may volunteer for a particular ship or station, or to recommission a ship. If the request can be granted he may be drafted without regard to his position on the roster.

Preference drafting

When a rating is due for U.K.-based service ashore or afloat he completes a drafting preference card. The principal preferences indicated are:

(a) Area, ship or type of service in which he wishes to be employed

(b) Station or ship in which he wishes to serve when next due for overseas service.

A man's Divisional Officer is responsible for seeing that the card is correctly filled in and is to assist him to do so. On completion the form is forwarded to the appropriate drafting authority, by whom it is attached to the man's drafting record. It is considered on each occasion of his being drafted. Ratings *must* ensure (through the normal Service channels) that the appropriate drafting authority is kept informed of any changes on this drafting preference card.

Courses

Ratings are normally selected for higher specialist qualifications on coming into Port Service. It is important therefore that ratings wishing to undergo higher specialist qualification courses should obtain the necessary recommendations before coming ashore, as these recommendations can only be obtained from seagoing ships. Courses are arranged by the appropriate drafting authority in conjunction with the Schools in order to maintain the proper numbers of such men to meet the requirements of the Fleet.

Leave

Before being drafted abroad every man is granted Foreign Service draft leave or advanced General Service leave if circumstances permit.

Before taking up a draft for Port Service (if he is away from the port), a man can request up to seven days' leave. If circumstances permit this to be granted, it will come out of the total number of days' leave allowed for the year.

Compassionate drafts

Any man who considers he has compassionate grounds for draft to a special area, or for the cancellation of a draft for which he has been detailed, may request for the matter to be investigated. He should be prepared to produce written evidence to support his application, e.g. doctor's certificate, local welfare reports, etc. The man's Commanding Officer will, where necessary, arrange for the man's appropriate Welfare authority (see Chapter 7) to make an investigation and recommendation. All information concerning the application is then forwarded to the appropriate drafting authority for consideration and decision.

ADVANCEMENT

See B.R. 1066, *Advancement Regulations*

'Advancement' means promotion to a higher rate. It involves the acceptance of greater responsibility and increased duties, for which greater privileges and higher pay are given and which in due course result in an increased pension. To be advanced, four main conditions must be fulfilled. A man must be:

Qualified for advancement
Recommended as being in all respects suitable to carry out the duties of the higher rate
Medically fit for advancement
Qualified as regards conduct.

To become fully qualified a man must satisfy certain provisions; he must, above all:

Pass the requisite educational examination

Pass professionally for higher rate

Serve the prescribed time in the rate at present held.

Naturally, individual branches require variations of the above: some require more, others less. These variations are many and cannot be separately listed here.

Advancement to Able Rate

This is governed by the time served in the lower rate and is subject to the man being qualified and recommended. Advancement may be accelerated by a few months as a result of reaching a high standard whilst under training and during service at sea in the Ordinary rate.

Advancement beyond Able Rate

THE ROSTER

The number of higher ratings in the Navy is limited and advancement is dependent upon there being a vacancy. Men who are qualified and recommended have their names placed on advancement rosters kept by drafting authorities. Ratings are advanced when their names reach the top of the roster, provided that there is a vacancy and that they are still recommended. Names are added to the roster half-yearly, and all men qualified continue to have their names forwarded half-yearly.

POSITION ON THE ROSTER—THE POINTS SYSTEM

The points system is divided into two parts:

(a) *Basic points*. These are awarded by the appropriate drafting authority according to the date against the man's name on the roster.

(b) *Merit points*. These are awarded by the man's Commanding Officer on the half-yearly return. The points are scaled according to whether a man is 'highly suited for advancement' down to 'qualified but not recommended'.

The sum of the two parts determines a man's place on the roster; therefore the man with most points will be at the top of the roster. The system is designed to take into account both length of time on the roster and just how deserving a man is to be advanced.

Acting time

In some cases advancement is on an acting basis, a man being required to serve for 12 months in the acting rate before being confirmed. This probationary period is arranged to ensure that men are capable of performing the duties of the higher rate before confirmation.

Promotion to the Special Duties List

The exact qualifications required by the individual branches for promotion to the S.D. List vary. But here again certain basic requirements have to be fulfilled.

(a) *For promotion to the Seaman S.D. List* a man must:

Be recommended by his Commanding Officer

Be within the correct age limits

Have served the prescribed period at sea

Pass a Preliminary Selection Board

Be educationally and professionally qualified

Pass final Selection procedure

Undergo pre-qualifying courses at the S.D. school

Undergo post-qualifying courses at the Royal Naval College, Greenwich, and at the professional schools at Portsmouth

Proceed to sea 'additional for training'

Undergo post-qualifying professional courses at his appropriate professional school.

(b) *For promotion to all other Branch S.D. Lists* he must:

Be recommended by his Commanding Officer

Be within the correct age limits

Be qualified educationally and professionally

Be serving in the correct rate

Have completed a qualifying amount of service, including sea service (where applicable)

Pass final Selection procedure

Undergo post-qualifying courses at the Royal Naval College, Greenwich, and at Portsmouth.

Promotion to the General List—Upper Yardmen Scheme

This scheme is designed to permit young ratings who possess a high general standard and character to become officers in the General List. There is an upper age limit of 21 years. Basically, a candidate must:

Be recommended by his Commanding Officer

Be within the correct age limits

Be educationally qualified

Pass a Preliminary Selection Board

Appear before a Ministry of Defence (Navy Department) Interview Board

Undergo further educational and professional training at Britannia Royal Naval College, Dartmouth.

On completion of the above he will be promoted to midshipman and carry out the same training as a Cadet Entry officer. His career, employment and promotion are as those of a General List officer from then onwards.

CHAPTER 5

Discipline and its Maintenance

See B.R. 11, *Admiralty Memorandum on Court Martial Procedure*

'Nothing is achieved without order and discipline'.

Admiral Lord St. Vincent, 1798

The meaning of discipline is often misunderstood. In the same sense as a disciple means a 'follower', so does discipline mean the 'act of following'. Only when discipline fails does disciplinary action have to be taken.

On board ship, in cramped quarters, life would be intolerable without order. Method, neatness and tidiness have therefore always been among the first principles of the Royal Navy.

How naval discipline is achieved

First of all, discipline is achieved by habit. From the moment of joining the Navy a man is taught discipline. It is essential for him first to discipline himself, his behaviour, his appearance and bearing and his ability to look after himself and his possessions. He must then understand and obey the rules for conduct towards the Navy, his seniors, his job, and those he lives with.

Discipline demands the intelligent and quick-witted understanding of orders and the intelligent anticipation of what will be required—in other words, the carrying out of orders in the spirit as in the letter. To achieve this a man must know his own job thoroughly and also the jobs of those around him. Officers and senior ratings are taught to lead. Thus in a ship which has good discipline, officers and men follow the lead given by their seniors and the ship's company works together as a team. It is our proud claim that whatever the emergency the Navy is able to cope with it. Each man must be able to adapt himself quickly to a new situation; this is one of the severest tests of good discipline.

Where the discipline is good a ship is happy and her company get on happily together, living for long periods and in trying climates in a ship designed primarily for fighting rather than for comfort.

Although good discipline ensures that men will normally do the right thing instinctively, some rules are necessary to protect the efficiency of a ship from the weakness, ignorance or bad leadership of individuals. These rules are enforced by a code of punishments which may be regarded as a prop to discipline.

The Articles of War and the Naval Discipline Act

The Naval Code. The Naval code came from the famous 'Black Book' of the Admiralty, whose contents dated back to the reign of Henry VI. They were ultimately derived from the medieval Rules of Oleron, themselves based on the older sea laws of the Romans and, before them, of the Phoenicians. These ancient laws and customs have found their way into most of the sea codes of the maritime nations of Europe. They were rough-and-ready rules for the day-to-day maintenance of discipline afloat, and were often very severe in the punishments awarded to offenders dealt with 'in accordance with the laws and customs of the sea'.

In 1645 the first 'Articles of War' were laid down, which combined current British Common Law and Naval Law for serious offences against naval discipline. The articles were amended from time to time until, in 1847, the first important Naval Discipline Act was passed. This act brought punishments into line with those used in courts ashore, and since that time Parliament has modified and amended these acts, although they are in some cases still based on 'the customs of the sea'.

The Naval Discipline Act. This act embodies the Articles of War and is essentially an Act of Parliament and therefore one of the laws of the country. It is designed for the governance of the Navy, the maintenance of discipline and the administration of justice. The Act lays down:

Who shall be subject to it
What acts and omissions shall be offences against it
How offences shall be tried
How offences shall be punished.

Discipline in battle

One of the supreme tests of discipline comes in battle. The sight of your messmates being killed or wounded in action; the accompanying noise and damage; fire, smoke, and perhaps the ship flooding and listing, can all be very frightening. It is under circumstances such as these that disciplined officers and men reap the benefit of their training and stand fast to fight their ship.

CHAPTER 6

Saluting, Ceremonial and Kit

SALUTING

See B.R. 1834, *Royal Naval Handbook of Parade and Rifle Drill*

The personal salute of officers and men of the Royal Navy in its present form is of comparatively recent origin, having been introduced in 1890 to conform with the practice of the Army. The original method of saluting in the Navy was to uncover the head, both when making the salute and acknowledging it, and amongst officers this was accompanied on ceremonial occasions by a bow. On board ship where many men did not wear hats, the recognised salute was to go through the motions of removing one's headgear, or just to touch the forehead, this salute being acknowledged in a similar manner. The original salute of removing the cap is still retained on certain occasions, and this manner of saluting is a custom which we honour as one of the traditions of our Service.

Why we salute

Generally speaking, we salute persons, flags and places in recognition of the Sovereign and her Government's authority which may be vested in them, or for traditional reasons, e.g. the Cenotaph in Whitehall, London. It is also an act of greeting. Saluting is the outward sign of good manners and respect.

The old saying that 'anything worth doing is worth doing well' can apply to saluting. A sloppy, half-hearted or furtive salute reflects no credit on the giver and may lower him in other people's estimation. The salute should be given smartly, ungrudgingly, and in good time for it to be observed and returned. You can find the full details in the reference quoted above.

You are to salute:

(a) Her Majesty and all members of the Royal Family.

(b) Heads of foreign States and members of reigning Royal Families.

(c) Whenever the National Anthem or any Commonwealth or foreign National Anthem is played within hearing.

(d) During the ceremonies of 'Colours' (when the ensign is hoisted) and 'Sunset' (when it is hauled down).

(e) When boarding or leaving any of H.M. ships or foreign men-of-war. This is a salute to the ship and her company and is given irrespective of the place or means of entry or departure, e.g. the gangway and jackstay.

(f) When coming on to the quarterdeck of a ship or establishment.

(g) When passing or being passed by a party of any country's fighting Services with uncased Standards or Colours, or when the White Ensign is paraded on shore.

(h) When passing or being passed by the coffin in a funeral procession.

(i) When passing the Cenotaph, in Whitehall, London.

(j) When meeting or passing any officer of any of the fighting Services of any country. This applies whether either or both are on foot or in or on a vehicle (including bicycle), except in public transport. Do not salute if, as a result of doing so, there would be a risk of a traffic accident occurring.

(k) When passing or being passed by a car flying a distinguishing flag or 'starred' plate.

(l) When approaching to report to, or be addressed by, an officer and when taking leave of him.

(m) When meeting or passing an officer whom you know and who is wearing plain clothes.

(n) When greeting relatives, civilians or guests on formal and social occasions.

Salutes are to be given at any time when it is sufficiently light to discern the person saluted.

FIG. 6-1. The hand salute

How to salute

(a) *When in uniform and wearing a cap* give the hand salute. The correct attitude is shown in Fig. 6-1. When saluting, always look the other person straight in the eyes.

(b) *When in uniform and not wearing a cap, or both hands are occupied, or your right hand is injured,* stand to attention and face in the required direction: or if on the move, turn the head and eyes smartly in the required direction, but do not pin your arms to your sides. When your hands are both occupied put the load down, if possible; otherwise salute as just described.

(c) *When in plain clothes and wearing a hat,* raise your hat.

(d) *When in plain clothes without a hat* use the normal hand salute or stand to attention only and face in the required direction, whichever is appropriate.

(e) *When in sports rig and wearing a cap* salute as in (a).

(f) *When in sports rig without a cap* salute as in (b).

(Both (e) and (f) include the wearing of track suits over the sports rig.)

When not to salute

(a) When passing or being passed by an officer on board a ship.

(b) In narrow gangways or other confined spaces; instead, you are to stand to attention.

(c) When a member of a boat's crew or a passenger in a boat. Instead, you are to stand or sit to attention as ordered.

(d) When actively engaged in work or when a member of a working party, unless addressed by an officer.

(e) Whenever in the ranks at the halt or on the march; on these occasions only the officer or rating in charge gives the hand salute, at the same time ordering the remainder to attention if at the halt, or giving the order 'Eyes right (or left)' if on the march.

(f) In such places as railway stations, football stands or whilst watching organized sport in an establishment (except when complying with (l) on page 53).

(g) In messes or recreation rooms when actively engaged in recreation.

When to take your cap off

At Divine Service and in places of public worship, except for tri-Services religious ceremonies.

When ordered for inspections, reading of the Articles of War, as a defaulter, etc.

On entering a Flag or Commanding Officer's quarters, officers' cabins, messes, messrooms, sick bay, administrative offices, civil courts, private houses and apartments.

Salutes by sentries

A sentry is to present arms:

To Her Majesty and all members of the Royal Family in uniform and all members of reigning foreign Royal Families in uniform.

During the playing of National Anthems within earshot.

When Colours are hoisted or lowered.

To officers of Lieutenant-Commander's rank and above and their equivalent ranks in any Armed Service of any country.

To uncased Standards or Colours of all three Services.

To a body when a funeral procession passes.

To all Chaplains.

A sentry is to give a 'butt salute' to:

Officers of Lieutenant's rank and below and their equivalent ranks in any Armed Service of any country.

Officers of the W.R.N.S., W.R.A.C. and W.R.A.F., irrespective of rank.

During the period between dusk and dawn the salute 'at the slope' is to be used, unless the sentry can clearly distinguish that an officer's rank is such that he is entitled to the 'Present Arms'.

Remarks on saluting and marks of respect

When a salute is made to two or more officers, it is returned by the senior officer only. An officer passing, or being passed, is not saluted when the rating is in the company of a senior officer. All individuals in company salute on passing or being passed by a senior officer (unless they are marching in the ranks).

The custom of saluting the Quarterdeck is derived from the fact that in olden times ships used to have a small shrine or crucifix under the break of the poop; it was customary to pay respect to this by uncovering the head.

On board a ship it is customary to salute officers on the first occasion of meeting or passing them on deck in daylight, and thereafter only when reporting to or being addressed by, or acknowledging the order of, a senior officer.

When an officer makes his way along a ship a gangway should be cleared for him and all ratings should stand to attention as he passes.

Officers entering or leaving the ship are saluted by the Officer of the Watch, if they are of equal or higher rank; he returns the salutes of others. The gangway staff salute all officers. When entering or leaving a boat, officers are saluted by the officer in charge of the boat or the coxswain; the crew stand or sit to attention.

When an officer enters a compartment during an inspection, or to address an assembly in it, everyone in the compartment should stand to attention until given the order 'Carry on'. When an officer enters a classroom the class is called to attention. They are to sit upright with their arms folded until ordered to 'sit easy'.

The cap

The cap is the symbol of the authority vested in the wearer and is therefore worn whenever he is exercising that authority. Caps are not removed by officers or men under arms or in the execution of their duties.

The custom of removing your cap on entering a mess, living space or private house is a common courtesy in accordance with the manners of our country.

When a body of men is about to be inspected it is customary for the order 'Off caps' to be given. This is, in fact, a salute to the Inspecting Officer, all leading rates and below removing their caps and all senior rates saluting. It also enables the Inspecting Officer to see if you need a haircut.

In some ships it is the custom for an officer to carry his cap under his arm should he wish his presence to be disregarded (except for clearing a gangway) when making his way during silent or recreational hours.

CEREMONIAL

See *The Queen's Regulations and Admiralty Instructions*, Chapters 12 and 13

PERSONAL SALUTES

Salutes and marks of respect are accorded in different ways, examples being:

The hand salute
The sword salute
Blowing of bugles
Piping the side
Parading of guards and bands

Playing of national anthems and musical salutes
Lowering or dipping of Colours
Gun salutes

The hand salute

The hand salute is the personal salute of all officers and men and is described on page 53.

Bugle salutes and the 'Alert'

The 'General Salute' is a bugle call sounded as a personal salute paid to rank. It is only sounded when there is no band available to play the appropriate anthems or musical salutes.

The 'Alert' sounded on the bugle is not a salute, but a mark of respect paid to rank or on specified occasions. With certain exceptions, it is only accorded to persons who are specifically entitled to it. When a bugle is not available the 'Still' is piped on the boatswain's call or blown on a whistle instead of the 'Alert'. The 'Alert' is sounded on the following occasions:

At the hoisting and hauling down of Colours.

Between 'Colours' and sunset, on the arrival and departure of Royalty and certain other persons specifically entitled to it (see *Q.R. & A.I.*, Chapter 13).

Between the hours of sunrise and sunset in a warship not under way, when a boat or tender passes which is wearing a standard of Royalty or the flags or other emblems of persons entitled to it.

Between the hours of sunrise and sunset when one of H.M. ships passes another ship not under way, and if one of the ships is flying a Standard or distinguishing flag, or is a flagship or a foreign warship.

Whenever the 'Alert' is sounded, all hands on deck stand to attention and face outboard until the 'Carry on' is sounded. However, at 'Colours' and at sunset, all hands stand to attention, face the Colours and salute, remaining at the salute until the 'Carry on' is sounded.

Piping the side

In the Royal Navy, piping the side is a mark of respect normally paid between Colours and sunset only. It is accorded to:

The Sovereign.

Members of the Royal Family of the rank of Captain and above, in naval uniform.

Officers of flag rank and Commodores in uniform; officers in command of seagoing ships or tenders in commission, in uniform.

Foreign naval officers in uniform irrespective of Branch or rank, and at all hours of the day and night.

Civilian members of the Naval Board of the Defence Council when visiting H.M. ships, wearing a peaked cap with the Naval Board badge and representing the Board.

The President of a Court Martial when proceeding to or returning from the Court.

The Officer of the Guard when flying a pendant.

A body when brought on or taken off a ship.

This mark of respect owes its origin to the days when captains of ships visited other ships at sea. On these occasions they were hoisted aboard from their boats in a chair slung from a whip rove from the lower yardarm. Such arrivals were accompanied by the pipes of the boatswain's call when passing the necessary orders to the men manning the whip. It is not piped at any shore establishment.

Parading of guards and bands

'Guards of Honour' are only paraded for Royalty and other persons entitled to them, and they vary in size with the importance of the personage concerned.

The parading of bands for the playing of musical salutes is of comparatively recent origin. Sovereigns, Presidents of Republics and the Heads of States are saluted with the anthem of their country; other dignitaries are saluted by the playing of specified tunes.

Guards and bands are also paraded on certain other occasions, such as 'Colours', and on entering and leaving harbour.

Flags and discs

These are displayed on boats, cars and aircraft, as follows:

(*a*) The Minister of State for the Navy, Naval Members of the Naval Board of the Defence Council and officers entitled to fly flags or broad pendants, fly them on ceremonial occasions; at other times, when they are in boats on duty or proceeding informally they display red or white discs.

(*b*) All other officers in command are entitled to fly pendants in boats on ceremonial occasions or on formal occasions.

(*c*) Officers of Flag rank and Commodores not entitled to fly their flags or broad pendants display a blue or white disc on boats and a blue disc on naval aircraft on ceremonial occasions, but on cars they fly the appropriate flag or broad pendant and may display 'star plates'.

(*d*) The Officer of the Guard when proceeding by boat flies a pendant in the boat, both by day and by night, and is entitled to certain marks of respect.

Note: Personal barges and boats of Flag Officers are painted either green for Commanders-in-Chief or dark blue for other Flag Officers and have a flag on the bows in lieu of a ship's crest.

Dipping of ensigns

As an act of courtesy and recognition, merchant ships dip their ensigns on passing a warship. Whenever this salute is given the warship acknowledges it by dipping her ensign and rehoisting it. The merchant ship will not rehoist her ensign until she has seen the warship rehoist hers. On no other occasion (except when they are half-masted) are the Colours of H.M. ships lowered out of routine times. H.M. ships do not dip their Colours to each other or to foreign warships unless the latter first, or at the same time, dip their colours to them.

Gun salutes

The firing of salutes in honour of a Royal or other personage or of a country is a very old custom. Gun salutes are always given in odd numbers; in former days even numbers were always reserved for occasions of mourning. The interval between successive guns is five seconds. Gun salutes are not fired between 1030 and 1300 on Sundays, or between sunset and 0800 except to return a salute from a foreign man-of-war.

Court Martial gun. The ship in which a Court Martial is to be held, on the day of the Court Martial, fires a gun when the Colours are hoisted and at the same time hoists the Union Flag at the peak.

Minute guns. These are fired at funerals of Members of the Naval Board of the Defence Council, Flag Officers, and Commodores entitled to fly their broad pendants. They are fired whilst the body is being borne to the place of interment. They are not to exceed the number laid down for the deceased's rank.

SOME NAVAL CUSTOMS AND CEREMONIES

Official visits

On the arrival of one of H.M. ships in a foreign port, visits are exchanged between the Flag or Commanding Officer of the ship and various government, naval, military or civil authorities in the port. The scope and rules for such visits are laid down in *Q.R. & A.I.* On some occasions they may extend over several days.

The Officer of the Guard

On the arrival of a foreign man-of-war, or one of H.M. ships for the first time, in a British port it is customary for the Senior Officer of the port to send the Officer of the Guard (as detailed by the guard ship) to visit her and to offer her the usual courtesies and facilities of the port. There may be occasions when the Officer of the Guard is sent to a merchantman or yacht if circumstances warrant such action.

Ceremony ashore

On all ceremonial occasions the Royal Navy, as the senior of the armed Services of the Crown, is accorded the position of honour, i.e. on the right of the line in review order, and in the van in marching order. The naval marches are 'Heart of Oak' for the march-past, and 'Nancy Lee' for the advance in review order.

Badges, trophies, etc.

The badge of the Royal Navy is the naval crown, which consists of a circlet surmounted by the sterns of four men-of-war (each with three poop lanterns) and four square sails, each sail being spread on a mast and yard and fully filled and sheeted home; the ships and sails are positioned alternately. This badge and the imperial crown are mounted on the trucks of the jackstaff and the ensign staff respectively.

Each ship has a badge or crest which is allotted to her on commissioning by the Ships' Badges Committee, a body on which the College of Heralds is represented. It is left to each ship to select a motto, which must be approved by the Committee before use. The badge and/or motto is displayed prominently on board and also on the bows of the ship's boats.

Ships display their battle honours, and those of their predecessors of the same name, in some prominent position on board. Any trophies of war, presentation plate or cups, etc. belonging to the ship and her predecessors are displayed between decks. All such trophies, etc. are the property of the ship and are recorded in the Ship's Book.

The ship's bell always bears the name of the ship and the date of her launching. Unless it is damaged it remains with the ship until she is sold or broken up, when the bell is either presented to some public body or offered for sale, preference being given to anyone who has served in her.

New Year's Day

It is the custom for the youngest member aboard (officer, man or junior) to 'ring out the old year and ring in the new' by striking sixteen bells at midnight on New Year's Eve.

Crossing the Line

When circumstances allow, unofficial ceremonies are held in ships as they cross the equator to initiate novices into the Brotherhood of the Seas and as subjects of 'His Oceanic Majesty, King Neptune'. The ship is usually placed out of routine for the day and officers and men share impartially in the proceedings, which are made the occasion for harmless, good-natured skylarking (see Fig. 6-2).

Whistling

The practice of whistling is forbidden in H.M. ships because the noise is apt to be confused with the piping of orders. It is usually anything but sweet, except in the ears of the perpetrator, and is more often than not a cause of annoyance to his messmates.

FIG. 6-2. King Neptune arriving for the ceremony of 'Crossing the Line'

UNIFORM, CLOTHING AND BEDDING

See Appendix to the *Navy List*.

HISTORY OF NAVAL UNIFORM

Uniform originated in the need to distinguish friend from foe. Subsequently it was also used to distinguish one kind of warrior from another, leaders from the rank and file, and soldiers from non-combatants or civilians. Uniform is the outward sign of the authority which may be vested by the government of a country in the wearer by reason of his profession or his status therein. It also protects the wearer in the execution of his duties against charges of espionage or irregular warlike activities.

Uniform was not introduced into the Royal Navy until comparatively recent times, because in the old days there was not the same need at sea to distinguish individual friend from foe as there was in land warfare. When the need arose, as when boarding the enemy, devices such as coloured scarves or headgear were worn as distinctive emblems.

Up to the middle of the last century sailors did not wear prescribed uniform and had to provide their own clothing; but a certain uniformity in dress was achieved, for the reason that each article had to be serviceable for the job and all were either made by the sailor or purchased by him from the limited resources provided by the ship's stores, or from outfitters in the main manning ports. It was not until 1857 that detailed uniform regulations for officers and men of the Royal Navy were laid down and the sailor was given a complete issue of kit on joining the Service. Many changes have been made since then, but the main principles remain the same.

The sailor's *collar* dates from the time of wigs and pigtails, when seamen used to wear a scarf over their shoulders to protect their clothes from powder and grease. This scarf eventually became standardized in the form of the present collar, and was made detachable so that it could be washed.

The *tapes* on the collar were originally a trimming which became common practice, the number of rows varying with individual taste. When the uniform for seamen was standardized, three rows of tapes were decided upon. There is no foundation for the story that they commemorate the victories of Lord Nelson.

The *scarf*, of silk or other good material and of any colour (black included), was part of the sailor's dress long before the days of Nelson, when it was worn as a comforter or a sweat-rag. It cannot be said, therefore, that it was introduced as mourning for Lord Nelson. In 1857 the colour was standardized as black and the material as silk.

The *bell bottoms* of the trousers were originally designed so that the trousers could easily be rolled up to the knee, to prevent them from getting wet when scrubbing decks or in heavy weather.

ISSUE OF UNIFORM AND KIT

Uniform is primarily the property of the Crown and is only allowed to be issued to, or worn by, those persons who are so entitled by regulations. It is unlawful to dispose of any articles of uniform to persons not entitled to wear them.

Each rating, on entering the Service, is issued free with a complete kit of uniform. At each establishment or ship which he joins he is loaned a set of bedding, which must be returned before he leaves for his next draft.

Tropical rig (No. 6s and No. 10s). A free issue of tropical rig is made to each rating on the first occasion of drafting abroad or to ships where tropical clothing is required.

Optional items of kit

There are certain articles of uniform which a rating may 'take up' (i.e. buy from the ship's clothing store) for his own use in addition to the standard kit. He may also take up additional items of standard kit provided that his total kit does not exceed the stowage space allowed for it.

Slops

All articles of uniform which make up the various kits can be purchased from the ship's clothing store for cash and are known under the general term 'slops'. Each article is made to naval specification, and its price, which varies from time to time, is published in Defence Council Instructions (R.N.). Cash payments are made, at the time and place of purchase, to a Supply Officer or senior Stores rating detailed by him, and no money may be given to any other person for the purchase of clothing.

Demands for clothing are made out on Form S.80, which is handed in to the clothing issue room. The prices are inserted against each article and the issue is made against cash payment.

Uniform suits can be supplied made to measure, and for this purpose self-measurement forms are available at the clothing stores. When uniforms are made up by shore tailors the kit must comply with the uniform regulations; otherwise the suit is liable to be confiscated.

In some special cases the cost of slops can be debited against a rating's pay in the ship's ledger, and this is done by means of the casual payment procedure. Special arrangements are in force in Junior Training Establishments.

Declared clothing

Articles of kit may not be sold, given away or exchanged, unless the Divisional Officer's permission has first been obtained. Men leaving the Service who have no further use for articles of kit often dispose of them by permission; also, dead men's effects, unless willed otherwise, are usually sold by public auction for the benefit of their dependants. Any such articles so acquired should be taken to the Regulating or Divisional Office, where the old marking is defaced by a special stamp with the letters D.C. (Declared Clothing) and the new owner's name inserted. This is an essential regulation to check illegal possession and to trace lost or stolen articles.

Loan clothing

In addition to bedding, certain articles of equipment and clothing may be required by a rating carrying out special duties; these are known as 'loan clothing'. The various methods of issue are:

Personal loan—items needed by a man for most or all of his service and taken with him when he goes on draft. Issues and periodic replacements are noted in his pay-book.

Individual loan—items only needed while in a particular ship or duty, and returned on leaving or ceasing that duty. Issues are recorded on cards held by the Supply Department, Departmental Officer, etc. This system is also used for bedding.

Temporary loan—items only needed for a very short time, which may be borrowed from the Supply Department, Departmental Officers, etc., and signed for in special books.

Loan clothing items generally carry the Government's 'broad arrow' stamp. Personal loan items may be neatly marked with the holder's name, but not nicknames or emblems: individual loan items may be marked with the holder's name (when appropriate), unless the ship runs a serial number system or the like.

If loan clothing is lost or damaged by neglect, including defacement by unsightly or unauthorized marking, the person responsible is charged a sum of money representing the loss to the Crown; disciplinary action may also be taken.

DRESS

The type of uniform which is worn at any time is known as the 'dress of the day' or 'rig of the day'. The dress of the day for a number of ships in company is signalled by the senior officer and is piped at breakfast time.

Uniform classification
 Class I—all Chief Petty Officers
 Class II—all men dressed as seamen
 Class III—all Petty Officers and men not dressed as seamen.

Classes I and III are commonly known as 'fore-and-aft rig' and Class II as 'square rig'.

The '*pattern*' is the composition, material and style of each article of each rig. All ships and reputable outfitters should hold a copy of the various patterns. Articles of clothing that are not of uniform pattern are liable to confiscation. Pattern books of authorized materials for uniforms are held on board frigates and above, so that it can be seen whether privately purchased suits meet the required standards.

DRESSES FOR SHIPS' COMPANIES

Dress No.	Occasions on which to be Worn	Description of Dress	
		For men not dressed as seamen (Classes I and III)	For men dressed as seamen (Class II)
1	Inspections; musters; ceremonial occasions; Sundays in harbour (except for Signal Ratings on duty who may wear No. 2 dress) and on leave, and when proceeding on long or week-end leave. Optional on leave on week-days.	Cloth suit, gold badges and medals. Diagonal serge suits, with gold badges and medal ribbons may be worn for week-end leave or long leave.	Worsted serge or best serge suit, gold badges, medals.
2	Sundays at sea and, for Signal Ratings on duty, Sundays in harbour. Optional on leave on week-days. Unless otherwise directed duty-men, duty boats' crews and signalmen are to wear this dress when the rest of the ships' company are in No. 3 dress.	Best blue serge or cloth suit (serge suit may have single or double-breasted jacket), gold or red badges, medal ribbons.	Worsted serge or best serge suit, gold or red badges, medal ribbons.
3	On working days for all ordinary duties (see dress No. 2 above).	Cloth or serge, tartan or diagonal serge suit (serge suit may have single or double-breasted jacket), red badges. Medal ribbons optional.	Worsted serge or serge suit, red badges. Medal ribbons optional.
3A	By Air Crews at sea, and in aircraft at all times. In ships in harbour, Naval and Dockyard Establishments, Naval Air Stations and Naval Air Sections during working hours and non-ceremonial occasions.	Serge blouse and trousers, red badges, navy blue beret with badge or flash, as appropriate.	Serge blouse and trousers, red badges, navy blue beret with flash.

Dress No.	Occasions on which to be Worn	Description of Dress	
		For men not dressed as seamen (Classes I and III)	For men dressed as seamen (Class II)
4	For night clothing and in wet weather.	Any old but respectable cloth, tartan, diagonal serge or serge suit. Red badges. Medal ribbons optional.	Serge suit, red badges. Medal ribbons optional.
6	In place of No. 1 at the discretion of the Senior Officer.	Drill suit. Medals.	Drill suit with medals.
7	In place of No. 2 at the discretion of the Senior Officer.	Drill suit, medal ribbons.	Drill suit with medal ribbons.
8	At action stations in hot climates and also in temperate or cold climates, when ordered by the Senior Officer, in conjunction (if necessary) with other clothing. On working days for all ordinary duties as an alternative to No. 3 dress. On shore as an anti-malarial dress if ordered by the Senior Officer.	Light blue shirt and dark blue trousers, blue rating badges. No medal ribbons.	Light blue shirt, dark blue trousers, blue rating badges. No medal ribbons.
9	Fuelling, refitting or dirty work when other clothing might be spoiled.	Blue overall suit.	Blue overall suit.
10	At the discretion of the Commander-in-Chief on foreign stations on which tropical rig is allowed.	Tropical shirt and shorts, cap.	Uniform cotton vest, tropical shorts, belt, cap.
10A	As a working dress on tropical stations at the discretion of the Senior Officer.	Light blue shirt, dark blue shorts and (a) blue stockings, black boots or shoes, or (b) sandals.	Light blue shirt, dark blue shorts and (a) blue stockings, black boots or shoes, or (b) sandals.

How to wear your uniform

Uniform must be cut and worn correctly, and each individual must be dressed smartly so that he is a credit to both himself and the Service. Slovenliness in dress is a sure reflection of slackness in character and is therefore discouraged. The incorrect wearing of uniform is a punishable offence; when it occurs in public it is particularly reprehensible, since it brings discredit on the Service. The full regulations for uniform are laid down in the Appendix to the *Navy List*, but a few of the more important details are listed here.

Jumpers. The 'V' opening of the jumper should never extend lower than one inch below the lower end of the breast-bone and should never be cut square. The jumper should be fitted with a zip-fastener front, and should be loose enough to allow a jersey to be worn underneath it in cold weather. Special attention should be paid to the material; Service issue material is made to resist shrinking and fading and is the best value obtainable. Made-to-measure suits may be obtained on repayment from Service sources.

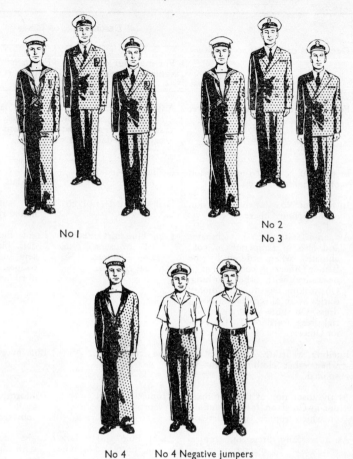

FIG. 6-3. Naval uniforms

Trousers should be fly-fronted, zip-fastened, and have a $2\frac{3}{4}$-in. waistband. The leg of the trouser should be 2–3 inches larger in circumference at the bottom than at the knee, according to the build of man. They are worn with the bottom just touching the instep.

Caps are always to be worn square and neither 'flat-a-back' nor perched on the eyebrows: chin stays should always be well secured. The compulsory kit includes two white caps which are worn, both at home and abroad, with blue and white uniform.

Cap ribbons are issued free to every rating in Class II uniform whenever he first joins a ship. They are to be tied with a 2-inch bow over the left ear and worn with the centre of the lettering over the nose.

Black silk scarves, for wear with Class II uniform, are worn under the collar of the serge jumper, with the ends stitched together. They are secured by the jumper tapes so as to allow a bight one to two inches long below the bows of the tapes. When ironing a silk scarf use a piece of damp linen between the silk and the iron.

Tapes should be 23 inches long, secured on the bight to a becket fitted one inch above the 'V' of the jumper. The bow of the tapes should be 2–3 inches across: the ends should be fish-tailed and not more than 7 inches in length.

Lanyards are worn with dresses Nos. 1, 2, 6 and 7. The lanyard is rove round the neck, under the collar and along the top of the silk so that the Turk's head rests just above the 'V' of the silk (approximately 2½ inches). The end is passed under the silk from right to left, brought right round its own standing part and then stowed in the left pocket of the jumper.

Knives should be worn by all seamen in working dress.

Overcoats, raincoats or waterproof coats P.V.C. are always to be correctly buttoned up and collars turned down (except in bad weather).

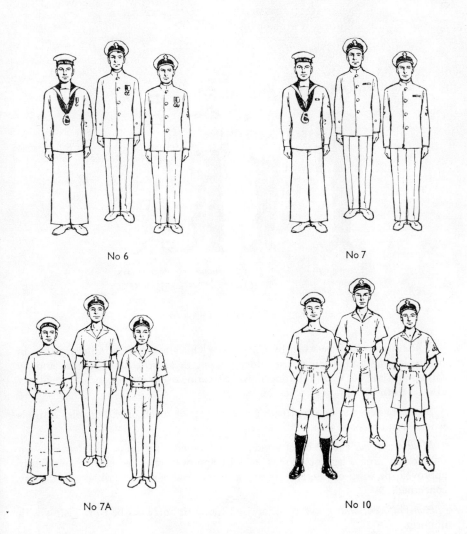

No 6   No 7

No 7A   No 10

FIG. 6-4. Naval uniforms (*cont.*)

C*

No 3A   No 9   No 8   No 10A   No 10A   No 10A
                       With sandals   With sandals,
                                    optional or
                                    neg. shirts

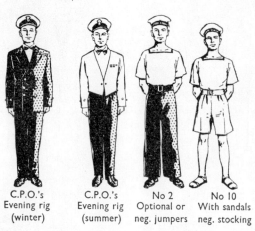

C.P.O.'s   C.P.O.'s   No 2   No 10
Evening rig   Evening rig   Optional or   With sandals
(winter)   (summer)   neg. jumpers   neg. stocking

FIG. 6-5. Naval uniforms (*cont.*)

White scarves may be worn by Chief Petty Officers and Petty Officers when in night clothing and when not on duty (except in shore establishments) and by ratings in Class I or Class III uniform when wearing overcoats or raincoats; they may also be worn by all ratings when on leave.

Boots are never to be fitted with studs, tackets or metal on either soles or heels when worn on board ship.

Mourning bands should be of 2-inch-wide doubled black crêpe and may be worn on the left arm. Flags or favours sold by approved charities may, if specifically approved, be worn on the lapel or stuck in the bow of the cap ribbon on the day concerned.

Non-uniform clothing (except authorized sports rig) may not be worn visibly with uniform.

Beards, moustaches and hair. Beards with moustaches may be grown by permission of the Captain. When permission is granted, a full set must be grown (i.e. a moustache or a beard by itself is not allowed) and shaving must be discontinued, the hairs being trimmed with scissors only to achieve neatness and uniformity. 'Comic opera' face adornments are forbidden. Hair must be kept short and the forelock should not reach below the eyebrows. 'Sideboards' are not allowed.

Badges

Badges of rate and command are worn on the left arm.

Good conduct badges are worn on the left arm below badges of rate and command.

Branch and specialisation badges are worn on the right arm.

Badges of skill are worn on the right cuff.

The principal badges are shown in Plate 2.

Decorations and medals. The more general decorations and medals which may be awarded to officers and men of the Royal Navy are shown, in the order in which they may be worn, in Plate 3. Medals are worn with Nos. 1 and 6 dresses, and ribbons only with Nos. 2 and 7 dresses.

Medal ribbons with medals should:

(*a*) be $1\frac{3}{4}$ inches long (2 inches if two or more rows are worn);

(*b*) be worn with the head of the Sovereign showing;

(*c*) be mounted on a detachable bar and worn immediately above the top row of ribbons in blue uniform and 2 inches below the point of the shoulder in white uniform;

(*d*) overlap when there are more than three medals in a row;

(*e*) be so hung that they completely cover the ordinary ribbons on the suit behind them; if necessary, a piece of suitable cloth should be used as a backing.

Medal ribbons without medals should:

(*a*) be sewn close together on a cloth backing which is sewn on the uniform;

(*b*) be $\frac{1}{2}$ inch long, touching each other in any one row;

(*c*) have $\frac{1}{8}$ inch between rows;

(*d*) in white uniform be mounted on a detachable bar.

Decorations and medals are awarded to a particular individual for some specific act or service and it is an offence to sell or make away with them.

Plain clothes

Entering or leaving naval establishments. All ratings over the age of $17\frac{1}{2}$ years (other than those undergoing disciplinary or technical training) on first entry may, when granted leave, be allowed to wear plain clothes on leaving or returning to naval establishments. The standard of dress of men entering or leaving naval establishments is subject to control by the Commanding Officer. This concession may be withdrawn in certain circumstances.

Leaving or returning to H.M. ships. Ratings below P.O. are not permitted to proceed on leave or return to any of H.M. ships, or proceed in a Service boat or dockyard launch in plain clothes. C.P.O.s and P.O.s over 21 years of age may be allowed to wear plain clothes in certain circumstances when proceeding on leave from or returning to H.M. ships.

CARE, CLEANING AND STOWAGE OF KIT

Many ships are fitted with laundries, but where such services are not available the following hints will be of value for the washing, care and maintenance of kit.

Wash clothing

Regulations for 'Wash clothing' are necessary for the preservation of health, to prevent loss or theft, to preserve orderliness and to provide for the general safety of the ship in emergency. Washed clothing is only allowed to be hung in certain places at certain times. It is not allowed to be hung in mess-decks or other living spaces. A drying room is sometimes available where clothes may be hung under lock and key, and times of opening and closing are laid down in Ship's Orders. Other spaces between decks may also be allocated for drying clothes.

Upper-deck dressing lines may also be used in fine weather between specified times. Clothing is to be securely stopped to the lines. Normal hours for the use of upper-deck clothes lines are after working hours until sunset.

FRESH WATER AND WASHING

Fresh water is always limited on board, and to preserve stocks a good system of washing clothes is essential.

Wash white clothes before blue or coloured articles. This avoids coloured dyes staining white clothing.

Before washing white suits remove all dust and tobacco shreds from the pockets to prevent staining.

For the first two or three washes use warm (not hot) water for a white jumper and avoid contact between the blue and white materials. Rinse thoroughly and hang it upside down when drying it out.

Boiling water should only be used for linen or cotton materials and drill suits. Never boil silk, wool or coloured articles.

Turn blue clothes inside out when drying in the sun; this lessens the risk of fading.

Ironing. Electric irons should be treated with the utmost care, and should only be repaired by an authorized person. Any defects resulting from misuse are chargeable to the mess or rating responsible.

Hints on maintenance

Removing stains

Paint: on serge—rub with another piece of serge while paint is still wet.

Grease: turn garment inside out, place it on brown paper and scrub it hard with a cloth moistened with hot water. To remove grease from collars: place brown paper over the grease spot and press with a hot iron. This draws the grease into the paper.

Gold braid can be cleaned with an old toothbrush and soap and water. Dry bread is also a good cleaner.

Plastic caps. To keep the crowns of plastic caps clean and white, clean them frequently by wiping over the plastic material with warm soapy water, and then rinse with clean water. If oil or grease is found on the plastic, wipe it off with a clean cloth as soon as possible and then clean the plastic in the normal way. If a pen has to be used to mark the cap inside, do not press too hard. Never use detergents for cleaning plastic caps.

Pressing blue uniform. When pressing blue uniform a piece of linen should be placed between the iron and the suit—this avoids iron-marks on the nap of the cloth. Uniforms wet with salt water should be soaked in fresh water as soon as possible to remove the salt.

Wet boots and shoes. Wet footwear should be stuffed with newspaper or dry rags to soak up the damp and maintain the shape. Never place them on hot pipes or too near a fire, because this will crack the leather. Footwear soaked in salt water should be carefully cleaned with fresh water before drying. Dubbin will waterproof boots, but will never produce a good polish.

Damp climates and airing. Airing boots, shoes and clothing prevents mildew forming in damp climates. Airing and mothballs discourage moths and silverfish.

Folding of Class II trousers
1. Turn Class II trousers inside out.
2. Lay them 'athwartships' and fold one leg over the other.
3. Using a baton 3 or 4 inches wide, fold each leg concertina-fashion as far as the fork.
4. Roll tightly to the top.
5. Secure with stops.

Marking of kit

All articles of kit must be marked clearly with the owner's name, initials and, in cases of doubt, his number; this is most important, not only to enable anything mislaid to be returned to its owner, but also to enable anything stolen to be traced and the thief caught.

On board a ship many personal effects or articles of kit have to be stowed with those of other men and much trouble can be saved by ensuring that every item is clearly marked. Every man is issued with a 'type' on entry and is to mark his clothes as follows:

Blue clothes—with white paint
White clothes—with black marking ink.

Jerseys. To be marked on the inside, at the bottom, with red worsted, or on a white tape in ink and sewn over with blue worsted.

Overcoats and raincoats. To be marked with white paint on the cloth inside the coat on the right-hand side, in a vertical position. The first initial is to be in line with the second buttonhole.

Trousers and drawers. On the inside waistband, at the back.

Jumpers. On the back, close up to the collar seam.

Cotton uniform vests and action working dress shirts. On the tail.

Caps. On the crown.

Cap covers. On the inside of the band.

Towels. Centrally and horizontally at each end.

Scarves. Diagonally across the corner.

Boots and shoes. Inside the upper.

Kit bags. At the bottom with the owner's name and official number, in **black.**

Note: The marking of Class I and Class III uniforms is to conform as far as possible with that laid down for Class II. Jackets are to be marked across the shoulders inside.

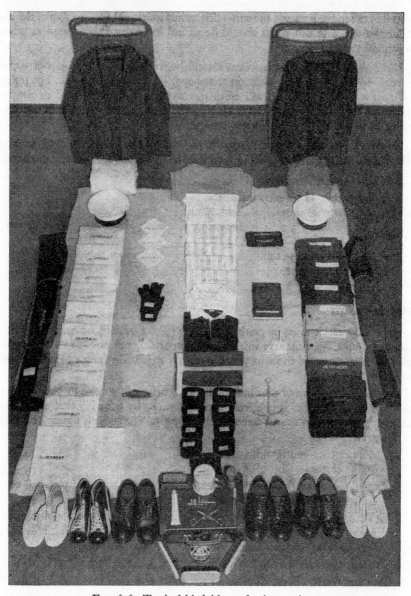

FIG. 6-6. Typical kit laid out for inspection

Stowage of kit

In a ship, stowage space is strictly limited and the proper and neat stowage of kit is important. Each rating is responsible for the stowage of his own kit, and all kit is to be stowed correctly and not left lying about (sculling). Each man is provided with a kit locker for his ready-use clothing and kit. In addition, he is allowed an attaché case for his personal effects. Racks are provided for boots and shoes, and special lockers are provided for the stowage of raincoats. Towel-rails are provided with each locker and should be used. Damp towels should not be stowed inside the

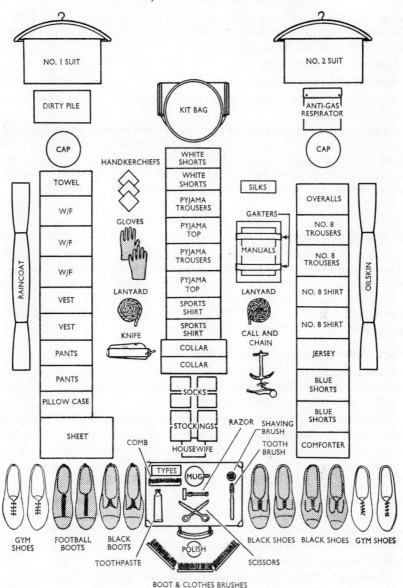

FIG. 6-7. Key to kit layout in FIG. 6-6

NOTES

1. According to the Branch of the rating and the rig worn by him, so the number of articles in the spaces will vary. With his No. 3 uniform the rating is assumed to be wearing at least one cap, one set of underwear, one seaman's belt, one pair of socks and one pair of black boots.

2. It is assumed that two sheets are on the rating's bunk.

3. Kit is folded.

4. Jumpers and trousers are hung nearby on coathangers.

5. Cook ratings will have four sets of cooks' caps, knitted shirts, aprons and white drill trousers. These should be at the top of the kit.

6. J.M.E.s and J.N.A.M.s will have two additional overall suits. H.M.E.s will have one steaming cap.

locker. All other clothing should be stowed in suitcases and kit bags, which must themselves be kept in the stowages provided for them. Suitcases should not exceed the dimensions of the Admiralty Pattern.

Never stow kit away while damp.

Separate blue from white kit.

Wrap white clothing in paper or polythene bags to prevent its picking up stains and dust.

Scran bag. All articles of clothing found lying about or stowed in improper places are handed to a member of the ship's Regulating Staff at the Regulating Office, where they are placed in the 'scran bag'. Any such articles can be redeemed by the owner for a forfeit. Unmarked articles, or those not claimed within a reasonable period, are disposed of by order of the Executive Officer.

KIT ALLOWANCES

Kit upkeep allowance

Every rating is expected to maintain his kit in good condition and to replace when necessary any unserviceable or worn article of the free kit originally issued to him. For this purpose he is allowed regularly a sum of money in addition to his pay, which is credited to him in advance in the ship's ledger. The amount of the sum varies from time to time in accordance with the cost of clothing, its value being quoted in current Defence Council Instructions (R.N.).

Other clothing allowances and gratuities

When advancement to a higher rank or rating involves a complete change of uniform, e.g. to Petty Officer (other than on Local Acting Advancement), a gratuity is paid to the rating to effect the change.

Compensation is made for clothing lost or damaged in the execution of duty.

On leaving the Service, ratings who have served 3 years or more are, subject to certain conditions, eligible to receive a civilian clothing outfit or a gratuity in lieu.

KIT INSPECTION AND MUSTERS

Divisional Officers are to muster the kit of men in their Divisions to ensure that a rating is fully kitted up and that his kit is in good condition, particularly when he is drafted to sea, abroad or to another ship. Kit musters may also be ordered for ratings who by slovenliness in dress or habits show that they have kit that is incomplete, incorrect or in poor condition.

The formal method of laying out kit (Figs. 6-6 & 7) may, apart from its use in New Entry Training Establishments, also be considered suitable for Senior Officers' Inspection, kit displays, etc. To enable Divisional Officers to examine individual articles and to avoid wasting time, the method shown in Fig. 6-8 may be found to be more practical for use at sea and outside New Entry Training Establishments.

Leading rates and above are exempt from kit musters, but should muster their own kit periodically.

When you lay out your kit you should:

(a) Fold each item so that it is as wide as this book is long, except for:
    Cotton uniform vests, which should be folded ready to wear,
    Collars, which should be folded lengthways,
    Class II trousers, which are to be folded as described on page 69.

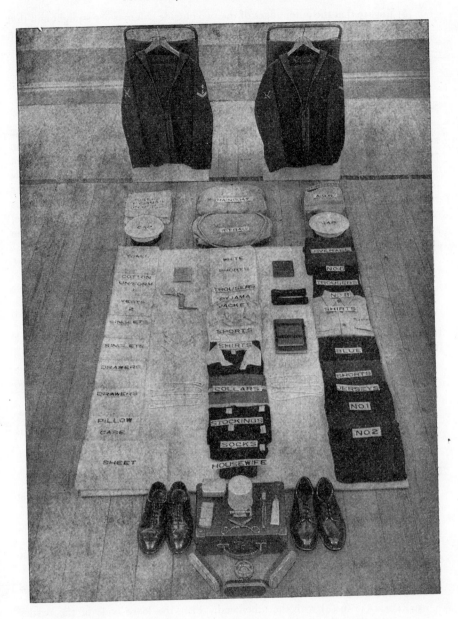

FIG. 6-8. Typical kit laid out for muster

(b) Ensure that the outer edges of the two outside columns are straight and that the edges of the centre column are in line (except for the collars, as shown in Fig. 6-6).

(c) Ensure that the articles are spaced in each column to take up the full length of the column.

Search of kit and effects

All ratings below Leading Rate are liable to personal search on entering or leaving a ship. This is to guard against smuggling. Leading Rates and above are exempt from personal search unless especially ordered to be searched by the Officer of the Watch, Duty Commanding Officer, Executive Officer, or the Captain. All ratings are liable to a search of their kit and effects by order of the officers listed above, for a specific reason. Such searches are necessary to establish the innocence of persons in cases of theft, to trace lost or stolen articles, and to catch thieves. Whenever possible, such searches are carried out by the Regulating Staff under the supervision of the rating's Divisional Officer and in the presence of the rating concerned.

BEDDING

The bedding issued depends upon the type of berth a man is allocated.

The *combined camp-bed and hammock* fitting can be used as a camp-bed or a hammock. For use as a camp-bed, pack metal fittings are drawn. The hammock fittings used are:

Clews. One pair issued. Each consists of a lanyard spliced to a steel ring. The ring also carries 8 nettles, each one being middled round the ring; the two ends are dipped through the eye of the bight to leave 16 ends.

Lashing. A length of sisal long enough to permit seven turns round the hammock (each marling-hitched) and the end to secure to its own part. The lashing has an eye splice in one end.

To sling a hammock (Fig. 6-9)

1. Secure one lanyard to the hammock bar so that the nettles' ends are at chest level.
2. Pass the outer nettles through the outer eyelets at the hammock corners; take a half-hitch, and leave about 6 in. hanging down.
3. Take the two centre nettles and secure them in the same manner to their corresponding holes, leaving 4 in. hanging down.
4. Working out from the centre, repeat (3) with the remaining nettles, adjusting evenly the amount left hanging down.
5. Repeat (1) to (4) with the other end. Plait the loose ends of the nettles together in threes and stow inside the hammock.
6. Now sling the hammock between two bars, passing the lanyard over the bar, up through the ring, and making a sheet bend round the top of the nettles. Then distribute the bedding over the length of the hammock, tautening up nettles if necessary.

To keep the sides of the head of the hammock apart, a stretcher can be used. This consists of a piece of wood about 2 ft. long, notched at each end and inserted between the two outside nettles at the head. Pass the lashing over the hammock and reeve the end through the eye, coil up the lashing and stow it on the head nettles.

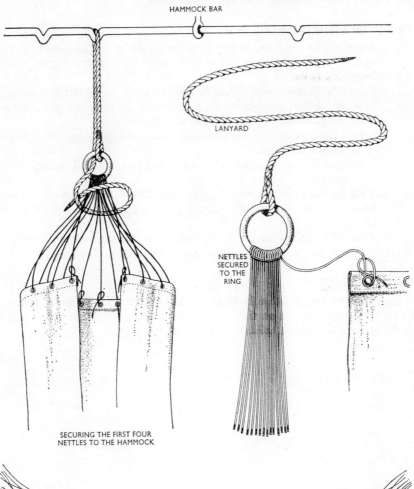

HAMMOCK BAR

LANYARD

NETTLES
SECURED
TO THE
RING

SECURING THE FIRST FOUR
NETTLES TO THE HAMMOCK

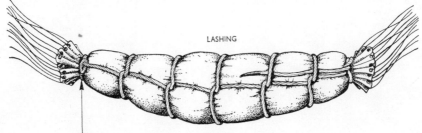

LASHING

The first turn is passed through the eye of the lashing.
The next five turns are marling-hitched.
The last turn is half-hitched to its own part.

FIG. 6-9. Slinging and lashing up a hammock

Hammocks should be triced well up to the deck head to allow passage below, and should never be slung in unauthorized places.

To lash up a hammock (Fig. 6-9)

1. Distribute the bedding evenly over the length of the hammock, leaving a space of about 6 in. either end to prevent the bedding sticking out when the hammock is lashed up.
2. Lower the hammock to breast height and stand on its left side facing the head. Bring the lashing down the nettles on to the hammock and draw taut.
3. Take six turns (or marling hitches) as follows:

   Pass the lashing over the hammock with the right hand. Bring it under with the left hand.

   Bring it over, then under, its own standing part and haul taut by swinging back on it.
4. Take the final turn round the neck of the foot of the hammock and secure on its own part by a half-hitch; then pass the end neatly under the previous turns.
5. Twist the nettles right-hand and tuck under the turns of the lashing.

Ship's Orders specify how frequently hammocks should be changed.

Airing bedding

Ship's Orders specify when bedding should be aired. Each mess or division has its own allocated position on the upper deck. Bedding should be lashed securely to the guardrails, without holidays and clear of the deck.

CHAPTER 7

Leave, Pay, Education, Religion and Welfare

LEAVE AND LIBERTY

See *Q.R. and A.I.*

Leave with full pay and allowances is granted in accordance with the regulations whenever possible, but always subject to the exigencies of the Service generally, to the safety of the ship in particular, and to any local circumstances which may prevail.

Leave can be curtailed or withheld on account of misconduct.

Types of leave

Leave is classified under three general headings:

Liberty: daily leave of under 24 hours
Short leave: leave of under 48 hours
Long leave: leave of over 48 hours

Public holidays

The following days are observed as far as possible as general holidays in Home Waters and in shore establishments at home, except in Junior Training Establishments, for which special regulations are laid down:

Good Friday   First Monday in August
Easter Monday   Christmas Day
Whit Monday   Boxing Day

The Sovereign's official birthday is not considered as a public holiday for purposes of leave, but an extra day's leave may be granted in lieu on either the Friday preceding or Tuesday following Whit week-end.

Leave at home

ANNUAL OR SEASONAL LEAVE

This is granted in Home Waters at Christmas and Easter and in the summer. The annual allowance for leave is laid down in regulations and is, as far as possible, split into three equal portions.

WEEK-END LEAVE

Short week-end leave. This may be granted, in addition to annual or seasonal leave, in shore establishments and in certain ships lying in their Home ports.

Long week-end leave. This may similarly be granted, but not more than twelve times per year.

Leave abroad (local leave)

Local leave abroad may be granted up to a maximum of 14 days per year to those ratings on Foreign Service who can be spared. In General Service ships local leave is only given when the ship is refitting abroad.

Miscellaneous leave

Compassionate leave. This may be granted at the discretion of the Commander-in-Chief of the station abroad, and by a man's Commanding Officer in ships at home in urgent cases (e.g. the serious illness or death of a wife or child; the imminent death—or, in certain circumstances, the serious illness—of a parent).

Sick leave. This is granted in special circumstances on the advice of the medical authorities to help in the recovery of a rating from an illness.

Watchkeeper's leave. Short leave is granted outside the normal daily leave periods to watchkeepers who keep continuous periods of watch, day and night, in harbour.

Travelling leave. Extra leave, added to long leave (but not to long or short week-end leave), may be granted to ratings who live at a long distance from the place where leave is being granted.

Marriage leave. Ratings should arrange for their weddings to take place during a seasonal or other long leave period. If this is not possible, long leave may be granted outside the seasonal leave periods, but only if the rating's services can be spared. Such leave will be deducted from annual leave.

Re-engagement leave. Up to 28 days' re-engaging leave may be granted to ratings on re-engagement.

Terminal leave. Twenty-eight days leave is granted to ratings prior to discharge on completion of a normal regular engagement to enable them to seek civil employment.

LEAVE REGULATIONS

Leave is granted by watches or parts of watches to all rates (except Chief Petty Officers, who are granted leave irrespective of watch) whenever their duties allow. Daily leave is piped daily, other leave being notified as circumstances demand.

Chief Petty Officers' and Petty Officers' leave

All C.P.O.s and P.O.s request permission of the Officer of the Watch before proceeding on leave, and report to him on return from leave.

Liberty boats; inspection of libertymen

The times of liberty boats are laid down in Ships' Orders and libertymen are piped to fall in at those times. Libertymen are also fallen in for inspection on return from shore. On both occasions they are inspected by the Officer of the Watch. Before proceeding on leave they are warned of the times of expiry of their leave, regulations regarding dress and patrols ashore, of the Customs regulations, and of any other matters to which their attention should be drawn.

Free gangway

In ships lying alongside and in shore establishments certain times are laid down between which ratings are permitted to use a 'free gangway'. On these occasions ratings are permitted to pass close by the Officer of the Watch and salute, instead of reporting or falling in for inspection.

Leave cards

All Leading rates and below are issued with station cards on joining a ship. These cards are surrendered on going on leave and reclaimed on returning aboard.

By this method a check is kept of ratings who may be absent, and it is a serious offence for a rating to have another rating's station card in his possession. Petty Officers and above personally tick off their names on a board before proceeding ashore and cross-tick on their return.

Leave passes

These are issued to all ratings proceeding on Long Leave and in some cases on Short Leave. These passes list all particulars about the leave they have been granted. The following details and instructions may be found on the back of the pass:

(a) Instructions to be followed in the event of sickness while on leave.

(b) Action in the event of loss of return ticket.

(c) Instructions regarding change of address on leave and notification to be forwarded to the ship's Commanding Officer. (A rating's address must permit a message to reach him within 24 hours of its despatch.)

(d) Action to take if delayed for reasons beyond the man's control.

These details are also listed in the naval rating's paybook, and should be referred to prior to proceeding on leave.

What to do if sick on shore

Before proceeding ashore on any form of leave a rating should know what to do if he falls sick. He should know whether he can get medical attention from his ship or the port, and the address of the Surgeon and Agent for the area. If he falls sick he should:

(a) Call in a doctor from one of the three sources above (in the order given); or, failing that, call in a civilian doctor.

(b) Inform his ship.

(c) Forward a doctor's certificate as soon as possible.

(d) Ensure that a doctor's certificate is forwarded to his ship at weekly intervals from the date of (c), until he is fit to travel.

(e) As soon as he is fit to travel, return to his ship with a final certificate stating that he is fit to do so.

Doctor's certificate. A rating must always return from leave if he is *fit to travel*. A doctor's certificate is valueless if it states only the nature of the illness and fails to state whether a man may travel or not; illness alone is not sufficient reason for absence over leave. In cases of discharge from hospital fitness to travel must be included in the discharge note, and hospital authorities should be requested to report the disposal of a patient direct to the man's ship as well as providing him with a discharge note.

Restrictions on persons refusing inoculation or vaccination

All officers and men are vaccinated and inoculated on entry and re-vaccinated, re-inoculated (or inoculated) as occasion demands. Anyone may refuse to undergo these precautions, but should he do so, permission for him to land may be withdrawn wherever there is any danger of his contracting disease. This precaution is most necessary in order to safeguard the remainder of the ship's company.

Free travel

Each rating may be allowed three free travel warrants a year, between 1st March and the end of the following February, enabling him to go on leave and return free of cost. A free travel warrant may be allowed for Drafting and Foreign Service leave.

Privileged leave list

There may be certain occasions when it is possible to grant a limited amount of leave, but when leave-breaking would cause great inconvenience and when misbehaviour ashore might reflect badly on the Service or the nation. In these special circumstances leave may be piped only to men who have not broken their leave and who can be trusted ashore and to return from leave. On first commissioning a ship all men are considered to be in this category and their names are said to be on the 'privileged leave list'. Men who subsequently show that they cannot behave ashore or return to their ships have their names removed from this list. Both removal and restoration are made at the discretion of a man's Commanding Officer.

Conduct on leave

While on leave ratings must not bring discredit on the Navy by misbehaviour. If a man is dealt with by the civil power for a civil offence committed while on leave, naval penalties can be awarded quite apart from any sentence given by the civil court. The severity of any such penalty is governed primarily by the degree of discredit brought upon the Service as a result of the case.

Drunkenness. Any rating returning from leave who, owing to the influence of alcohol or any drug, is unfit to be entrusted with any duty he may be required to carry out, or who behaves in a disorderly manner, may be immediately placed under restraint. This is done for both his own good and that of his messmates. Drunkenness is punishable according to a scale and may be accompanied by additional punishments.

Returning from leave

Every rating is himself responsible for returning from leave at the correct time. Excuses such as failure of alarm clocks or 'just missing' public transport are not acceptable. Should there be, however, a breakdown of public transport, or a similar event beyond the control of the rating, a certificate in confirmation of the event should be obtained from a recognized official of the company or from the local police. Unnecessary watchkeeping and manning problems are created if a ship sails short-handed as a result of personnel being absent over leave. Such shortages could endanger the efficiency or even the safety of the ship and her company in wartime or in an emergency.

Absence over leave

This is an offence which is strictly dealt with, and failure to make every effort to return at the earliest possible time after the expiration of leave is regarded as aggravating the offence. Remaining absent over leave may be involuntary by lack of means of transport (e.g. missing the last boat back to the ship). In such cases the rating should report to the nearest naval authority such as a ship, shore establishment or naval patrol, or to the civil police, who will give him any necessary instructions and endorse his leave pass with the time of reporting. This time may be taken into consideration in the subsequent investigation of the offence.

Leave-breaking is punishable by a stoppage (mulct) of pay and forfeiture of leave under a scale laid down in regulations, which varies according to the period of absence. In awarding punishments within the limits of the scale, the investigating authority can take into consideration extenuating circumstances and the absentee's general behaviour.

An offence of improper absence can be 'aggravated' under certain circumstances such as an emergency, time of war, the ship being under sailing orders, etc. It may also be regarded as 'repeated' for a second or subsequent offence occurring within a prescribed time.

Both repeated and aggravated offences may entail additional punishments being added to those laid down in the scale.

General recall

Whenever flag 'P' (commonly known as the 'Blue Peter') is hoisted in any ship, it is to be understood as recalling all officers and men belonging to her who may be on leave. As soon as a rating sees this he is to return to his ship immediately.

The General Recall may also be promulgated through the naval and civil police by notices, announcements in the streets, canteens, cinemas, places of public entertainment, etc. It must be obeyed immediately.

PAY, ALLOTMENTS AND REMITTANCES

See B.R. 1950, *Naval Pay Regulations*

The Naval Pay Regulations

The pay and allowances of officers and men of the Royal Navy and Royal Marines are set out in B.R. 1950, *Naval Pay Regulations*. The basis of the Pay Code is payment of increased rates of pay for higher qualifications and length of service. This ensures that all members of the Royal Navy and Royal Marines receive rates of pay which, after allowance for difference in Service conditions and qualifications, give overall parity with the other armed Services.

The ledger

Pay accounts of officers and men are kept in 'the ledger'. The Supply Officer is responsible for its maintenance and correctness. The ledger is kept in duplicate, each maintained separately by two different Writers in order to avoid errors in accounting and as a cross-check. The ledgers are called the 'working' ledger and the 'loose-leaf' ledger (S.50).

Besides details of pay, allowances, income tax, etc., the ledger contains a great deal of information concerning a man's career. From the ledger the naval authorities are able to reconstruct the details of a man's career should his Service documents become lost or destroyed.

For larger ships the ledgers are kept on board: for small ships they are kept at a base on shore. The base provides Commanding Officers with the information required in order to pay the ship's company and to inform the latter of matters concerning pay and allowances, savings accounts, etc.

The loose-leaf ledger (S.50)

At the end of each pay period a man is given a form (S.50) showing all payments, allotments and deductions concerning his pay during that pay period. It should be checked and retained, as it is an official document and the only means by which a man is informed of the state of his pay.

Method of payment

Main payment. Payment is made fortnightly. Hands are piped to payment at the time stated and are fallen in according to ship's book number. A Writer sits at the pay table with the ledger: the Paying Officer is close by with his envelopes, each containing a man's pay. Another officer stands by the table to witness payment. When all is ready, the Writer calls out the name of the first man on the ledger; the man replies by calling out his ship's book number, salutes the Paying Officer and steps up in front of him, showing his pay book. The Writer then calls out the wages due, the Paying Officer pays them and the man doubles away.

Miss-muster payment. Certain ratings, such as watchkeepers, may not be able to attend main payment. A suitable time is fixed to pay these men and the payment is known as 'miss-muster payment', the men being referred to as 'miss-musters'.

Allotments

Ratings can make regular weekly payments to wives or other dependants, and monthly payments to tradesmen, etc. by means of allotments. An allotment declaration is made out in the Pay Office and is signed by the man. The Pay Office then makes the necessary notations in the ledger which will result in the amounts being deducted from pay. The form is sent to the Principal Director of Accounts, who pays the money regularly to the person concerned on behalf of the man who has made out the allotment.

The number of permissible allotments is:

two monthly and one extra to a recognized Savings organization,
one weekly to a man's wife or dependant.

Normally, no more than two allotment changes may be made in one pay period.

Payment of marriage allowance

The payment of marriage allowance is normally conditional upon a married man making a weekly allotment from his pay to his wife. This must at least equal the qualifying rate appropriate to his rating in the Service.

It is important to tell the Pay Office at once of any change in domestic circumstances which may affect the amount of allowances payable; otherwise overpayment may occur and recovery become necessary.

Remittances

Allotments are regular payments which continue automatically until stopped. There are, however, occasions when an officer or man wishes to send a sum of money to a wife, relative, friend, tradesman, etc. In such cases a sum can be remitted through the Supply Officer. The Supply Officer is handed the cash and he issues a receipt for it.

Money may always be handed to the Supply Officer for safe-keeping in Shore Establishments in the United Kingdom where savings facilities are not available. A receipt will be given for it, and it may be withdrawn when required.

Handling of money for remittance and custody. Cash for remittance, custody or deposit in a Savings Bank must always be handed to an officer and never to a rating.

EDUCATION

See *Q.R. and A.I;* B.R. 1066, *Advancement Regulations*

Education facilities exist in all ships and establishments and every opportunity is given to those who are keen to use them. In all but the smaller ships and establishments Instructor Officers are borne to give all possible help to those requiring educational assistance. If no Instructor Officer is borne, an officer is detailed to act as Education Officer.

The Instructor Officer or Education Officer is always available to tell ratings about the educational examinations they have to pass before they can become eligible for promotion or advancement.

Able Seaman's Test (E.T.A.B.). This simple test in arithmetic and dictation is the educational qualification for Able Rate, and all ratings must pass this test before leaving the New Entry Training Establishments.

Educational Test for Leading Rate (E.T.L.R.). A test in arithmetic and English, which is the educational qualification for Leading Rate and above. Exemption can be obtained in New Entry Training Establishments. Classes are held in ships and training establishments to prepare ratings for this examination, which is held three times a year.

General Certificate of Education and Higher Educational Test. This examination is held twice a year, in spring and autumn, in eight subjects. One or more subjects may be taken at a time and a candidate may qualify for a G.C.E. ('O' level) pass or, at one grade lower, an H.E.T. only pass. G.C.E. certificates are issued to successful candidates. H.E.T. certificates are issued to those who have passed in four subjects at H.E.T. level.

Apart from its importance in civilian life, G.C.E./H.E.T. also provides the educational qualification for S.D. list (4 subjects at H.E.T. level) and for Upper Yardmen (4 subjects at 'O' level).

The Instructor Officer arranges classes to prepare ratings for the G.C.E./H.E.T. examinations. Where no Instructor Officer is borne, the Education Officer can arrange suitable correspondence courses.

Further education

Apart from meeting Service requirements, there are educational opportunities for men to make good use of their spare time. Education centres exist at Portsmouth and Devonport and at some naval bases abroad. At these centres reading-rooms, libraries and courses on various subjects are always available. Information rooms, which are supplied with literature on matters of current interest, are maintained in some large ships and most shore establishments. The non-fiction and reference books in ships' libraries cover a wide range of subjects. There are also some hundreds of correspondence courses available under the Forces Correspondence Course Scheme, to enable men to study subjects in which they are interested. In addition, financial assistance is given towards the cost of other courses, provided certain conditions are fulfilled.

The scope of Further Education includes such cultural pursuits as play-reading circles, music-appreciation groups and discussion groups; and, where possible, opportunities are provided for men and women to follow the more important aspects of current national and world affairs.

RELIGION

The Church and the Navy

When you join the Navy you are asked to state your religion. You are not compelled to profess a religion; you can, as an alternative, declare yourself an 'agnostic' (i.e. one who holds that nothing is known or is likely to be known of the existence of God) or as having 'No religion'. If, however, you do state that you have a religion and belong to a certain Church, it is expected that you are sincere about it and that you understand, or at least are willing to learn, what that profession means and the obligations it demands.

Your Church in the Navy welcomes you, looks forward to your fellowship and is ready to help you at all times. The Christian Church ordains ministers to present the duty of obedience to God and bring it to expression in worship and conduct. The Navy appoints Chaplains to provide for your spiritual and moral welfare, and to whatever Church you belong you will find facilities provided to enable you to continue the practice of your religion. Your Church afloat is part of your Church ashore and not something separate or distinct. There is an age-old custom and regulation in the Navy that prayers should be said daily; it is a good one and draws everyone together in a family, and a good ship is one where there is this family spirit and feeling of comradeship.

Some of the Chaplain's duties

One is to lead worship.

Worship is the public acknowledgment of God's supremacy. Church attendance is voluntary; but, needless to say, it is the natural duty of believers to practise their religion and to take part in corporate worship.

Another is to instruct in the Christian faith. There will be many men who will wish to know more about their religion. Wherever men foregather religion comes in for discussion and the messdeck is no exception. Difficulties may arise which require an explanation. Do not hesitate to ask the Chaplain; he is ready and willing to help you in this matter to the best of his ability, just as he is ready at all times to help and advise you in other matters of a more personal or domestic nature. The Chaplain is regarded as the friend and adviser of all on board.

The Church and You

You on your part also have a responsibility to the Church to which you belong. Be faithful to it and give it your support by your personal conduct and by your presence at its acts of worship.

Whether you have been taught to believe in God or not, the fact remains that the majority of people in the Royal Navy believe that:

We came from God,

We belong to God,

We are on our way to God,

and that it matters very much how we live our daily lives.

WELFARE

SOURCES OF ADVICE AND HELP

A man gives of his best for his ship and the Service when he is content with his surroundings and his mind is at rest about his family affairs at home and about his future.

THE DIVISIONAL OFFICER

A Divisional Officer is instructed to study his men's interests so as to be well acquainted with their conditions of life both on board and ashore. He keeps in close touch with his men and is ready at all times to advise and help them to the best of his ability.

THE CHAPLAIN

The Chaplain, who holds no rank, is concerned primarily with spiritual matters, but his experience enables him to advise in many problems, and he is always pleased to give help and counsel.

THE COMMANDING OFFICER

The Captain is concerned with the welfare of the entire ship's company, and any man may ask, through his Divisional Officer, to see his Captain for advice on private matters.

THE WELFARE COMMITTEE

Every ship with a complement of 50 or more has its own Welfare Committee. Ships and craft whose complements are less than 50 form a Flotilla Welfare Committee. The Committee consists of a number of officers detailed by the Commanding Officer, including the Executive Officer as *ex officio* chairman of the Committee, and a number of lower-deck representatives elected by the messes or divisions in the ship. C.P.O.s and P.O.s may be represented by their messes or their branches, according to the size of the ship.

Welfare Committees in ships and shore establishments provide for free discussion to take place between officers and men on matters of welfare and general amenities within the ship or establishment.

Matters discussed by the Welfare Committee include living conditions in the ship or establishment, messing arrangements, composition of meals, recreational activities, and any suggestions for the welfare of the ship's company. Responsibility for the administration of the ship's Welfare Fund is also undertaken by this Committee. General conditions of service, i.e. discipline, working hours, pay, leave scales, etc., are outside the scope of Welfare Committees. Questions of welfare amenities not directly connected with the particular ship or establishment are also outside their scope.

The institution of these Committees does not in any way interfere with or prejudice the right of an individual rating to put forward suggestions or complaints through his Divisional Officer or affect the responsibility of the Divisional Officer for looking after the interests of his men.

THE WELFARE FUND

The main source of income of the ship's Welfare Fund is a rebate on the value of goods sold at the ship's canteen. It is primarily intended to contribute to the cost of recreation and amenities for the ship's company and to be used for benevolent purposes connected with the ship. The Captain must satisfy himself that a sufficient allowance is made for these objects, with a due regard to the proportion of the ship's company who are able to take part in any particular form of recreation. In all respects the Welfare Committee has full discretion as regards expenditure, subject only to the right of veto on the part of the Captain of any proposed expenditure which appears to him subversive of discipline or otherwise improper.

Loans to individuals from the Welfare Fund are only permitted in exceptional circumstances. Any such loan must ordinarily be repaid while the borrower is serving in the ship in which the loan is made.

RECREATIONAL FACILITIES

Canteens

THE N.A.A.F.I.

The Navy, Army and Air Force Institute (N.A.A.F.I.) is the organization used by the Service to provide canteens in H.M. ships and establishments. Although it caters for the three Services, the Naval accounts are kept entirely separate from the Army and the Royal Air Force accounts, so that trading balances of one Service cannot be diverted to another.

The N.A.A.F.I. makes no profit and has no shareholders. A rebate on all sales is paid back to the ship's fund, a proportion of this rebate being subscribed by all ships and establishments to the Royal Naval Benevolent Trust. At the end of the financial year any surplus revenue is handed back to the Royal Navy to be spent on welfare purposes.

CANTEEN COMMITTEES

The affairs of the canteen in ships and establishments are administered by the Welfare Committee or by a standing sub-committee called the Canteen Committee appointed by the Welfare Committee from its members. Its duties are to investigate any questions and complaints that may arise in regard to prices and quality of canteen goods, weights and measures, and the general working of the canteen.

At each of the Home ports a committee, consisting of representatives from ships and establishments at the port, meets periodically to discuss canteen matters affecting the port. Similarly, the Fleet, squadrons, etc. hold meetings to discuss canteen matters which affect them. In addition, lower-deck representatives are elected annually to represent the point of view of the Fleet, establishments and Royal Marines at N.A.A.F.I. headquarters.

VOLUNTARY CANTEENS

In many places at home and abroad canteens are provided for all Service men by voluntary bodies, which include:

Y.M.C.A.   W.V.S.
Y.W.C.A.   Salvation Army
Church Army   Catholic Women's League
Church of Scotland   Toc H
Methodist Church Forces Centres   Church of England Soldiers', Sailors'
Missions to Mediterranean Garrisons   and Airmen's Clubs.

These bodies are co-ordinated by the Council of Voluntary Welfare Work.

OTHER SOCIETIES

In addition, seamen's societies provide canteens for men of the Royal Navy, Merchant Navy and fishing fleet. Among the larger of these organizations are the British Sailors' Society, the Royal Sailors' Rest and the Missions to Seamen (The Flying Angel Clubs).

Hostels and clubs

Hostels and clubs are provided at many naval ports and centres. In London the following are well worth remembering:

The Union Jack Club, for Servicemen ⎫
The Union Jack Families and Women's Services Clubs, for ⎬ Near Waterloo
   Servicemen and their families and Servicewomen ⎭ Station, S.E.1
The Red Shield Club, Buckingham Gate, S.W.1
The Nuffield Centre, Adelaide Street, W.C.2
The Chevrons Club, Dorset Square, N.W.1

Each of the Home ports has its clubs and hostels, details of which are given in local orders.

Cinemas

The Navy is fortunate in the supply of recreational films for seagoing ships. As a result of the generosity of the film industry the Royal Naval Film Corporation can distribute good films cheaply to ships when not in dockyard hands or alongside. The small regular payment for these films depends on the number of men in the ship (however many see the show) and the number of films shown. It is often paid out of the ship's fund. Officers' messes pay separately.

The Royal Naval Film Corporation (shore establishment). This operates in a similar way, but the shows must not cut across the legitimate trade of local cinemas. Payment in this case depends on the number of admissions to each performance.

Sports and games

The Navy pays officially for sports grounds and their upkeep. The Welfare Fund is intended to help to provide the gear and equipment required.

The R.N. and R.M. Sports Control Board helps to encourage sports and games. It makes grants and loans to ships and establishments, on commissioning, in order to buy sports gear, before any money has been collected in the ship's fund. Further grants and loans may be made as described in Defence Council Instructions (R.N.) or in *Sports and Recreation in the Royal Navy*.

FAMILY WELFARE

A booklet called *A Guide for Naval and Royal Marines Families* is issued to all naval wives on the first occasion of drawing their marriage allotment. It contains information concerning family welfare, leave, types of service, etc. which help the naval wife to understand how the Service works.

Married quarters

A scheme to provide married quarters supplemented by furnished hirings operates at ports and establishments in the United Kingdom and at most stations abroad. Where demand for accommodation is heavy a married quarter may not become available immediately it is required: quarters are therefore allocated from a waiting list.

Ratings who wish their names to be put on this list should apply to their Divisional Officer in the ship or establishment in which they are serving. This application is forwarded to the Staff Married Quarters Officer at the ship's base or refitting port in the United Kingdom.

A rating's Divisional Officer can always advise him on such matters as entitlement to a married quarter, length of time a rating may expect to wait for one, conditions of tenancy, etc., consulting the Staff Married Quarters Officer as necessary.

Family passages

Free passages are provided for the families of ratings serving in certain billets abroad where suitable accommodation is available. Concession travel for families of Service personnel is also permitted, subject to current regulations issued in Defence Council Instructions (R.N.).

Concession (CSN) Telegrams

These are provided to enable officers and men to receive communications from their families, and to send messages to them on urgent personal affairs. Next of kin and one other nominated person can obtain the special forms by application to a rating's depot; on these forms messages can be sent through the Post Office at inland rates. Messages can be sent home to the next of kin or second nominated person at concession rates as laid down in Defence Council Instructions (R.N.).

Family Welfare Section

A Family Welfare Section works under the supervision of the Commodore at Portsmouth and Devonport barracks, and the Flag Officer Air (Home) at Lee-on-Solent. The Family Welfare Officer and his staff are all civilians.

Any man, wherever he is serving, who has cause for anxiety about his family should first see his Divisional Officer and, if appropriate, consult the Chaplain; he may also request to see his Commanding Officer privately. The latter will, if the circumstances of the case demand, communicate by signal with the man's selected Welfare Authority, (i.e. the Commodore, R.N. Barracks, Portsmouth or Devonport, or the Flag Officer Naval Air Command). On receipt, the signal is referred to the Family Welfare Section, which, where necessary, arranges for a Welfare worker to visit the family if it is in the vicinity of the port. Families living further afield and to whom a visit may be necessary have their problems referred to specially selected workers in the area concerned. The Soldiers', Sailors' and Airmen's Families Association plays a great part in this work outside the ports.

In the same way, wives or dependants of serving men who are in need of help or advice can visit or write to the Family Welfare Section and discuss difficulties or troubles with the Family Welfare Officer. Should they not be able to contact the Family Welfare Section they can go to the local branch of S.S.A.F.A., which works in close co-operation with the Welfare Sections.

Welfare workers. Naval Welfare workers are highly experienced specialists; cases of distress, hardship and domestic difficulties are dealt with by them sympathetically and quickly, and no matter is too trivial or too great for them.

Home helps. A wife who is ill, has young children, or is temporarily incapacitated presents a difficult problem. The voluntary assistance of neighbours may be the solution in some cases, but in general it has been found better for paid local help to deal with the problem. Welfare workers who are Chief Wrens investigate the local conditions and make recommendations to the Family Welfare Officer concerned. In cases where the illness of the mother is likely to be permanent or of considerable duration, arrangements can be made for the children to be transferred, on either a temporary or permanent basis, to one of the Children's Homes set up for the care of children of Service personnel.

TRUSTS, FUNDS AND ASSOCIATIONS

The Royal Naval Benevolent Trust (R.N.B.T.). The R.N.B.T. has been established since 1922 as the central benevolent organisation for past, present and future C.P.O.s, P.O.s, N.C.O.s and men of the R.N., R.M. and R.N.R. It is controlled and administered by a central committee and local committees at Portsmouth and Devonport. There are a few officers on the central and local committees to help and advise; but there is a large majority on every committee of men who have served or who are serving as ratings, and the allocation of funds is entirely in their hands. One or more ratings on board every ship in the Royal Navy act as Corresponding Representatives of the Trust and are links between the men afloat and the committees of the Trust at home. The primary beneficial objects as laid down by Royal Charter are:

(*a*) To provide relief in cases of necessity or distress to those ratings mentioned above.

(*b*) To make provision for training such persons for civil life, and to give them assistance in order that they may obtain suitable employment after leaving the Service.

(*c*) To make contributions, either directly or through the agency of other benevolent or educational institutions, for the care, training, maintenance and welfare of the families and dependants of such persons in case of necessity or distress.

The Forces Help Society and Lord Roberts Workshops. This Society helps men and women during their service and after their discharge. There are representatives in most districts.

The Royal Naval Association. This is an association of ex-naval men who help each other. There are branches in most districts.

The National Association for the Employment of Regular Sailors, Soldiers and Airmen (R.F.E.A.). This is the principal organization for helping a man to find employment on return to civil life, its objects being to recommend to employers selected men of steady character and of the necessary qualification or calling.

Men are given cards before leaving the Service to enable them to register in their own districts. The Association provides 'job-finders' in most districts, and issues Resettlement Bulletins from time to time.

King George's Fund for Sailors. This is a centre for information about all nautical charities, as well as the principal distributing medium for them.

The Nuffield Trust for the Forces of the Crown. This makes monetary grants for the provision of amenities not procurable through public funds. In addition, the Trust assists a number of Service clubs at home and abroad.

RESETTLEMENT

Both Devonport and Portsmouth have Command Resettlement Officers, who promulgate information on resettlement and advise personnel who are about to leave the Service for civil life. Each ship and establishment has an officer appointed for resettlement duties who performs the same function.

Courses

Resettlement courses are available before leaving the Service for personnel who meet the required qualifications. An effort is made to enable a man to start one of these courses during the latter part of his service, but much depends upon the circumstances.

National organization

A number of associations (e.g. R.F.E.A.—see page 89) and the Ministry of Labour work closely with the Service in the field of resettlement. Anyone who is leaving the Service is well advised to contact his ship's or establishment's Resettlement Officer, who will make every effort to put him in contact with a resettlement organization.

CHAPTER 8

Organization and Routines

ORGANIZATION

Command

A warship is commanded by a seaman officer who is known as the 'Commanding Officer' or the 'Captain'. He may be of any rank from Captain to Lieutenant, depending upon the size and type of ship he commands.

Next to the Captain is the 'Executive Officer', who may be of any rank from Commander to Sub-Lieutenant. He is specially appointed to carry out executive duties in the ship, and he is responsible to the Captain for the overall fighting efficiency of the ship, the general organization and routine of her ship's company, and the discipline, morale and welfare of all on board. In ships where the Executive Officer is of Commander's rank, he is known as 'the Commander'; otherwise he is known as 'the First Lieutenant'; in ships where the Executive Officer is a Commander, the officer of the seaman specialisation next in seniority to him is known as 'the First Lieutenant'.

In the event of death or incapacity of the Captain, the command of the ship devolves upon the senior surviving officer appointed for seaman duties.

During the temporary absence on leave or on duty of the Captain, the command of the ship for the time being is vested in the senior officer on board appointed for seaman duties. Different rules apply in shore establishments.

Departments and divisions

The men who man a warship are known collectively as the ship's 'company'. They are divided into departments, each of which is related to a particular task, e.g. the Engineroom department, Supply and Secretariat department, etc. In a large ship a department may consist of several hundred men. The senior officer of a department is known as the 'head' of his department and is responsible to the Captain for its efficiency.

For general administrative and welfare purposes the ship's company is divided into 'divisions', which normally correspond as closely as possible with the departments in which they work. The ideal size of a division is about 25 men. In a large ship there may be several divisions within a department, but in a small ship the men in a department may form one division. The main principle of the divisional system is that each division is composed of a body of men who normally work and mess together, and who therefore know each other well.

The Divisional Officer. Each division is under the charge of an officer of the department concerned, who is responsible for the administration, training, instruction, advancement, welfare and general efficiency of everyone in the division. He is expected to know all members of his division well, and to give each man's problems consideration, sympathy and understanding, ensuring that every action necessary is taken to maintain the general welfare and efficiency of all those under him.

The Divisional Senior Rating. The Divisional Officer has a senior rating to assist

91

him, who may be a Chief Petty Officer, a Petty Officer or a Leading Hand. He attends to the day-to-day administration and work of the division. He must work closely with his Divisional Officer. He plays a vital part in the divisional system, acting as a link between the Divisional Officer and the men of his division.

All problems, queries, requests, complaints and personal matters which ratings wish to discuss or bring to the Divisional Officer's notice must be forwarded through the Divisional Senior Rating. The Divisional Senior Rating is to assist members of his division in making their representation to the Divisional Officer, and in many cases provide the guidance and help required, calling on his own experience as a rating in the Service.

Offices

The general organization and administration of a warship are directed through several offices, the more important of which are briefly described below.

The *Captain's Office* deals with the questions of general policy in the administration of the ship, with the records and documents relating to all her officers and men, and with all Secret and Confidential correspondence. All official mail is delivered to this office. This office may, in small ships, be combined with the Pay Office.

The *Pay Office*. Here are kept the ship's ledgers and all matters concerning pay, allowances and allotments are dealt with.

The *Commander's* or *Routine Office*. The administration of the ship's internal organization is done in this office. Routines, daily orders and general ship notices are originated here.

The *Regulating* or *Coxswain's Office*. This office is concerned with the discipline, liberty and leave of the ship's company, and with the victualling and checking of officers and men in and out of the ship.

The *Victualling Office*. This office administers the victualling of officers and men, the stowage and issue of provisions and clothing, and the preparation, cooking and serving of meals.

The *Naval Store Office*. This office is concerned with the stowage, issue and return of naval stores, except departmental stores such as armament stores. This office is usually adjacent to the main naval store, where every kind of article from a nut to an aircraft tail plane is kept.

The *Technical Office*. This office is concerned with the main domestic and weapon machinery in the ship, as well as the administration of the ratings concerned with the engineering and weapons departments. In small ships this office is usually integrated in the ship's NBCD organization.

The *Specialist Branch Office(s)*. The T.A.S., Gunnery and R.P. departments sometimes combine their administration in one or more offices.

The *Main Signal Office* or *Communications Centre*. This office deals with all signals and communications (other than official mail), attending to the routeing and distribution of all signals.

The *Mail Office*. This office handles the despatch, receipt, collection and internal distribution of both official and private mail.

WATCHES

A continuous watch must be kept in a ship both by day and night, at sea or in harbour, to ensure her safety and to keep her in working trim. A proportion of her complement of officers and men must therefore always be on watch, either actively engaged or standing by at immediate notice. The size of that proportion depends upon the type of ship, whether she is at sea or in harbour and the duties on which she is engaged. To provide a continuous watch of varying size to suit the occasion, and to allow for the rest and recreation of the men, a ship's company is divided into watches and parts of watches. In each there are sufficient men of the various branches and with the necessary technical qualifications to carry out any duty which the watch or part thereof may be required to perform.

There are two main types of watch organization, known respectively as the 'three-watch' and 'two-watch' system. In either system each watch may be divided into two parts: thus a part of the watch is the smallest body of men that is used to fight and work a ship. Modern ships are complemented for a three-watch system.

The Three-watch system

Here the watches are 'Red', 'White' and 'Blue' and each has its own first and second parts. In this system the men can be worked in three watches (four hours on and eight hours off at sea, and one day on and two days off in harbour). The system provides for two-thirds, one-third or one-sixth of the total ship's company to be used for any work or duty required.

The Two-watch system

Here the watches are 'Port' and 'Starboard' and again have their first and second parts. In this system the men can be worked 'watch and watch' (four hours on and four hours off at sea, or one day on and one day off in harbour) or in 'four watches' (four hours on and twelve off at sea, or one day on and three off in harbour). The units of this system are three-quarters, half and a quarter of the ship's company.

In either system the men off watch carry out their general ship's duties in accordance with the routine in force at the time. Owing to the complementing of ships it is generally best to work in three watches, but it may be more feasible to work in two watches at sea. In harbour watches are worked according to the requirements, but it is easiest to work in units of the system worked at sea.

Parts of ship (Seaman department)

For purposes of cleaning and ship husbandry, a warship is divided into what are known as 'parts of ship'. Typical examples of this are shown below.

Four parts	Three parts	Two parts
Forecastle (FX)	Forecastle (FX)	Forecastle (FX)
Foretop (FT)	Top (T) or Irondeck	Quarterdeck (AX)
Maintop (MT)	Quarterdeck (AX)	
Quarterdeck (AX)		

Seaman Petty Officers and men are detailed in approximately equal numbers from each part of the watch to each part of ship; they are known by their part of ship, e.g. forecastlemen.

Each part of ship is thus composed of approximately equal numbers from each watch or part of watch: and conversely each watch or part is composed of approximately equal numbers from each part of ship. Care is taken to ensure that each different rate and qualification is spread equally between the watches and parts of ship and that they are balanced as regards seniority and experience.

Employment of the hands

For general harbour duties the watch systems allow for the employment of varying numbers of hands, as shown below:

(a) *Clear lower deck.* This calls all men of all branches, except those actually on watch, and completely disrupts the work of the ship.

(b) *Both watches of the hands.* This can include all departments, and is normally used as the first muster of each working day. Certain members of the ship's company are excused this muster: these are enumerated in the ship's 'Excused List'.

(c) *Watch, or part of the watch, of the hands.* This calls all seamen and marines of the watch or part concerned except those actually on watch.

(a) and (b) are usually reserved for the main musters of the day, for drills or evolutions.

If comparatively few hands are required unexpectedly during working hours, the call 'Hands working on the upper deck' is usually piped in preference to a watch or part of a watch, because it is not desirable to disturb the work of the ship and the training classes more than is strictly necessary.

Quarters

In war different circumstances require that either the whole or only a portion of the armament of a warship be kept manned and ready for instant action. This manning of her armament is, therefore, based on the watch system, so that the whole or only a portion of the ship's company are at their quarters according to the 'degree of readiness' required by circumstances. Basically these are as follows:

DEGREE OF READINESS	STATION	PROPORTION OF THE SHIP'S COMPANY CLOSED UP AT THEIR QUARTERS	CIRCUMSTANCES
First	Action Stations	All hands.	Action with enemy forces imminent.
Second	Action Stations Relaxed	All hands except a small proportion from each quarter who are allowed to fall out for their meals or relaxation.	Action with enemy less imminent or during a lull in an engagement.
Third	Defence Stations	One watch or a part of a watch, according to the proportion of the armament required to be manned: governed by the degree of threat from the enemy forces.	Action with enemy possible, but not imminent. The watch not closed up carry out normal routine duties in their parts of ship.
Fourth	Cruising Stations	A part of the watch or a proportion of one.	Action with enemy possible, but fairly remote. Normal ship's duties are carried out by men not at their quarters; hands working in their part of ship.

Degrees of readiness should not be confused with Nuclear, Biological and Chemical Defence (NBCD) states of readiness, which are described on page 193.

A man's action station or 'quarter' is that part of the armament of a ship to which he is detailed, and it may vary with the degree of readiness in force.

A watch or part of the watch is not only balanced proportionally between each part of ship, but also includes a balanced proportion of the hands necessary for manning and fighting a portion of the armament.

Watch and station bills

Every member of the ship's company, in addition to being detailed for routine duties and shipwork, is allocated to specific quarters for fighting the ship and to special stations for certain emergencies. This is done by entering his name and other details in a *watch and station* (or watch and quarter) *bill.*

Copies of the watch and station bill are posted on the notice boards, and from it a man can tell at a glance his more important stations. The NBCD watch and station bill, which details the various parties in the ship's NBCD organization (such as fire and repair parties, monitors, etc.), is either incorporated in it or displayed separately close to it. Every man has a specific station for action, etc., and he may also have a specific task to perform in the ship's NBCD organization. Detailed orders for other evolutions are usually included in a separate station bill or in ship's Standing Orders.

Duty watches

At sea the duty part of the watch changes once a watch, i.e. every four hours (every two hours in the dog watches), but in harbour it changes daily at 1230.

Whichever watch system is adopted, it is convenient to maintain a regular sequence of watches, and for this a roster is useful; a typical example is shown below.

	Days	FOUR WATCH				THREE WATCH			
		2	3	4	5	1	2	3	4
Middle	1P	2S	2P	1S	1P	R	W	B	R
Morning	1S	1P	2S	2P	etc.	W	B	R	etc.
Forenoon	2P	1S	1P	2S		R	W	B	
Afternoon	2S	2P	1S	1P		B	R	W	
First Dog	1P	2S	2P	1S		W	B	R	
Last Dog	1S	1P	2S	2P		B	R	W	
First	2P	1S	1P	2S		R	W	B	

The method shown for the three-watch system breaks the sequence for the forenoon and afternoon, so as to avoid the middlewatchmen having an afternoon for their next watch. This is known as working 'West Country watches'. In either system the afternoon watchmen shown are the duty watch for the following 24 hours if the ship enters harbour.

Watch duties in harbour

Out of working hours, both by day and at night, the 'watch on board'—and, more particularly, the 'duty part'—must be ready at all times to turn to for any work or emergency which may arise. In addition, the duty part provides parties for the duties indicated below.

Duty hands. These consist of a small section of the duty part of the watch, and are usually employed for all work out of working hours for which only a small party is required.

Fire and emergency party. This is drawn from all men of all branches. Their prime function is to deal with fires, but they may be used to take action in any emergency.

Anchor watch. When a ship is at anchor in heavy weather or in a strong tideway, an anchor watch is detailed to watch the cable so that they can veer it, heave it in, let go a second anchor, slip the cable or weigh anchor as necessary.

Watch duties at sea

At sea it is usual for all hands to work within their departments and to work the daily routine from the time hands fall in to the end of working hours. Out of working hours, ship duties and any work that may be required to be done are carried out by the 'watch on deck'. The watch-keeping system is worked throughout the 24 hours of a day, and watch-keeping duties and 'tricks' are done by the watch on deck. Their duties include the following:

Seaboat's crew and lowerers (see Chapter 11). A boat is always kept ready for use while a ship is at sea. Hands from the watch on deck are detailed off to act as seaboat's crew and lowerers for the boat should she be required.

Lookouts. Lookouts perform a very essential task in a ship at sea, despite the introduction of radar into ships. They work tricks of 30 minutes, which may be reduced to 20 minutes in war.

Radar plotters. Radar plotters keep their watch in the Operations Room.

Helmsman and telegraphsman. A helmsman is detailed for a trick of up to two hours' duration. A telegraphsman is detailed to work the telegraphs for the duration of the watch. Both work under the supervision of the Quartermaster.

Lifebuoy sentry (see also page 144). A rating is detailed to stand by the lifebuoys, which are usually situated in the after part of the ship. He is stationed there so that he can quickly throw over a lifebuoy should someone be seen to fall overboard. He also acts as a sentry in the after part of the ship and as a lookout.

Bridge messenger. A seaman or junior detailed for the period of the watch.

In war, to prevent all ships changing sea watches at the same time and thus providing a suitable moment for an enemy to catch a group of ships 'off its guard', the times of the change-over of watches may be staggered not only between ships but within each ship.

EVOLUTIONS

In addition to her normal tasks a ship must be prepared to deal immediately and efficiently with any emergency. It would not be possible to issue detailed orders to meet every situation that might arise, but it is possible to issue such orders for certain duties or emergencies which it is known from past experience are likely to be encountered; these are generally known as 'Evolutions'. Typical examples are:

Replenishment at sea	Boarding party
Tow aft	Storing ship
Tow forward	

There are many more standard evolutions, the orders for which are to be found in the ship's Standing Orders. They usually affect all departments in the ship, and are exercised from time to time to ensure efficient execution in the shortest possible time.

Principal exercises and evolutions

Entering and leaving harbour. When a ship enters and leaves harbour she is especially in the public eye; therefore all that goes on must be done efficiently. Everything must be 'squared-off' (tidy and stowed correctly), and the ship's company dressed smartly and fallen-in.

Preparing for sea. Before a ship leaves harbour, all her equipment required for use must be tested. This includes such things as the main engines, steering gear, sea communications and compasses; setting wireless watch and switching on radar sets; equipping and rigging the seaboat, adjusting wires, ropes and cable; securing all loose gear, closing certain doors, hatches and watertight openings.

Divisions. This is a muster of all the ship's company (except men on watch and a few ratings specially excused). Its chief purposes are to muster the ship's company, to enable the officers to see their men and vice versa, and to ensure that each man is fit, alert and smart. Divisions may be held as ordered by the Captain in accordance with station orders.

Nuclear, Biological and Chemical Defence Organization. The ship's NBCD organization and general organization must be co-ordinated with each other. Ship safety is just as important in peace as it is in war, and that part of NBCD which is not applicable in peace must be easy to apply when the situation requires it. All members of the ship's company must know the NBCD organization thoroughly, as the practical application of that knowledge may make all the difference between reaching harbour safely and sinking. In order to ensure that everyone knows his responsibility in this subject exercises are held from time to time.

ROUTINES

The normal everyday life of a ship is run in accordance with a time-table known as the 'routine'. A routine must cover the general activities of a ship and her company wherever she may be; thus there are routines for harbour and sea, for weekdays and Sundays, for the Home and Foreign stations, for shore establishments, and for winter and summer.

Routines must vary considerably with the type of ship and her situation, but the principles on which any routine is based are governed by *Q.R. and A.I.* and there are therefore certain main features which are common to all of them. The day is divided into three main periods, from approximately 0600 to 0900, from 0900 to 1600, and from 1600 to 2200.

D*

PRINCIPLES TO BE CONSIDERED IN A ROUTINE

Different ships and different stations have so many varied requirements that it is impossible to give a definitive specimen. As new techniques and requirements come into the Fleet they all have to be fitted into the ship's routine, and standard routines get out of date very quickly.

The main points that must be considered in a routine are:

time to clean the ship above and below decks
time for ship husbandry
time for training and exercises
time for meal hours
time for recreation.

Communal duties

There is no one body of men carried in a ship to sweep, clean and polish; nor can any one department carry this out alone as well as its own duties. Therefore each department has to assume responsibility for the cleanliness and maintenance of certain compartments and equipment. Likewise all departments are involved in the running of the ship's organization: in order to share the duties evenly throughout a ship's company and to keep the number of dutymen to a minimum, the duty watch, duty ratings and certain special duties are drawn from and shared by all departments.

Petty officers' duties

Petty officers' duties vary according to the size and type of ship, and, like those of the duty watch or part, they are continuous for 24 hours. Typical duties are:

Petty Officer of the Day. The P.O. of the Day is employed for administrative duties and may be required to carry out such duties as attending the spirit issue, also the servery during meal hours, and machinery compartment rounds at night.

Duty Disciplinary Petty Officer. This P.O. attends to all matters concerning discipline during his period of duty. These may include calling the hands, inspecting libertymen before they go ashore and on their return, taking requestmen and defaulters before the Officer of the Watch, and rounds at night. In small ships this duty may be combined with those of the duty Petty Officer.

Duty Petty Officer. The Duty P.O. in small ships may undertake Regulating duties. He is normally responsible for the fire and emergency party, the employment of the duty watch or part should they be required to work, detailing members of the duty watch or part for any specific duties, and taking charge of the men under punishment.

Daily orders

Particulars of the work and duties of the ship's company are issued by the Commander's or First Lieutenant's Office as 'Daily Orders', usually on the afternoon of the day before they are to be carried out. These orders include the names of those officers and men detailed to carry out routine duties, any orders or instructions required for duties of a non-routine nature, and night leave. They are posted on the messdeck and it is the duty of every individual in the ship to read them. Lack of knowledge of such orders is not accepted as an excuse for any failure to carry them out.

Piping and the boatswain's call

Piping is a method of passing orders, especially routine orders, in the Royal Navy. The expression 'to pipe' describes generally the sound of the boatswain's call, together with the spoken order which may qualify it. Some pipes are orders in themselves and do not require any verbal additions, e.g. 'Pipe down'.

In order to reduce the noise level in a ship, pipes at routine times are kept to the bare minimum so that only essential orders are circulated throughout the ship.

Bugle calls

In larger ships the more important routine orders are passed by the bugle, if a bugler is borne. Most bugle calls are an order in themselves and require no qualifications by pipe, e.g. 'Flying stations'.

Time, and division of the day into 'watches'

The 24 hours of the day are divided into seven periods called 'watches'. The time is recorded in four figures, like the 24-hour clock system used on the Continent, starting and ending at midnight. The first two figures denote the hour, the last two the minutes.

Civil Time	*Naval Time*	*Watch*
Midnight to 4 a.m.	0001–0400	Middle
4 a.m. to 8 a.m.	0400–0800	Morning
8 a.m. to 12.30 p.m.	0800–1230	Forenoon
12.30 p.m. to 4 p.m.	1230–1600	Afternoon
4 p.m. to 6 p.m.	1600–1800	First dog
6 p.m. to 8 p.m.	1800–2000	Last dog
8 p.m. to midnight	2000–2359	First

The purpose of dividing the dog watches is to provide an odd number of watches each day. Midnight is never specified as 0000; it is either 2359 or 0001 in order to differentiate between adjacent days.

Watches are used to denote the period of the day, e.g. 'during the forenoon'.

Striking the hours

The ship's bell is struck every half-hour throughout each watch in the following manner:

First half-hour	1 bell
First hour	2 bells
First hour and a half	3 bells
and so on, until:	
Third hour and a half	7 bells
Last hour	8 bells

The sequence is repeated for each successive watch. Hence seven bells can indicate 0330, 0730, 1130, 1530 or 2330.

During the dog watches the sequence is broken as follows:

1630—1 bell		1830—1 bell	
1700—2 bells		1900—2 bells	
1730—3 bells		1930—3 bells	
1800—4 bells		2000—8 bells	

Apart from striking the hours, the ship's bell is struck only to indicate the position of the ship when at anchor in a fog.

Silent hours. This term denotes the period at night between 'Pipe down' and 'Call the hands'. It is the custom not to strike the bell during these hours, and pipes are restricted to those that are essential or for an emergency.

Make-and-mend

Formerly known as 'make and mend clothes', this was originally a half-holiday for the ship's company to repair and replace their kit. In those days few articles of clothing were supplied from store and men usually made most of their own clothing.

Nowadays make-and-mends are usually granted on every Saturday when circumstances permit, and in addition an extra make-and-mend may be granted occasionally for organized recreation when the ship is in harbour.

CHAPTER 9

Messing

MESSING SYSTEMS

All officers and men are entitled to be fed without payment, as a part of their wages. The provision of meals is traditionally known as *messing*, while the term *mess* is applied to a particular company of officers or men of a ship who are *berthed** together, and also to the space in which they pass their social life. In general terms, the division of messes is as follows:

C.P.O.s of all Branches ⎫
P.O.s of all Branches ⎬ In older ships Artificers mess separately.
Cooks (O) and Stewards ⎭
Ship's company, according to divisions or departments
Young ratings (for Juniors or ex-Juniors, all of whom are usually doing their first commission at sea).

A messdeck is a compartment in a ship in which there are one or more messes.

There are two main systems of messing for ratings:

(*a*) General messing.
(*b*) Cash victualling allowance messing.

These systems will now be explained.

General messing

General messing is the system used in all shore establishments and in all but the smallest ships (e.g. coastal minesweepers), under which the Supply Officer is responsible for the entire messing of the ship's company. The Supply Officer is credited with a money allowance for each man he has to feed, and he sets against this the cost of the food used for breakfast, lunch, tea and supper. There are three methods by which food may be served, namely Centralized, Modified Centralized and Broadside messing. The present policy is to install full Centralized messing in all ships down to coastal minesweepers, but this policy can only be effective in new-construction ships and (sometimes) during modernization or conversion of existing ships. In the meantime some ships still have to use Broadside messing, while in others it has been possible to install the 'half-way house' of Modified Centralized messing. The main features of these three systems will now be described.

Centralized messing. Serving counters are fitted, normally as part of the galley but sometimes in a separate servery. Each junior rating collects his own meal from the serving counter on a recessed self-service tray, by helping himself from the choice of dishes displayed on the counter. He carries his tray to an adjacent dining hall. Senior ratings have their meals in separate dining halls and they are served by messmen.

Modified Centralized messing. The essential feature of this system is a serving counter adjacent to the galley, from which individual junior ratings can collect their

---

* A *berth* is a space in a ship which is allotted to a person or a number of persons and in which they sleep and pass their leisure hours. In older types of ships they may also have to eat there. *Berthing* is the allotting of such places among the ship's company; it varies considerably in different classes of ships.

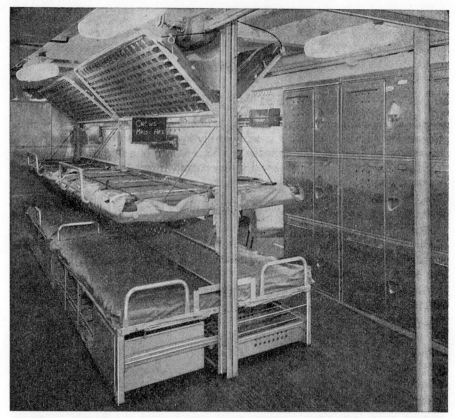

FIG. 9-1. Junior ratings' messdeck in a General-purpose frigate

FIG. 9-2. Junior ratings' dining hall in a General-purpose frigate

own meals, which they take to their messdecks. Only one class of ship (*Rothesay* class frigates) is especially built for M.C.M.; in other ships M.C.M. has had to be fitted to the best advantage into the existing layout of compartments. This means that minor inconveniences may have to be accepted (e.g. a serving counter sited a little awkwardly in relation to the messdecks). The important advantages that the M.C.M. system offers are:

(a) Ratings can collect their own meals individually, have them hot and help themselves to a sufficient quantity without being wasteful.

(b) A choice of meal can be offered.

(c) Waste of food is reduced (and therefore more money becomes available to raise the feeding standard).

Under the M.C.M. system some items of food may be taken to the messdecks in bulk, as under the obsolete Broadside system (e.g. soup). Washing-up has usually to be done on the messdecks.

Broadside messing. Meals are prepared and cooked centrally and the share for each mess is set out in some form of food-container, such as in meat dishes. The containers are collected by the Cooks of the Mess, who carry them to the messdecks, serve out the food and clear up afterwards. Dishes, etc. obtained from the galley are returned by the Cooks of the Mess. Cutlery and crockery are kept on the messdecks in specially provided lockers. This system of messing is rapidly dying out.

Cash Victualling Allowance messing

In certain small ships which are usually dependent upon a base organization for supplies, facilities and amenities, a form of victualling known as 'Cash Victualling' is used. A sum of money (usually the approximate total monthly messing allowance for all the officers and men on board) is advanced by the Base Supply Officer to the Captain. All provisions purchased are paid for in cash. At the end of the month a balance is struck between expenditure and the actual total messing allowance for that month. Any credit due is then paid to the Captain on behalf of the ship. After payment of mess savings or settlement of any excess expenditure, the Captain holds the amount of the initial advance.

Fittings

The system of messing in use determines what equipment is provided in the mess. For example:

(a) Under Centralized messing, meals are eaten in a central dining hall, so the only furniture required in the mess is for sleeping and recreational purposes;

(b) Under the remaining types of messing, meals are eaten in the mess, so each mess is provided with dining tables, stools or chairs and stowage for mess gear.

Mess gear

Mess gear comprises:

Tableware—articles used at table in dining halls and messdecks.

Galley gear—articles used in the preparation, cooking and serving of food.

Each category has:

Consumable gear—mainly crockery and glassware.

Permanent gear—the remainder.

Custodians are made responsible for the mess gear in particular compartments, e.g. the leading hand of each mess. Broken or worn-out permanent gear may be returned and replaced by drawing new articles. The expenditure of consumable gear is controlled by a monetary allowance. Replacements may be made in the same way as for permanent articles, their value being reckoned against the allowance. If the allowance is exceeded the custodian must provide an explanation, which, if not accepted by the Captain, must be further investigated to determine the degree of personal responsibility. Disciplinary action may be taken where there are cases of damage or loss by neglect of both consumable and permanent gear.

Under full Centralized messing the quantity of gear issued to messes is very small, sufficient only for tea, coffee and drawing the rum. However, the same rules regarding replacements apply as to gear used in dining halls.

ORGANIZATION OF MESSES

Below are described some of the more important details of the organization and duties of mess members; they vary from ship to ship and with the type of messing in force.

President of the mess. In Chief Petty Officers' and Petty Officers' messes the President is responsible for the conduct and general running of the mess, assisted as necessary by a small committee formed from the mess members. The President is appointed by election, subject to the Commanding Officer's approval.

Senior Hand of the mess. In other messes the senior rating (usually a Leading Rate) is in charge of the conduct and general running of the mess. It is his duty to check any irregularities and, if necessary, report them to the Officer of the Watch or other superior authority. His other duties vary with the type of messing in force; they include:

(a) Detailing the Cooks of the mess daily by roster, and ensuring that there is always a Cook of the mess of the watch on board.

(b) Issuing the grog ration to those entitled to draw it, on the basis of one man one tot. He is to ensure that non-entitled personnel do not receive any of it. He is to check any improper disposal, selling or exchanging of grog for a service or object, and the habit of offering 'sippers' to other ratings. ('Sippers' is the custom whereby a man lets someone else have a drink from his tot in celebration of an event or in payment for a good turn or favour.)

(c) Ensuring that the mess and its precincts are cleared up at the proper times.

(d) Representing complaints about food.

(e) Ensuring that money for mess issues on repayment, cinema subscriptions, etc. is handled correctly. If the Leading Hand of the mess is not also the caterer, he is to supervise the latter in his handling of these sums of money.

(f) Ensuring that the correct numbers are victualled in his mess and reporting any discrepancies to the Regulating Office.

(g) Notifying the Regulating Office if any members of his mess have not returned from leave or duty by the correct time, and reporting any mess-members who may be absent or whose absence cannot be accounted for.

(h) Notifying the Regulating Office of any mess-members who may be absent on duty during the dinner-hour and whose spirit ration should be set aside for issue later at miss-musters.

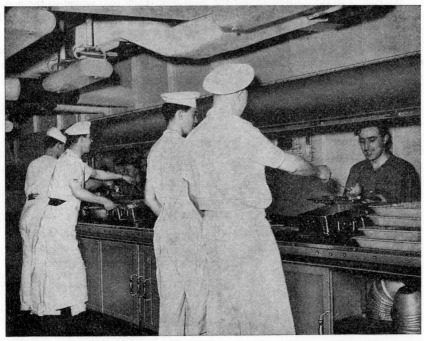

FIG. 9-3. Servery in an aircraft carrier

FIG. 9-4. Ship's company galley in a cruiser

(*i*) Acting as the 'custodian' for the mess gear (page 103) issued to the mess.

(*j*) Sharing food equally among the mess-members when Broadside and Cash Victualling Allowance mess systems are in force.

Messman. Chief Petty Officers' and Petty Officers' messes are allowed messmen, who are drawn from the various parts of the ship's company. Their duties are similar to those of Cooks of the mess, and they work under the supervision of the President of the mess.

Cooks of the mess. Not so very long ago ratings used to draw or buy fresh provisions for individual messes and used to prepare the food in their own messdecks, taking it to the galley for cooking. One or two ratings (depending upon the size of the mess) were detailed to act as 'Cook' of the mess each day. We still retain the term 'Cook of the mess', even though his duties have changed considerably in more recent times. The Cook of the mess's duties may include:

(*a*) Cleaning out the mess in the early part of the day.

(*b*) Attending the issues of grog and collecting the grog ration for the mess if no 'rum bo's'n' is detailed.

(*c*) Making Stand Easy tea.

(*d*) Obtaining repayment issues of tea, sugar and milk for the mess.

(*e*) Where meals are taken in the mess, collecting parts of the meal (e.g. the soup) from the galley or issue room, and cleaning up after meals.

Mess caterers. In some messes a rating may be detailed to deal with the handling of minor mess purchases, checking ratings for grog issue, collecting cinema money, etc. This duty is normally carried out by the Leading Hand of the mess.

The duties of Cooks of the mess and Mess Caterers vary according to the type of messing in force.

Messdeck and flat sweepers. This party of ratings, which is drawn from all parts of the ship, works under the supervision of the Messdeck Petty Officer. It is responsible for the general cleanliness and tidiness of areas outside the immediate precincts of the messes, such as corridors (gangways), lobbies, etc.

Dining hall party. In ships provided with dining halls a party of ratings is detailed to look after the cleanliness of the dining hall, wash up crockery and utensils and dispose of all waste.

Complaints

Immediate complaints about food are made in the following way:

Under Centralized messing to the Senior Hand of the dining hall
Under Modified Centralized messing } to the Senior Cook rating in the
Under Broadside messing } galley

Failing redress, complaints are to be taken to the Officer of the Watch.

VICTUALLING AND ALLOWANCES

Victualling and checking

A man is 'victualled' on entering a ship and 'checked' on leaving, in connection with the monetary allowance which can be claimed for feeding him. If he joins after noon or leaves before noon allowance cannot be claimed for that day: if he joins before noon or leaves after noon it can be claimed. This is called the 'noon rule', and originates from the time when the naval 'day' ran from noon to noon and not from midnight to midnight. It is continued because it simplifies the planning of meals and getting food up into the galley.

Ration allowance

Officers and men on long leave are paid ration allowance. Married officers and men serving in shore establishments and in some ships who live with their families ashore may elect to receive ration allowance under certain circumstances. The rules covering the eligibility for payment of ration allowance are in the *Naval Pay Regulations*, which may be seen at any Pay Office.

RUM, TOBACCO AND EXTRA ISSUES

Spirit ration

Every rating over the age of 20 (except an Apprentice under training) is entitled to be issued with one tot (one-eighth of a pint) of rum each day, or to be given a cash allowance ('grog money') instead, provided he is victualled in the ship for that day. The following symbols are accordingly entered against each man's name in the ledger and the mess books: G—grog, T—temperance, UA—under age. A man can elect to receive either the ration or the money from the first day of the month following his twentieth birthday, provision being made to change from one to the other subsequently, if he so wishes.

A man who draws the ration may have it stopped if he is sick or for punishment; grog money, however, is payable continuously. It is not payable to men on leave or R.A., to deserters, or to men in prison or detention.

METHOD OF ISSUE

The Petty Officer of the Day has to attend the issue of rum as a witness of its quality and quantity. When 'Up spirits' is piped (usually at about 1145 each day) an officer draws the keys of the spirit-room and, in the company of the Petty Officer of the Day (or a member of the Regulating staff, if borne), a member of the victualling staff and one rating, goes to the spirit-room. The total quantity of spirit required for issue that day is measured out, the neat spirit for entitled Chief Petty Officers and Petty Officers is collected by their messmen, and the remainder is put into a container called a 'barricoe' (pronounced 'beaker'). The barricoe is padlocked and shut away under lock and key, the officer attending the issue retaining the key.

At a time fixed by the Captain the barricoe is drawn and the contents poured into a tub ('rum tub') under the supervision of the issuing officer. The duty Victualling Rating removes rum for any men temporarily absent on duty ('stops'); and the remaining ration, which is for leading rates and below who are entitled to draw it, is then mixed with water in the proportion of two parts of water to one part of rum. This mixture is called 'grog'. It is stirred well and each mess representative draws the proper amount for his own mess. When the issue is completed, the remains of the grog, if any, are poured down the drain (scupper). The 'stops' for men absent on duty are then replaced under lock and key, to be issued, diluted as necessary, at a later time.

CAUTION. Each day's spirit is to be drunk before rounds on the day of issue. The saving of spirit is forbidden. It must be clearly understood that the spirit ration is issued *solely for the consumption of the individual entitled to it*, and that it must not be given away, exchanged, sold or otherwise disposed of. Apart from any infringement of the regulations, *if too much naval rum is drunk it is dangerous:* men have died from its effects.

Note on drawing rum. When drawing anything from a tub do not hold the mess kettle over the tub, as there may be dirt on it which may fall into the tub. Hold the kettle against the edge of the tub and tilt it so that the lip is just within the tub's rim, but the bottom safely outside.

Tobacco

Duty-free tobacco may be taken up by officers and men over the age of 16 and who are declared smokers serving in one of H.M. ships or establishments entitled to the privilege. The personal allowances and the type of tobacco permitted (i.e. Service or proprietary brands of cigarette and tobacco) in Home Waters vary according to the duty-free category of the ship or establishment and are under coupon control.

The quantities allowed to be landed duty-free are:

   1 oz of tobacco (or 25 cigarettes) for each night of leave, up to 6 nights
   8 oz of tobacco (or 200 cigarettes) for seven or more nights of leave.

Owing to the high rate of duty on tobacco, the duty-free concessions allowed to the Royal Navy have become extremely valuable. These privileges are, more than ever before, likely to be jeopardized by smuggling or unauthorized landing. Duty-free tobacco is solely for the personal use of the recipient, though this does not prevent an officer or man from offering an occasional cigarette to a guest by way of hospitality. Smuggling of, or trading in, tobacco or cigarettes is a serious offence against naval discipline. *The unauthorized landing of dutiable goods remains an offence even though the owner may offer to pay the duty on shore.*

Extra issues

Lemon or orange powder and sugar may be issued daily to officers and men in very hot weather on the advice of the Medical Officer. Their issue may also be authorized for men working in hot compartments.

Hot drinks. Men on duty at night may be given an issue of tea, coffee or chocolate for making hot drinks.

Food. Men exposed to unusually severe weather or engaged in particularly hard work, or for long hours at night, may be given extra meals.

Spirit. In very exceptional circumstances the senior officer present may authorize an extra issue of a tot of rum to men who have been subjected to particularly arduous conditions or exposure.

Splicing the mainbrace. This means an extra issue of rum to all officers and men over 20, and of lemonade to those under 20 and those who prefer it. This is only authorized on some special occasion.

Issue of milk to men under 18. A free issue of half a pint of fresh milk is made to all juniors and men under 18 in all shore establishments at home and in ships in the United Kingdom when fresh milk is available: when it is not, an addition is made to the money in the messing allowance to pay for extra food instead. Similarly, a monetary supplement for the purchase of extra food is authorized for persons under 18 in ships and establishments outside the United Kingdom.

Further details of these and other special supplements are given in *Q.R. & A.I.*, in B.R. 93, *Victualling Manual*, and in Defence Council Instructions (Royal Navy).

CHAPTER 10

Elementary Seamanship

See *Admiralty Manual of Seamanship*, Vols. I and II; A.T.P. 16, *Replenishment at Sea*; B.R. 2203, *Ship Husbandry Manual*

ROPES AND CORDAGE

For many centuries ropes and cordage have played a major part in the daily life of the sailor. In the latter part of the nineteenth century wire rope was introduced into the Royal Navy for general use, and more recent times have seen the introduction of synthetic or *man-made* fibre cordage into the Service. Today, no matter whether you are watching ships replenish at sea or simply lashing down deck gear when rough weather approaches, you will see a variety of rope and cordage in constant use throughout the Royal Navy.

Rope is of three main types:

    Cordage made of vegetable fibres,
    Cordage made of man-made fibres,
    Steel wire rope.

The size of a rope is measured according to its circumference. Rope is normally supplied in lengths of 120 fathoms (1 fathom = 6 ft).

A table of comparison between wire rope, manila rope and man-made fibre rope may be found in the *Admiralty Manual of Seamanship*, Vol. I (1964).

Vegetable fibre cordage

This type of cordage is made from manila, hemp, sisal and coir plants, whose fibres are combed out and twisted into yarns, which are themselves twisted into strands. The strands are then laid up (left- or right-handed) to form a rope. The ropes most commonly used in the Royal Navy are of three-stranded, right-hand-laid construction, and are known as *hawser-laid* ropes (Fig. 10-1).

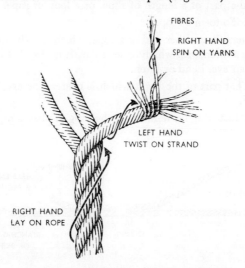

FIG. 10-1. Parts of a hawser-laid rope

Vegetable fibre ropes are used for a variety of tasks in the Royal Navy, according to their sizes and properties.

Manila rope is durable, strong and flexible and is therefore used where safety of life is concerned, e.g. boats' falls and cargo slings.

Sisal rope is less reliable and durable, and is therefore not used where the parting of the rope might endanger life.

Coir rope is light and will float, but it is not as strong as manila or sisal, and its commonest use at sea is for passing heavier lines between ships, e.g. during towing operations.

Hemp is used mainly for *small stuff*, the name given to all small ropes or lines of under half an inch in circumference.

Man-made fibre cordage

This cordage, introduced into the Navy in 1961, consists of fibres of Nylon or Terylene, which are products derived from coal or crude petroleum. These ropes have characteristics of their own which are in many ways superior to those of natural fibre and steel wire rope. Nylon and Terylene ropes are used in the Royal Navy where there is a requirement for heavy duty, long life, safety and ease of handling. Typical uses are for running rigging, boats' falls, slings and berthing ropes.

Wire rope

A number of small steel wires are twisted together to make up strands, and these are themselves 'laid up' to form the rope. The wires forming a strand are twisted left-handed round a jute or wire *core*, and the strands themselves are laid up right-handed round a hemp or jute *heart*.

Wire rope is used for standing rigging (such as the shrouds of a boat), for running rigging (such as a derrick purchase), for guard rail wires and jacob's ladders.

Terms used when handling a rope (Fig. 10-2)

Bight. The middle part of a length of rope, or a loop of rope.

To make a bight. To form a loop.

End. The short length at either end of a rope, which may be formed into an eye or used for making a hitch with which to secure it. It is also that length of rope left over after making an eye, bend or hitch.

Standing part. That part of the bight which is nearest the eye, bend or hitch, in contrast to the end.

Stopping. A light fastening for temporarily holding in place a rope or other object.

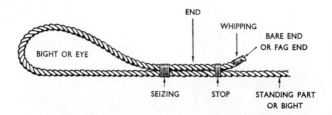

FIG. 10-2. Terms used in handling a rope

Seizing. This is used to fasten two ropes or two parts of the same rope securely together to prevent them moving in relation to each other.

Whipping. The binding round the bare end of a rope which prevents the strands from unlaying.

ELEMENTARY PRACTICAL SEAMANSHIP

BENDS AND HITCHES

Many bends and hitches (known to the landsman collectively as 'knots') are used in the Royal Navy. A few simple ones are listed below and you will find many practical applications of them in daily use throughout your time in the Service.

Most bends and hitches consist of a combination of two or more of the following (see Fig. 10-3):

(*a*) A bight   (*d*) A twist
(*b*) A round turn   (*e*) An overhand knot
(*c*) A half-hitch

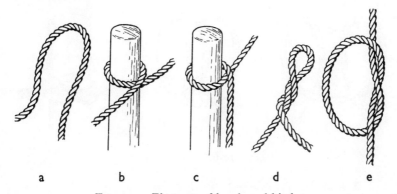

a   b   c   d   e

FIG. 10-3. Elements of bends and hitches

Reef knot

This consists of two overhand knots made consecutively and is used as a common tie for bending together two ropes of approximately equal size. To form a reef knot care must be taken to cross the ends opposite ways each time they are knotted (i.e. right over left and then left over right, or vice versa); otherwise a 'granny' will be formed, which will either slip or jam. (Fig. 10-4.)

(i)   (ii)

FIG. 10-4. Reef knot

Figure-of-eight knot

This is used to prevent a rope unreeving through an eye or a block. An overhand knot can also be used. (Fig. 10-5.)

FIG. 10-5. Figure-of-eight knot

Clove hitch

A clove hitch is used to secure a rope to a spar, rail or similar fitting. It will slip along the spar if subjected to a sideways pull. It can be made with the end or the bight of a rope. (Fig. 10-6.)

FIG. 10-6. Clove hitch

Rolling hitch

This hitch is used for securing a rope to a spar when the pull is expected to be from one side or the other, or for securing to another rope under strain. It is made by passing the end twice round the spar or rope, each turn crossing the standing part. A half-hitch completes the hitch. Always pass the two turns on the side from which the pull is expected. (Fig. 10-7.)

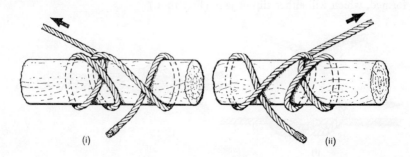

(i)   (ii)

FIG. 10-7. Rolling hitch

Round turn and two half-hitches

This combination is used to secure a heavy load to a spar, ring or shackle, such as a buoy shackle of a mooring buoy. It will never jam and can be cast off quickly. (Fig. 10-8.)

STOP

FIG. 10-8. Round turn and two half-hitches

Sheet bend

This is used to secure a rope's end to a small eye, e.g. the lazy painter of a boat at a boom to the foot of a Jacob's ladder; the hammock clew when a hammock is slung; or a small rope to a large one. It will not slip and is easily let go. (Fig. 10-9.)

Double sheet bend

This is a more secure method of accomplishing the same purpose as a single sheet bend. It is used, for example, to secure a boat's painter to the eye of a lizard when a boat is at a boom. (Fig. 10-9.)

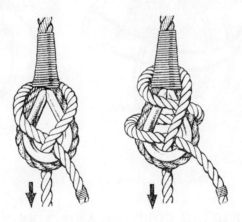

FIG. 10-9. Single and double sheet bend

Bowline

To make a bowline, take the end in the right hand and the standing part in the left; place the end over the standing part and hold the cross thus formed between the index finger and thumb of the right hand, with the thumb underneath; the loop so formed becomes the bight of the bowline, and if required it can be formed round the body of the man making the knot. Turn the wrist to the right away from the body and bring the end up through the loop so formed; this loop is sometimes called the 'gooseneck'. Now hold the cross of the gooseneck in the left hand, as shown in Fig. 10-10, leaving the right hand free to manipulate the end, and complete the bowline by dipping the end under the standing part, bringing it up again and passing it down through the gooseneck.

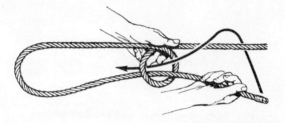

FIG. 10-10. Bowline

Bowline on the bight

This is made on the bight of a rope, the first two operations (Fig. 10-11) being the same as those for a simple bowline. It is used for lowering a man from aloft or over the ship's side, the short bight passing under his arms, the long one under his buttocks.

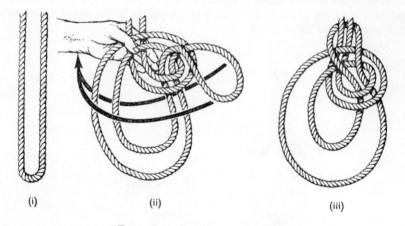

(i)   (ii)   (iii)

FIG. 10-11. Bowline on the bight

HANDLING CORDAGE AND WIRE ROPE

Precautions

(a) When coiling down a rope, the running end should be kept free to allow it to rotate and thus prevent it from becoming snarled up with kinks or turns (Fig. 10-12).

(b) Never allow a rope to chafe on a sharp edge. To avoid this, run it through a leading block to hold it clear of the obstacle.

(c) Never stand under any weight that is being hoisted or lowered (Fig. 10-13).

(d) Never stand within a bight or a coil (Fig. 10-14).

(e) Always stand on the opposite side of a leading block from that to which the rope will jump if the block carries away (see Fig. 10-14 (iii)).

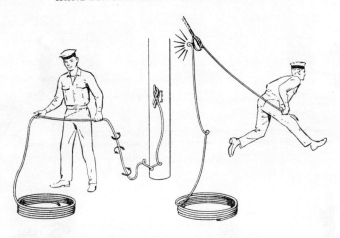

FIG. 10-12. Mistakes in coiling down

Orders and terms used in handling hawsers, ropes and cables

In the course of his normal work the seaman uses the word 'strain' as meaning the pull or tension on a rope (e.g. *take the strain* and a rope *under strain*), which is the sense given in the dictionary. In the mechanical sense, however, the term 'strain' is applied to distortion of material resulting from force or stress applied to it, and this distinction must be remembered when dealing with mechanism.

(*a*) HEAVING

A heave	A pull on a rope or cable; a throw or a cast with a rope.
To heave	To throw a rope or to pull on a rope or cable, either by hand or power.
Heave in!	The order to heave in with the capstan.
Light to!	The order to fleet a rope back along the deck so as to provide enough slack for belaying it.
Veer!	To pay or ease out a cable or hawser from the cable holder or capstan when these are connected to, and

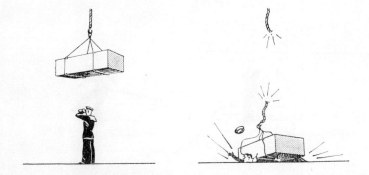

FIG. 10-13. Never stand underneath a hoist!

FIG. 10-14. Never stand within a bight or coil!

controlled by, their engines (veer on power); or to allow a cable to run out by its own weight or strain on the outboard end and under control by the cable holder brake (veer on brake).

To check To ease out a rope steadily by hand while keeping a strain on it.

To snub Suddenly to restrain a rope or chain cable when it is running out.

To surge To allow a hawser to ease out by its own weight or by the strain on the outboard end. A hawser slipping round the barrel of a capstan is said to surge whether the barrel is stopped or turning to heave in. Surging when the barrel is turning to veer is dangerous.

To render A rope is said to render when it surges under strain round a bollard, cleat or staghorn.

(*b*) HAULING

A haul A pull on a rope by hand.
To haul To pull by hand.
To haul hand over hand To haul a rope in quickly with alternate hands.
Haul taut! An order to take down the slack and take the strain.
Haul away! An order to haul in steadily.
Avast hauling! and *Avast!* Orders to stop hauling.
Hold fast To hold a rope under strain so as to keep it from moving.

(*c*) HOISTING

A hoist A system designed for lifting, or the load which is lifted.
To hoist To lift.
Hoist away! The order to haul away on a rope when hoisting something with it.
High enough! The order to stop hoisting.
Marry! The order to bring two ropes together side by side and handle them as one. Also a term used in splicing, meaning to butt two ropes' ends together with their respective strands interlocking.

(*d*) LOWERING

Lower away! The order to lower steadily.
Avast lowering! An order to stop lowering.

(*e*) GENERAL TERMS

Handsomely Slowly, with care (e.g. 'lower handsomely').
Roundly Smartly, rapidly.
Walk back! An order to ease a rope back or out whilst keeping it in hand; or the order to pay back a rope or cable for a short distance when brought to the capstan.

Well! or *Enough!*	Orders to stop heaving, hoisting, hauling, lowering, checking, etc. *Enough!* is usually only applied to hoisting and lowering and is preceded by *High* or *Low* respectively.
To back up	To haul on the hauling part of a rope when passed round a bollard or similar fitting so that you can assist the bollard to hold it. Also to reinforce men already hauling on a rope.

To coil a rope

Because the strands of a rope are twisted (laid) one way a rope turns and kinks if incorrectly coiled down. A rope of right-handed lay must be coiled down right-handed (clockwise), and a rope of left-handed lay must be coiled down left-handed (anti-clockwise).

Heaving lines

As its name implies, a heaving line is a light, flexible line that can be thrown. It is used as a *messenger* to pass hawsers from ship to shore, or vice versa. Old log line and signal halyard, being very flexible, make excellent heaving lines.

A heaving line consists of approximately 17 fathoms of 1¼-in. cordage, rot-proofed or natural, and well stretched; though it cannot be thrown much further than a distance of 12 fathoms, the extra length often proves extremely useful. One end should be whipped and the other weighted with a special knot called a 'monkey's fist', with a small sandbag or a heaving line knot.

To prepare a line for throwing, it should be wetted and from 12 to 13 fathoms should be coiled in the left hand, using rather small coils (Fig. 10-15). One-third of the line is taken in the right or throwing hand. The line is then thrown with the right

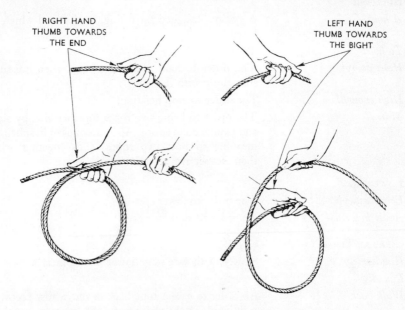

RIGHT HAND
THUMB TOWARDS
THE END

LEFT HAND
THUMB TOWARDS
THE BIGHT

FIG. 10-15. Making up a rope in the hand

FIG. 10-16. Throwing a heaving line

arm straight, and it must be allowed to run out freely from the coil in the left hand. The most frequent cause of bad casts is failure to have the coil free for running.

There is more than one method of heaving a line, and most good throwers have their own variations. Some men take rather less than half the coil in the right hand and throw both halves together, letting go with the right hand before the left. This method is very effective but harder to learn, and to achieve a good throw with the first method is generally sufficient. (Fig. 10-16.)

Many seamen think they can throw a line further than they can; 70 ft is a good cast. Before heaving a line the standing end must be made fast—to the top guard rail, for example—with a clove hitch. Many a good throw has been rendered abortive and valuable time wasted by omitting to do this. As soon as the line has been caught, the standing end should be bent to the hawser.

Remember that a heaving line is only meant to take the strain of the weight of the hawser while it is being passed ashore or into the ship.

To belay to two bollards

1. Lead the rope round the bollard furthest from the source of strain from out-board to inboard (Fig. 10-17).
2. Pass it between both bollards and round the second bollard.

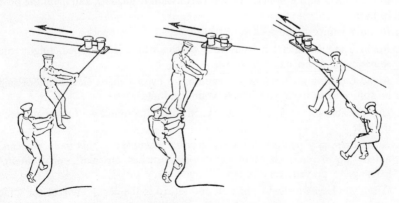

FIG. 10-17. Catching a turn round two bollards

3. Complete the figure-of-eight by passing it between the bollards and round the first bollard.

4. Pass as many turns of figures-of-eight as are required to hold the strain, then *rack* (bind) the turns together with a light line.

To place two hawsers on one bollard

If there is already one hawser on a bollard and it is required to put another hawser on it, the eye of the second hawser must be led up through the eye of the first. It is then placed over the bollard. This will allow either hawser to be slipped without the other having to be removed from the bollard. (Fig. 10-18.)

FIG. 10-18. Placing two hawsers' eyes on one bollard

SOME GENERAL SEAMANLIKE PRECAUTIONS

Going aloft

When you go aloft, you must strictly observe certain commonsense rules and precautions, which have been designed for your safety. You must:

1. Draw the appropriate 'Safe to Transmit' and 'Safe to Rotate' boards, which will immobilise the radio and radar aerials on the mast concerned; then report to the Officer of the Watch, request permission to go aloft, and hand the boards to him.

2. Remove your cap and tuck your trouser-legs into your socks.

3. Remove any loose items from your person which, if dropped, might injure someone or cause damage below.

4. Avoid touching an aerial or waveguide, for even a slight electric shock might be sufficient to make you release your handhold.

5. Use a boatswain's chair, if necessary. Rig a lifeline round your waist and secure it aloft.

6. Never carry any gear up with you, but rig a mast rope so that tools, etc. can be hoisted up to you; and, when using tools, brushes, etc. aloft, secure them by lanyards to prevent them from falling.

7. When you have finished work aloft and return to the deck, report to the Officer of the Watch and return the boards.

Going over the ship's side

Here again commonsense safety rules must be obeyed. When going over the side you must:

1. Obtain permission from the Officer of the Watch.
2. Take the same precautions regarding clothing and gear as for going aloft.
3. Use a boatswain's chair and a lifeline at sea, or a plank stage when in harbour.
4. Have someone tending the lifeline inboard.
5. Ensure that your gear is lowered to you on lanyards.
6. On returning inboard, report to the Officer of the Watch.

Securing for sea

On every occasion of getting under way to proceed to sea from a harbour or anchorage a ship is always 'secured for sea'. This means securing the anchors, boats and ship's armament properly: however, it also means that individuals secure their offices and messdecks, attending to small gear such as lockers, crockery, books, personal gear, etc. Once a ship starts to move in a seaway objects which are not secured are liable to fall out of their stowage and may break or cause damage to personnel and ship's fittings. It is important that whenever a ship goes to sea all articles which are not actually in use be properly stowed and, if necessary, lashed in their stowages. Every man on board must see that compartments and items for which he is responsible are properly secured for sea.

Manhandling of weights

All equipment used in rigging is designed to assist the sailor to move or hold heavy weights which he could not do by himself. However, there always comes a time when a man must manhandle either the weight itself or the equipment associated with moving it. If you overload a derrick or winch something is bound to break, and whenever you overload your body it, too, is liable to be damaged. Detailed instruction is given at New Entry Training Establishments on this subject, but there are some important points which are worth emphasizing here.

(a) *Never* bend over to pick up a weight—this is the most frequent cause of back injury and strain.

(b) Keep the *chin in* and do not look down when lifting; this helps to keep the back straight.

(c) Arms should be kept *close to the body* by keeping the elbows tucked in. This ensures that the weight being carried is kept close to the body, thereby causing less strain.

(d) When pushing or pulling heavy weights, place the feet carefully so that the body's weight can be used to do the work.

(e) Always take care to use a proper grip, using the palms of the hands where possible. To use the fingers only is wrong, as they can slip easily.

(f) When moving or lifting heavy boxes, drums, etc. with sharp edges gloves should be worn: accidents may occur to unprotected hands.

(g) When moving heavy drums lay them down and push them with *both hands*, keeping the back as straight as possible and bending the knees.

(h) Hand barrows and trolleys: Always keep both hands on the shafts when pushing loads. If this is not done, an obstruction may cause the barrow to swing, driving the handle into the groin or the stomach.

(*i*) When negotiating a ramp always *pull* a barrow. Always *pull* an empty barrow back to its loading position.

Remember—your back is not a crane!

RIGGING

Blocks

'Block' is the nautical word to describe what is commonly known as a *pulley*. A block is a portable pulley, and can be made of wood or metal, or of wood and metal, or of laminated plastic material (Tufnol). The principal parts of a block can be seen in Fig. 10-19; they consist of the *shell*, the *sheave* (over which the rope runs),

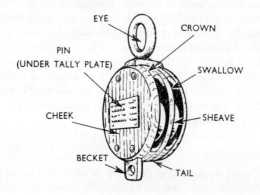

FIG. 10-19. A block

and the *eye*, *hook* or *strop* by which the block is secured in the required position. The top of the block where the eye is fitted is the *crown;* the bottom is the *tail*, the sides of the shell are the *cheeks*, and the opening between the sheave and shell through which the rope passes is the *swallow*.

A block with one sheave is a 'single block', one with two sheaves a 'double block', and so on. A rope rove through a single block and used for hoisting is called a *whip*.

Tackles

A tackle consists of an arrangement of two blocks rigged with a rope (called a *fall*) rove through both so that it will help a man to move a heavy weight. Any pull applied to the hauling part is multiplied by the 'mechanical advantage' of the tackle, which depends upon the number of sheaves in the block and the manner in which the rope is rove through them. The mechanical advantage is equal to the number of parts at the moving block if friction is disregarded. Friction does reduce the mechanical advantage. A tackle in which there are two parts at the moving block would give, for example, a mechanical advantage of two (friction being disregarded).

Derricks

A derrick is a spar made of wood or steel, rigged as a swinging boom and used for hoisting boats, stores, cargo, ammunition or gear in and out of a ship. The lower end or *heel* is pivoted so that the derrick can swing both horizontally and vertically. The upper end is supported by a *topping lift* which can be used to raise or lower it, and with *guys* to train it to one side or the other. The topping lift is taken to a point directly above the heel of the derrick and the guys are led to positions on the deck well to either side of the heel. The load is hoisted or lowered by a whip or a purchase, which is rove through a block at the derrick head and a leading block at the heel and then taken to a winch. (Fig. 10-20.)

There are many types of derrick, and the details of their rigging vary according to the tasks they are designed to perform.

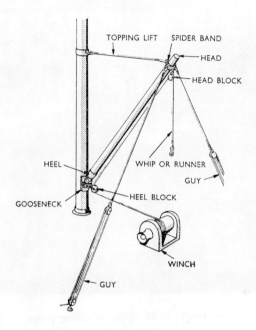

FIG. 10-20. A single derrick

Winches

A winch in its simplest form is a reel which can be turned in either direction by hand cranks. Power-driven winches vary in size according to requirements.

To bring a rope to a warping drum of a winch take two turns of the rope round the drum in the required direction and back up the hauling part. These two turns should be sufficient for the rope to grip the drum, but if the load is heavy or a man-made fibre rope is being used a third turn may be necessary. As the rope passes round the drum there is a tendency for the turns to ride away from the middle towards one end. The drum surface is curved so that the load on the rope forces the turns down to the narrowest part of the drum to counteract this tendency.

To hold the rope stationary while the drum is heaving in, ease the pull on the hauling part to allow the turns to slip or surge. Never do this when the drum is veering, as control will be lost. Never allow turns to ride over each other (*riding* turns), as you will lose control unless the drum is stopped.

FIG. 10-21. H.M. ships refuelling at sea

REPLENISHMENT AT SEA

To maintain a fleet at sea close to its operational area it is necessary to keep it supplied with fuel, ammunition, food and stores, etc. from supply ships (including tankers) organized in replenishment groups. Replenishment at sea provides the modern fleet with greater mobility at greater distances from its main bases. There are several methods of replenishment, of which the commonest forms you will see are the *light jackstay* (for personnel and light stores) and *abeam fuelling* (for fuels), which are described briefly below.

When replenishing at sea the ship supplying the stores also supplies the gear and steers a steady course at a steady speed; it is called the 'supplying' ship. The other ship, the 'receiving' ship, steams close alongside the supplying ship and tries to maintain a steady position relative to her. To guide the receiving ship a distance line, appropriately marked, is passed between the two ships, secured to the guard rails in the supplying ship and kept in hand in the receiving ship. The line must be kept taut at all times.

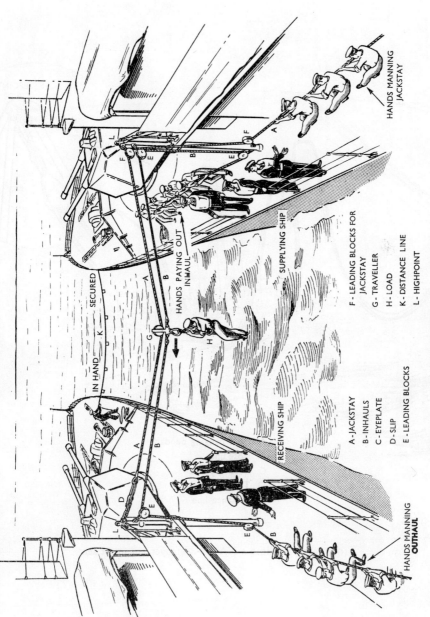

FIG. 10-22. A transfer by light jackstay

A - JACKSTAY
B - INHAULS
C - EYEPLATE
D - SLIP
E - LEADING BLOCKS

F - LEADING BLOCKS FOR JACKSTAY
G - TRAVELLER
H - LOAD
K - DISTANCE LINE
L - HIGHPOINT

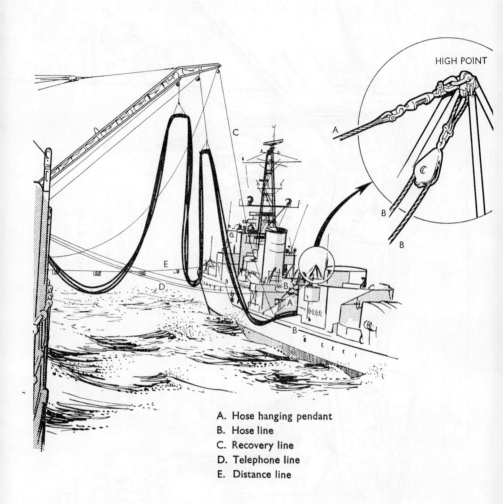

HIGH POINT

A. Hose hanging pendant
B. Hose line
C. Recovery line
D. Telephone line
E. Distance line

FIG. 10-23. Fuelling a NATO destroyer abeam at sea

Initial contact between the two ships is made with a line-throwing rifle. The line is used to pass over a messenger, to which are clipped telephone cables, distance line and the heavier lines for the required transfer.

The light jackstay (Fig. 10-22)

The jackstay, of 4-inch manila, is hauled over by the outhaul, which is clipped to the messenger. The outhaul and inhaul are secured to the traveller block, which is free to run along the jackstay and which carries a suitable container for the load. During the transfer the jackstay must be kept taut so that the load is kept out of the water and can move quickly from one ship to the other. On completion of the transfer all gear must be paid out under control by the receiving ship, and must be clear before she leaves from alongside.

Precautions during transfer. The jackstay, inhaul and outhaul must always be tended by hand when transferring personnel. All personnel being transferred or working in the vicinity of lowered guardrails must wear lifejackets.

Crane and derrick fuelling abeam

Fuel and water are transferred from one ship to another by means of flexible hoses. The two ships having made initial contact, as described above, the hose is hauled over by a hose line, which is clipped to the messenger. The hose is supported by two or three troughs whose weights are taken by trough wires, and the end by a recovery wire when it is being passed or recovered. These wires are worked from the head of a derrick, or from the head and centre of a crane (Figs. 10-21 and 10-23). (An auxiliary will normally use a derrick and a warship a crane; some aircraft carriers may be fitted with a special fuelling boom.) During fuelling the supplying ship controls the height of the hose and the amount of hose in the bights by heaving in or veering the trough wires, to allow for the movements of the ships as they keep station.

Here again, on completion of fuelling all gear must be paid out under control by the receiving ship and must be clear of her side before she leaves from alongside.

SHIP HUSBANDRY

The maintenance of a ship and her equipment in a state of seaworthiness, efficiency and cleanliness is a most important task, and ratings must possess a general knowledge of the various materials provided for these purposes and the manner of their use. A useful guide to the subject may be found in B.R. 2203, *Ship Husbandry Manual*, but some of the more important details of it are described below.

PAINTS AND PAINTING

Paint is used to provide a protective coat to materials such as steel and wood, which would soon corrode and rot if their surfaces were left bare. To be effective a coating of paint must be:

(a) of the correct type for the job in hand,

(b) properly applied over a prepared surface so that it will be waterproof, damp-proof and corrosion-proof.

Two or more layers of paint must be used, and each coat must be applied correctly and worked well into the surface. If paint is applied too thickly it will not dry; if too thinly, it will not provide sufficient protection and will let in damp.

Paint coats

The first layer of paint, which is called the 'priming' coat, should be brushed on and worked well into the surface. (Bare metal must always be given a priming coat, as this is an important part of the paint scheme.) Over this goes a 'finishing' coat, or, where some schemes include them both, an *under coat* and a *top coat*. The top coat is a glossy or semi-glossy paint which gives a smooth, hard surface which will stand up to wear and tear and cleaning.

Paint is heavy and adds to the weight of a ship. Therefore it must not be applied excessively, and old paint should be removed before repainting a surface if it is in bad condition or too thick.

Types of paint

Oil paints and *enamel* are flammable and are therefore never used for painting inside a ship.

Synthetic resin paints are more fire-resistant after application and are used as interior top coats. In bulk, in a tin, they often contain solvents, etc. which make them flammable.

Priming paints commonly used are aluminium primer ('Silverine'), zinc chromate and red lead. The type used varies according to the surface to be primed.

Flatting is chiefly used for interior surfaces such as deckheads, especially over cork-granulated surfaces, as it is porous and allows the cork to absorb the moisture.

Distempers are made with water or an oil emulsion, and give a matt surface. They are used for lagging of steam-pipes and ship's-side lagging in living-spaces.

FITCH OR LINER
Used for cutting in lines

SASH TOOL
Used for delicate
and intricate work

FLAT BRUSH
Used for general purposes

FIG. 10-24. Paint brushes

They are not as durable as oil paints, but are not so liable to crack or peel when the surface on which they are painted contracts or expands.

Paint brushes

The choice, use and care of paint brushes are very important. Typical examples of paint brushes are shown in Fig. 10-24. Paint brushes are supplied in various sizes. Efficient painting cannot be done with a brush whose bristles are distorted or splayed out.

Preparing a surface for painting

The preparation of a surface for painting is of the utmost importance. It must be clean and dry: all scale, rust, loose paint, oil, grease, moisture, salt deposits and other corrosive agents must be removed before paint is applied. If this is not done the coating will crack and peel off, or blister, and under it corrosion will spread unseen and unchecked.

Applying the paint

Cordage and rubber should never be painted, because paint rots them. Do not paint such articles as wire ropes, rigging-screws, insulators, tallies and any article which commonsense shows would be harmed or prevented from functioning by painting.

Start painting from the top and work downwards. When painting a compartment it should first be swept clean; deckcloths should be laid down, and furniture and fittings not required to be painted should be covered over. Paint the deckhead first, then the bulkheads, starting from the corner furthest from the door. The use of paint brushes lashed to broom handles ('long toms') should be reduced to a minimum, because the paint cannot be worked in effectively with them. Always have a rag dipped in white spirit handy, to wipe off smears on fittings not to be painted. Remove smears while they are still wet. When painting an intricate fitting such as a watertight door, use a piece of cardboard to cover parts which are not to be painted.

Brushwork

Painting is a job that requires skill and the correct technique.

(a) Hold the brush between the thumb and the first three fingers (Fig. 10-25).

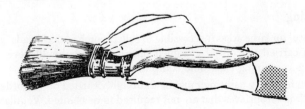

FIG. 10-25. How to hold a paint brush

(*b*) Never have the paint kettle more than two-thirds full.

(*c*) Keep the paint well stirred with a stick.

(*d*) Only dip the bristles half-way into the paint and press them gently against the inside of the pot to remove excess paint.

(*e*) Apply the paint firmly with smooth, even strokes backwards and forwards across the surface, the brush being held at an angle of about 45 degrees to the work.

(*f*) The initial (laying-on) strokes should be made horizontally over an area of about 2–4 square feet if a 3-inch brush is being used.

(*g*) The final (laying-off) strokes should then be done vertically.

(*h*) Paint should be brushed on thinly. If applied thickly it will not dry properly and will have a poor appearance.

Cleaning brushes on completion of work

1. Work all surplus paint out of the bristles against the side of the paint kettle.
2. Thoroughly clean the brush in white spirit, working it well into the heel of the brush and squeezing the solvent out against the side of the container.
3. Rinse the brush in clean white spirit when the bristles are quite free of paint.
4. Dry by spinning the brush handle between the palms of the hand.
5. Wash the brush in clean, soapy water and rinse in clean, fresh water.
6. Dry it, and lay it flat in its stowage.

Roller painting

This is the most economical method of painting large surfaces. It saves paint, personnel and time. The paint is held in the lower end of a tilted tray. To charge the roller, immerse a narrow strip of it in the paint and then roll it up and down the tray until the paint is evenly distributed over the roller. It is better to under-charge than over-charge.

Rolling. First paint inaccessible parts with a brush; then roll round the brushed area to make an inconspicuous joint. Roll in any direction, avoiding skidding and sliding. It is best to work twice horizontally and vertically, laying off vertically. Never use a roller to apply the priming coat, as this requires to be brushed in well.

Cleaning. Remove as much paint as possible by rolling out on newspaper. Wash the roller in white spirit, then in warm soapy water. Rinse in cold water, wipe on a clean rag and hang out to dry.

Spray painting

This is useful for large areas inaccessible to rollers, such as deckheads of messdecks. It should be carried out only by trained operators, and should never be done in compartments containing electronic equipment.

Preparation for spray painting must be thoroughly carried out, in order to prevent the paint settling on surfaces that are not required to be painted. Ventilation must be good and the operators properly clothed. On completion of the work the operator must ensure that his gear is cleaned and that he cleans himself thoroughly.

CLEANING SHIP

Brightwork. Emery paper should be used only to smooth down rough castings or to remove heavy accumulations of rust. Brass should be cleaned with metal polish, rubbing it in vigorously and polishing with rags or paper. Steel and very dirty brass, or brass covered with verdigris, should be cleaned with cleaning paste and metal polish rubbed on with a rough cloth.

Stainless steel. This should be cleaned with soap (or a mild detergent) and warm water, and wiped dry. Never scratch or rub with an abrasive such as wire wool, as this will mark the surface.

Chromium. This should be cleaned in the same way as stainless steel. To remove rust, rub with a chromium cleaner.

Canvas. Scrub heavy canvas with salt water and then thoroughly rinse with fresh water. Wash light canvas with soap and fresh water and then rinse in fresh water. To remove paint rub it with hard soap when wet. This will remove the paint at the next scrubbing.

Glazed surfaces. Clean in the same way as stainless steel. The use of cleaning powder may be necessary occasionally to remove stains.

Corticene or linoleum. Keep this type of surface treated with plastic or wax polish. If this is not possible, wipe over with detergent on a damp cloth. Never swill water over linoleum. Paint or other marks can be removed with white spirit and very fine steel wool.

Glass. Clean glass with soap and fresh water and polish with soft paper, such as newspaper. Paint can be removed by wetting it, then rubbing it with a copper coin laid flat.

Lagging and insulation. This should be brushed with a soft brush, washed with a damp cloth rinsed in fresh water and repainted with distemper.

Leather, hide and P.V.C. leather cloth. Wash with soap and warm fresh water. Dubbin should be rubbed well into real leatherwork exposed to the weather.

P.V.C. weather covers used on the upper deck. These should be washed with soap and water. P.V.C. covers can be repaired on board in a similar manner to a cycle puncture, using the correct adhesive. The patch should be sewn on before the adhesive dries and the edges coated with adhesive before leaving it to dry.

Plastic-topped tables. These table-tops are not completely heat-resistant, so never use them for ironing and always use mats for hot dishes. Avoid scratching them. Clean them with a damp cloth or hot, soapy water. Remove stubborn stains with detergent, and not with abrasive powders.

Painted surfaces. Clean with fresh water and clean cloths. Soda, cleaning powder, soft soap and caustic soda all destroy paint and should never be used. Remove stains carefully with cleaning paste on a damp cloth.

Rubber. Clean with soap and fresh water and dry thoroughly. To prevent sealing strips from becoming tacky, rub on powdered chalk. Remove paint splashes with a smooth piece of wood. Never allow paint, oil or grease to come in contact with rubber.

Woodwork. Bare woodwork should be scrubbed with salt water or sand and salt water. Do not use soap on woodwork, as it is liable to turn it yellow and leave a greasy surface. Polished woodwork should be wiped with a damp cloth, thoroughly dried and then polished with furniture polish.

Varnished wood. This should be washed with fresh water. To revarnish: remove old varnish with varnish-remover, wash with fresh water, dry thoroughly, then revarnish.

Salt

Nothing that has been soaked in salt water will keep dry until all traces of salt have been removed. Whenever possible, therefore, wash out the salt with fresh water before allowing the article to dry.

CHAPTER 11

Boats and Lifesaving Apparatus

See *Admiralty Manual of Seamanship*, Vols. I and II

SHIPS' BOATS IN GENERAL

Every man in the Royal Navy should be prepared to play his part as a member of a boat's crew. Details of boat construction, handling and sailing may be found in the *Admiralty Manual of Seamanship*, Vol. I, and only the more important aspects of the subject are dealt with here.

A warship carries a variety of boats, for both transport and recreation. The Motor Whaler is the standard general-purpose boat used in the Royal Navy; it can be propelled by power, sail or oars. Certain ship's boats are specially prepared for lowering and use at sea: these are called *seaboats*. The Motor Whaler is designed for this purpose, and when supplied to a ship is so used. In this chapter all references to a boat, and quoted orders to members of its crew, are made with the Motor Whaler in mind.

Behaviour in boats

The way in which Service boats' crews conduct themselves when away from their ship reflects credit or discredit upon themselves, their ship and the Royal Navy. Boats' crews should maintain a high standard of behaviour also in the interests of safety. Therefore when away from your ship in a Service boat remember the following:

(*a*) Boats' crews must be correctly dressed in the rig ordered, and must always wear their chin-straps down.

(*b*) Do not move about the boat except when necessary.

(*c*) Keep your hands, arms, etc. off the gunwale.

(*d*) Do not lounge, shout or skylark in a boat.

(*e*) Concentrate on your duty in the boat and do not let your attention wander.

(*f*) Keep your boat clean at all times.

(*g*) Ensure that ropes' ends, fenders or any other gear are not left hanging over the side while the boat is under way.

(*h*) If you are a non-swimmer or you are going out in a small boat you are to wear a lifejacket.

(*i*) If you are the bowman of a sailing boat keep a good lookout ahead and to leeward.

(*j*) Oars should never be shipped or used in a boat under sail except in emergency.

Principal parts of a boat

The hull of a pulling boat is like the hull of a ship except that the keel runs outside and beneath the bottom from end to end (Fig. 11-1). Extending upwards and outwards from the keel at short intervals along the whole length of the boat are the *timbers*, which form what are virtually the ribs of the boat. The timbers are curved up on either side and are held in position inside the boat by long fore-and-aft strips of wood called *stringers*. The timbers are covered on the outside by *planking*. The plank edges may either overlap (*clinker build*) or fit flush together (*carvel build*).

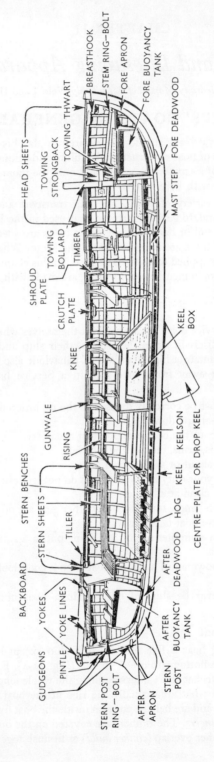

FIG. II-I. Parts of a 27-foot whaler

If the planks run fore-and-aft they are called *strakes*. The length of wood lying inside the topmost strake at the boat's side is called the *gunwale*. The stringers which support the ends of the seats (*thwarts*) are called *risings*.

When pulling, the boat's crew sit on the thwarts facing aft, their feet braced against adjustable wooden footrests (*stretchers*) placed in the bottom of the boat at a convenient distance from each man. The aftermost oarsman (*stroke oar*) sits on the aftermost or *stroke thwart*, and the foremost oarsman (*bowman*) sits on the forward or *bow thwart*. The space abaft the stroke thwart is the *stern sheets* and each side of and athwart the after end of this space are fitted seats called *benches*. Thwarts are fixed rigidly to the boat's sides by wooden brackets (*knees*). The boat's bottom beneath the thwarts is covered by *bottom boards*. To enable the boat to be hoisted and lowered, slings are hooked into suitably placed plates and eyebolts in the boat.

A boat is hoisted and lowered from davits by rope *falls*, which are hooked on to the slings.

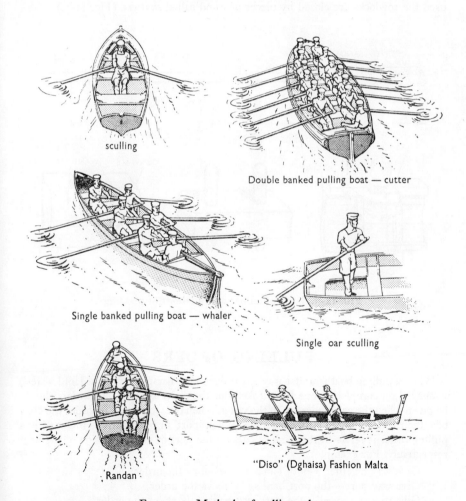

sculling

Double banked pulling boat — cutter

Single banked pulling boat — whaler

Single oar sculling

Randan

"Diso" (Dghaisa) Fashion Malta

FIG. 11-2. Methods of pulling a boat

Seating of the crew

An oarsman sitting on a thwart manning a pair of oars is said to be *sculling*. When only one oar is manned at each thwart (i.e. on alternate sides of the boat at alternate thwarts) the boat is said to be 'single-banked'. When an oar is manned at each side on each thwart she is said to be 'double-banked'. (Fig. 11-2.)

A boat's crew is always numbered from forward, but the bowman is known as 'Bow' and not as 'No. 1'. Similarly, the stroke oarsman is always referred to as 'Stroke' and not by a number. In a motor whaler used for pulling the crew members are Bow, No. 2, No. 3, Stroke and Coxswain.

Crutches and rowlocks

An oar's weight can be taken in either *crutches* or *rowlocks*. Crutches are U-shaped metal fittings which are shipped in crutch plates fitted inside the gunwale. They are always unshipped when oars are not being used. Rowlocks are U-shaped spaces cut in the *washstrake* (a thick plank fitted above the gunwale). When oars are not being used the rowlocks are closed by pieces of wood called *shutters*. (Fig. 11-3.)

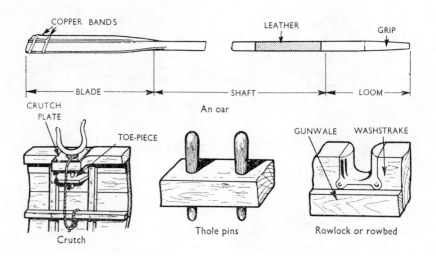

FIG. 11-3. Parts of an oar and methods of pivoting

PULLING ORDERS

When a pulling boat is under way any order to the oarsmen (except 'Hold water') is obeyed on completing one full stroke after the order is given. All orders should be given when the oar blades are in the water. When obeying a pulling order the crew take their time from the stroke oarsman. When 'port' or 'starboard' is included in a pulling order it refers to the bank of oars on the port or starboard side of the boat respectively. For example:

'Give way together'—both banks of oars obey the order;
'Give way port'—the port bank only obeys the order;
'Give way starboard'—the starboard bank only obeys the order.

Leaving from alongside

It is assumed that the motor whaler is alongside the jetty or gangway, that the crew has been detailed for its thwarts, that the boat is manned and is in all respects ready to get under way.

ORDER	ACTION
'Shove off'	The bowman shoves off the bows and lays in his boathook. The stroke oarsman lays in his boathook and springs the boat ahead.
'Ship your oars'	The crew unship their shutters and ship their oars.
'Oars'	Each man grasps the loom of his oar and brings the oar to the athwartships position, with the oar and blade horizontal.
'Give way together'	This is the order to start pulling and is obeyed together by the whole crew. If only one bank of oars is required to give way the order is 'Give way port (starboard)'.

Orders given while under way

ORDER	ACTION
'Easy all'	This means 'pull less vigorously' in order to reduce the speed of the boat. To resume normal pulling the order 'Give way together' is given.
'Mind your oars'	A warning to the crew to keep the blades of their oars clear of some obstruction.
'Eyes in the boat'	An order to the crew to keep their gaze from wandering abroad and to pay attention to their duties.
'Hold water'	An order to reduce or stop the way of the boat by holding the oars at right angles to the fore-and-aft line of the boat, with their blades in the water; it should be obeyed immediately.
'Back together'	An order to back water together by pushing on the loom of the oars instead of pulling.
'Stroke together'	An order to the crew to give one stroke together.

Going alongside

ORDER	ACTION
'Bow'	The bowman takes one further stroke after the order and lays in his oar (blade forward).
'Way enough'	The crew take one further stroke after the order and then lay their oars in the boat.

Bow and Stroke use their boathooks, and, if necessary, check the boat's way as it comes alongside.

These orders may be given at any time and need not necessarily be confined to going alongside.

THE SEABOAT

A ship at sea always has at least one boat available for immediate lowering for a variety of reasons, including, for example, the saving of life, picking up an object in the water, and transferring stores or personnel between two ships. This boat is rigged in a special way and carries extra equipment suitable to these purposes. The full details of the rig and gear are shown in the *Admiralty Manual of Seamanship*, Vol. I, and some general points concerning rig and gear are dealt with below.

Although in normal circumstances the seaboat is manned, lowered, and sometimes hoisted, by men of the Seaman Branch, there are occasions when any man on board may have to act as a crew member or assist in lowering, particularly if the saving of life is involved. Therefore everyone on board ought to know the drill and understand what the gear and fittings are for. So that you can learn the drill for hoisting and lowering, it is described in detail here. In some ships where the seaboat is hoisted by hand, all ratings on board man the falls under the supervision of Seaman Branch ratings.

Safety precautions when hoisting and lowering

Whenever a boat is being hoisted or lowered from davits no one is allowed to stand before the foremost fall or abaft the after fall, because if one fall parted a man would be crushed between the other fall and the bow or stern of the boat. No one is allowed to place his hands on the falls, and everyone in the boat must hold on to a lifeline.

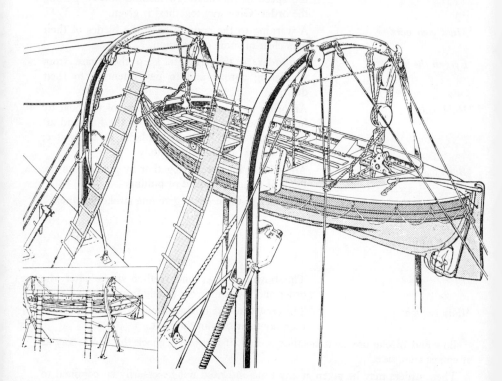

FIG. 11-4. A motor whaler rigged as a seaboat

Rig and gear of a seaboat (Fig. 11-4)

The boat-rope. This is a rope led from the boat to a position well forward in the ship, and secured in the boat in a special manner to ensure quick release. Its purposes are:

(*a*) to keep the boat heading in the same direction as the ship, thus preventing the boat from broaching to if the after fall fails to release on slipping;

(*b*) to haul the boat ahead if she is slipped with the ship stopped, thus giving her steerage way to sheer out from the ship's side;

(*c*) to haul the boat forward under the bows when the ship is coming to a buoy or going alongside, if the boat is not under power;

(*d*) to haul the boat forward under her davits when she is approaching to hook on in a seaway;

(*e*) to hold the boat under her davits while she is being hooked on; with the help of a sternfast aft in the boat, to prevent the boat from surging as she is being hoisted or lowered in a seaway.

Lifelines and falls. Lifelines (one to each thwart) are secured to the span between the davits. The falls are belayed to the staghorns or davit cleats, or reeled up on the davit winches.

The tiller. The tiller is stopped over towards the ship's side by a split yarn, so that when the boat is slipped she will sheer away from the ship's side.

Disengaging gear. It is essential when lowering a seaboat, and when the ship has way on her, that both falls should be disengaged from the boat simultaneously, so that the boat can be slipped above the level of the waves. To effect this all ships' boats in the Royal Navy are fitted with 'Robinson's disengaging gear'. A full description of its setting-up and action may be found in the *Admiralty Manual of Seamanship*, Vol. I. Fig. 11-5 shows how the disengaging gear is rigged in a seaboat.

Boat's gear. The gear in the boat includes:

Oars and boathooks—these should be lightly stopped in place to prevent them rolling about;

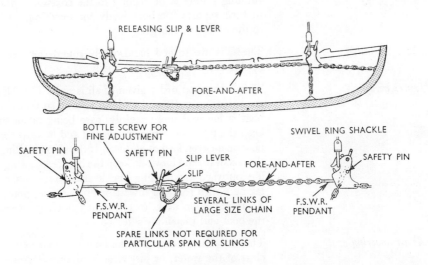

FIG. 11-5. Robinson's disengaging gear set up in a seaboat

Inflatable lifejackets—there should be a lifejacket for each member of the crew and one spare one;

Boat's bag—this contains gear such as tallow, tingles, etc., for emergency repairs, hand signalling equipment, boat's lead and line, candles and matches;

Boat's distress box—this contains distress signals (pyrotechnics);

Additional gear—jerrycans of water, boat's compass and lantern.

Lowering a seaboat

For seaboat drill to be carried out efficiently a standard sequence of orders must be adhered to. Usually the seaboat on the lee side is ordered to be manned. In rough weather oil may be used to lessen the breaking of the waves, and a sternfast may be secured to a suitable fitting aft in the boat. Both the sternfast and boat-rope are manned and tended inboard.

The drill described below is that for lowering a 27-foot motor whaler from quadrantal davits. The gripes have been slipped, the davits turned out and the davit slips, if fitted, knocked off (Fig. 11-6).

ORDER	ACTION
'Away seaboat's crew, man the port (starboard) seaboat'	The crew man the seaboat at the rush, put on their lifejackets, position themselves by their respective thwarts, grasp their lifelines, and await further orders. The coxswain and bowman unmouse the safety pins on the disengaging gear and take the sea jackstay lizards in hand. The M(E) makes sure that the exhaust is clear and the shaft clear to rotate, then starts the engine.
'Turns for lowering'	The lowerers remove the outer turns from the davit cleats. When the M(E) is satisfied that the engine is running properly, he reports to the coxswain, who in turn reports 'Seaboat ready for lowering, Sir', to the officer in charge.
'Start the falls'	The falls are surged handsomely round the cleats so that the boat is lowered slowly.
'Lower away'	This is the next order given, if all is well. The falls are surged roundly and without jerking so that the boat is lowered more rapidly, care being taken to keep the falls under perfect control and to keep the boat on an even keel *at all times*. If the ship is rolling the coxswain and bowman keep the boat from swinging outward by tending the lizards, if necessary taking a turn round a thwart or other strong point. Spare hands on deck lower rattan fenders between the boat and the ship's side.
'Avast lowering'	This order is given when the boat is a foot or two clear of the water, or just clear of the wave crests. The lowerers stop lowering and back up the falls.

FIG. 11-6. A seaboat about to be lowered

ORDER	ACTION
'*Out pins*'	The bowman removes the safety pin from the forward disengaging gear and raises his hand to indicate to the coxswain that the pin is clear. At the same time the coxswain removes the safety pin from the after disengaging gear, grasps the slip lever of the fore-and-after, removes its locking pin, raises his hand and reports 'Pins out, Sir', to the officer in charge. The sea-jackstay lizards must be in hand at this stage and not secured in the boat. The sternfast should also be in hand in the boat.
'*Slip*' (In rough sea, or if the ship is rolling, this order is timed so that the boat will land on the crest of an approaching wave.)	The coxswain slips the fore-and-after and the boat drops into the water. He grasps the tiller and parts its strop. He orders 'Half ahead', orders the lizards to be cast off, and casts off the sternfast. The crew shove off hard from the ship's side, if necessary. (If there is no way on the ship, the boat may have

Order	Action
	difficulty in shoving off; to help her in getting clear, the boat-rope is manned and the boat hauled forward a short distance to give her sufficient way to sheer off.) The boatrope is slipped by the bowman on orders from the coxswain.

As soon as the boat is clear of the ship, the gripes and falls are hauled inboard, the latter being rove ready for hoisting the boat on her return. The boat-rope and sternfast are recovered and made ready for passing into the boat. The sternfast should have sufficient strength to withstand the shock of the boat surging forward. The lizards are recovered and their ends stopped to the lower blocks of the falls.

Hoisting a seaboat

The majority of ships in the Fleet have cordage falls fitted, and can hoist their boats either by power or by hand. The drill described below is for hoisting a motor whaler as a seaboat by cordage falls, by hand. It is assumed that the weather is bad enough to use Nylon anti-shock slings, and that falls are already manned inboard. The anti-shock slings consist of 3-ft Nylon strops and steel wire pendants.

A lee is formed by the ship, if possible. The Nylon strops are spring-hooked to the lower blocks of the falls, which are then lowered over the side until there is the right amount of scope between them and the waterline. Care has to be taken in doing this to prevent the lower blocks 'thoroughfooting' themselves, i.e. tumbling over upside-down. The steel wire pendants are shackled to the davit heads (one to each davit). These pendants are longer than the Nylon strops, and their lower ends are fitted with spring-hooks.

The functions of the anti-shock slings are:

(a) to absorb the shock of the boat plunging up and down when alongside, during the first stages of hoisting;

(b) to prevent damage to the boat and davits;

(c) to keep the lower blocks clear of ratings hooking on in the boat.

Immediately the returning boat gets within reach the boat-rope and sternfast are passed to her and made fast in the bow and stern respectively.

Order	Action
'*Marry to your marks*'	Hands inboard marry the falls so that their strips of bunting are in line. The bunting marks ensure that the boat is hoisted on an even keel.

As the boat rises to a wave the foremost fall Nylon strop is hooked on, and immediately afterwards the after fall Nylon strop is hooked on. The coxswain reports 'Hooked on in the boat, Sir'.

'*Hoist away*'	Hands manning the falls run up the boat clear of the waves as quickly as possible. The boat-rope and sternfast must be manned to prevent the boat surging as she is hoisted. The coxswain and bowman tend their sea-jackstay lizards, and the M(E) stops the engine. As a further step to prevent surging the lifelines may be crossed. Hands on deck man their fenders and follow the boat up as she is being hoisted.

ORDER	ACTION
'Avast hoisting'	This order is given when the boat is high enough for the steel wire pendants to be hooked on. The hands on the falls stop hoisting. The coxswain and bowman hook on their respective pendants to the top shackle of their respective disengaging gear, each holding up one hand when the pendant hook is properly engaged. Two crew members tend the sea-jackstay lizards while this is going on.
'Walk back to the pendants'	The hands keep the falls in hand and walk back towards the davits until the pendants take the weight of the boat and the Nylon strops slacken, and continue to walk back as the coxswain and bowman remove the Nylon strops from the lower blocks of the falls and from the hooks of the disengaging gear. The coxswain and bowman then overhaul the falls until the lower-block swivel-ring shackles can be hooked directly on to the disengaging gear.
'Well'	The hands manning the falls stop walking back.
'Hoist away handsomely'	The hands manning the falls walk away and continue to hoist the boat. As soon as the weight is off the steel pendants the coxswain and bowman unhook them and keep them clear of the falls.
'High enough'	This order is given when the boat's falls are nearly *two blocks* (when each lower block on each fall comes up against its upper block). The hands stop hauling, but keep their weight on the falls.
'On slips'	The bowman and coxswain pass the tongues of their slips *down and through* the shackle provided on the boat's slings and secure the tongue with the link and pin of the slip. The bowman reports 'Forward slip on' to the coxswain, who then reports 'Both slips on, Sir' to the officer in charge.
'Ease to the slips'	The hands keep the falls in hand and walk towards the davits until the slips take the weight of the boat and the falls slacken.
'Light to'	A bight of about two fathoms of each of the slack falls is lighted towards the davits and the remainder let go. The hands positioned at the davits belay the falls ready for lowering again and report 'Foremost (after) fall belayed, Sir'.

The boat is once more prepared for use as a seaboat and all gear restowed correctly.

Use of a seaboat as a lifeboat

If the seaboat is required for an emergency such as 'man overboard', the pipe 'Away, lifeboat's crew' is made, whereupon the boat is manned by any officers, seamen or other ratings qualified to act as boat's crew. Spare hands act as lowerers.

Use of a swimmer for lifesaving

In some ships a swimmer is used to recover a man from the water as an alternative to using a lifeboat. In this case the swimmer must be qualified in lifesaving, and he should wear a lifejacket and be attached to a lifeline. The ship manoeuvres close to windward of the man to be rescued, and the swimmer jumps into the water and swims out to him. The swimmer grapples the man and takes him back to the ship.

LIFESAVING APPARATUS

See *Admiralty Manual of Seamanship*, Vol. II; B.R. 1977(1), *Liferaft Handbook*

Lifebuoys and lifebuoy sentry

H.M. ships carry lifebuoys hung in conspicuous and handy positions on their upper decks. In frigates and larger ships two of these are placed aft, and at sea a rating from the watch on deck, who is known as the *lifebuoy sentry*, is always stationed near them. In the vicinity is a telephone to the bridge and an electric buzzer operated from the bridge according to a special code. This code is displayed on notices on the bridge and by the lifebuoy sentry's position. The normal code used is:

One ring—Throw over the starboard lifebuoy
Two rings—Throw over the port lifebuoy
Three rings—Throw over both lifebuoys.

On closing up at his station at the beginning of his watch the lifebuoy sentry telephones the bridge and requests that the buzzer be tested.

To mark a lifebuoy's position in the water it is fitted with a lanyard, which is attached to a combined smoke and electric light marker. The action of water on sea cells in the marker ignites the smoke composition which it contains and illuminates the electric lights. The marker is fitted with plastic plugs which are attached to an orange-coloured line. The line is secured to the stowage bracket.

When the lifebuoy is thrown overboard the marker is drawn out of its stowage by the lanyard, and the plastic plugs are pulled out of the marker by the coloured line, so that on entering the water the sea cells can function.

The naval inflatable lifejacket

The lifejacket (Fig. 11-7) is designed to keep you floating on your back at an angle of 45°, and swimming must be done on your back. It is fitted with a lifting harness and a line and toggle for securing to other personnel floating in the water. There are also a whistle, a lamp and a battery (which must not be wasted). The jacket must be inspected daily and the operation of its mouthpiece thoroughly tested. Points to look for are the state of the rubber, harness, lamp, battery and whistle (for clogging).

The jacket is kept in a pouch worn in the small of the back. When you need to use it, slide it round to the front of your body, unbutton the flap, and slip the stole of the jacket over your head.

To INFLATE

1. Remove the inflation tube from its loop and unscrew the mouthpiece.
2. Depress the light valve spring with the mouth, puffing air into the jacket at the same time. Four or five puffs are sufficient to ensure flotation, but the jacket should be fully inflated to ensure that it is self-righting.
3. Screw the valve shut and stow the tube back in the loop.

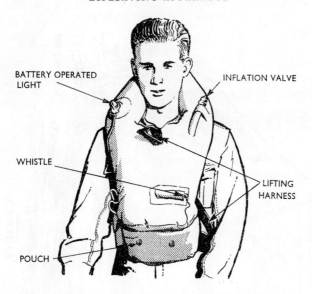

BATTERY OPERATED LIGHT

INFLATION VALVE

WHISTLE

LIFTING HARNESS

POUCH

Fig. 11-7. The naval inflatable lifejacket

To Deflate and Stow

1. Unscrew the valve, press against the spring and deflate.
2. Lay the lifejacket out flat. Dry, and dust with French chalk.
3. See harness is secured by the three press-studs. Replace mouthpiece in the retaining loop.
4. Fold in sides to the width of the pouch.
5. Stow the bottom of the jacket.
6. Starting from the neck, roll up tightly and stow the jacket in the pouch.

Self-inflating lifejackets

Trials have recently been carried out with self-inflating lifejackets. These jackets are worn in a similar manner to the naval inflatable lifejackets and automatically inflate when the wearer is in the water.

Inflatable liferafts

In H.M. ships, boats are not included in the lifesaving complement, but inflatable liferafts are supplied on a scale that provides for the war complement required for a ship. The two sizes in use in the Service are the 8- and 20-man liferafts. They are packed in rot-proof canvas valises, and are fitted with survival packs which contain food, water, first aid kit, repair outfit, distress signals, etc. The 8-man survival pack is stowed inside the liferaft, whereas the 20-man pack is separate and is stowed above the liferaft valise. Packs and liferafts are held in place and protected by a cover, which is either slipped by hand or released hydrostatically if the ship founders before the cover can be slipped by hand.

When the pack and valise have been launched overboard, the valise remains secured to a strong-point (eyeplate) near the stowage by an operating cord, which, when given one or more sharp pulls, operates a gas-release mechanism. The raft then inflates and bursts out of its valise.

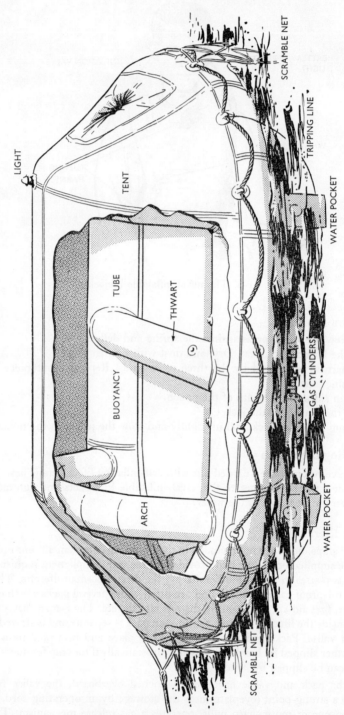

FIG. 11-8. The 20-man liferaft

THE 20-MAN LIFERAFT

This liferaft, with its accompanying survival pack, is designed to carry the essentials of life for 20 men for a period of five days. Fig. 11-8 shows the construction of the raft and its principal fittings. Occupants of the raft are protected by a layer of air which insulates them from the extremes of temperature outside the raft.

When launched, the main buoyancy tube, arches and thwart are automatically inflated from the gas cylinders attached beneath the raft. The floor and seat tubes are inflated by hand bellows. The main buoyancy tube is divided athwartships by two vertical bulkheads, each half having its own inflation, safety and topping-up valves and deflation plug. Defects in one half will not, therefore, affect the other.

Fittings

Some of the more important fittings are:

A towing bridle at each end,

A drogue attached to the forward bridle,

A scramble net at each end,

A lifeline secured round the main buoyancy tube in loops,

Adjustable sleeve entrances each end, which can also be used as awnings in the tropics,

On the underside, four handling loops for use when righting the raft if capsized, and four water-pockets to check wind drift. Each pocket is fitted with a trip line for spilling the water when it is desired to increase drift or to manoeuvre, or when being towed.

The raft contains equipment to aid survival and rescue.

Boarding the raft from the water

Either

(a) hold the lifeline nearest the scrambling net with one hand and put one foot on the bottom rung of the hauling-in ladder; then transfer both hands to the ladder and scramble aboard; or

(b) grab the lifeline; place both feet on the scramble net; grab the hauling-in ladder as far up as possible; now put both feet as high as possible on the scramble net. Straighten your legs, pull upwards with your arms and lunge, face down, into the raft.

Righting the raft

Manoeuvre yourself to a position close to the gas cylinders and grasp the lower set of handling loops. Climb on to the cylinders and grasp the upper set of handling loops. Sway backwards and push with your feet (Fig. 11-9). Provided that its topside is up-wind, the raft should turn right side up. To get clear from underneath the raft, push it away with the feet to avoid being struck on the head by the cylinders.

Cutting loose

When the raft is full, use *only* the safety knife fitted to cut the painter. Manoeuvre the raft clear of the ship, using the drogue. Keep rafts together and keep a good lookout for other survivors.

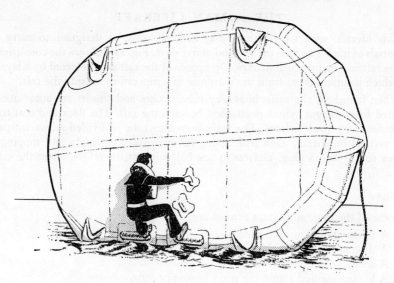

FIG. 11-9. Righting a capsized raft

The survival pack

The survival pack is stowed on top of the raft and is attached to the valise lifting handle by a painter. The length of the painter permits separate launching of pack and raft. The pack contains rations for the full complement for five days and certain equipment listed in the handbook B.R.1977(1). Distress signals are stowed in the pockets on the outside of the survival pack valise.

Survival

The officer or senior rating in charge of the raft will organize watches, lookouts, distribution of food, etc. Remember that you are not the only one who is suffering discomfort and that the best hope for your individual survival lies in co-operating with those around you, doing what you are told, keeping cheerful and helping those less fortunate than yourself.

CHAPTER 12

Navigation, Conning and Steering, and Rule of the Road

See B.R. 45 (1) and (2), *Admiralty Manual of Navigation*, Vols. I and II; B.R. 67 (1) and (2) *Admiralty Manual of Seamanship*, Vols. I and II

THE SEA

The sea covers 70 per cent of the world's surface area. Although Man has been sailing on it for many centuries and in recent years submerging in and flying over it, there is still a great deal that is not known about it. Although he is constantly investigating its structure and behaviour, it still has many undiscovered secrets and will retain its mystery and fascination for many years to come.

Units of measurement

Depth is measured in *fathoms*, six feet being equal to one fathom. A measurement of the depth of water is called a *sounding*, and making a measurement is called *taking a sounding*.

Distance is measured in *nautical miles*, one nautical or sea mile being 6,080 feet or approximately 2,000 yards. One-tenth of a nautical mile (200 yards) is one *cable*.

Speed is measured in *knots*, one knot being one nautical or sea mile per hour. A ship proceeding at thirty knots or thirty nautical miles per hour represents a land speed of 34½ miles per hour.

Soundings

The sea bed, like the land surface, consists of hills and valleys. The greatest known depth is deeper than Mount Everest is high. Before 1925 it was not possible to measure

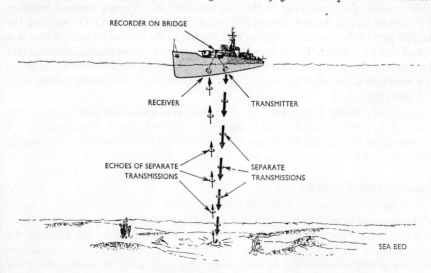

RECORDER ON BRIDGE

RECEIVER   TRANSMITTER

ECHOES OF SEPARATE TRANSMISSIONS   SEPARATE TRANSMISSIONS

SEA BED

FIG. 12-1. Diagrammatic representation of echo sounding

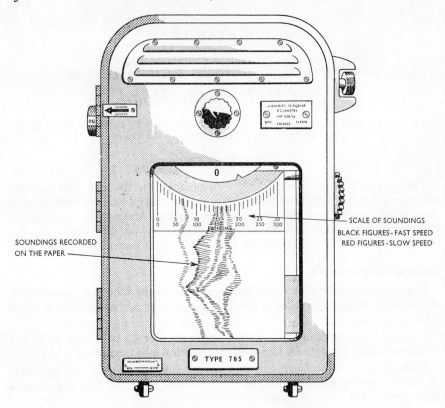

SCALE OF SOUNDINGS
BLACK FIGURES - FAST SPEED
RED FIGURES - SLOW SPEED

SOUNDINGS RECORDED
ON THE PAPER

TYPE 765

FIG. 12-2. Echo sounder recording unit

depth except by using a weighted line. Today ships are fitted with an echo sounder. This consists of a transmitter in the ship's bottom which emits a sound impulse; this impulse travels through the sea at a uniform speed (Fig. 12-1). On reaching the sea bed part of the sound is reflected and returns to the ship as an echo, where it is picked up by a receiver. This echo is passed to a recorder, whose mechanism combines the speed of sound in water and the time interval between transmission of the signal and reception of the echo into depth. This is shown on a continuously moving strip of paper (Fig. 12-2).

Hand lead and line. For sounding in shallow water at speeds not exceeding 10 knots a lead on the end of a long line can be hove over the side by hand. The line is marked at intervals so that the leadsman can read the depth. This method is seldom used in H.M. ships, where accurate echo sounding gear is fitted.

Tides and tidal streams

The periodic rise and fall of the sea constitute what are known as *tides*. The theory of the cause of tides is complex, but the following simplified explanation is based on it (Fig. 12-3). The combined gravitational forces of earth, moon and sun raise the water level of the oceans and seas on the earth. The pull is concentrated at any moment at two points on the earth's surface, one of which is approximately below the moon, and the other on the opposite side of the earth. At these two points the water level is raised, and a high tide occurs. The moon can be said to revolve round the earth once in about 25 hours, and it is found that the two banks or waves of raised water travel round the earth at about the same speed as the moon, their axis keeping in line with the moon. Thus at any point on the earth's surface one would expect two high tides to occur within one day, with two low tides in the intervals, the period between a high and a succeeding low tide being about 6¼ hours. Such a tidal oscillation is called *semi-diurnal* (twice daily) and is found over large parts of

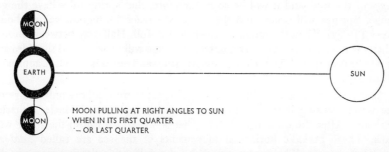

MOON PULLING AT RIGHT ANGLES TO SUN
WHEN IN ITS FIRST QUARTER
— OR LAST QUARTER

AT LAST QUARTER OR FIRST QUARTER HIGH WATERS ARE LOWEST AND LOW WATERS ARE HIGHEST
Neap Tides

SUN AND MOON PULLING TOGETHER
AT FULL MOON OR NEW MOON

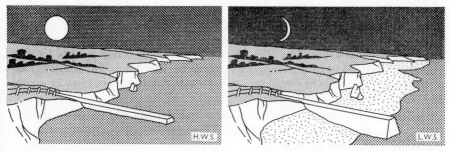

AT FULL OR NEW MOON HIGH WATERS ARE HIGHEST AND LOW WATERS ARE LOWEST
Spring Tides

FIG. 12-3. Spring and neap tides

the earth's surface. However, the tide found around the coasts bordering a sea or ocean depends on the configuration of the coastlines and the contours of the sea bed, and the response of the shape of that sea to the tide-raising forces. Thus in some parts of the world only one high water will occur each day, this being called a *diurnal* tide.

At full and new moon the attractive force of the moon is allied to that of the sun, and the highest (and lowest) tides will occur. These are called *spring* tides. The vertical distance between the water level at low tide and that at high tide is called the *range* of the tide, and it will be seen, therefore, that spring tides have the greatest range. Springs will occur, and the range will reach its highest value, about once every 14 days, when the moon is either new or full. Half-way between these times, when the moon is at first or last quarter, the range will be least, and the tides are then said to be *neap* tides. The period between springs and neaps is therefore approximately seven days.

As the tide-raising wave approaches the coast there is a horizontal movement of the water, causing it to flow towards the coast and into channels, estuaries and harbours. After the time of high tide (that is, after *high water*) the water will flow back. These periodic horizontal movements of the sea are called *tidal streams* (or *tidal currents*). The stream caused by the rising tide flowing into a harbour is called the *flood* stream; the reverse is the *ebb* stream. The direction of the tidal

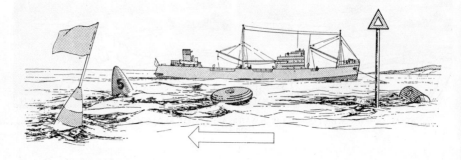

FIG. 12-4. Buoys and ships give indication of the set of the tidal stream

stream at any point is called the *set*, and its speed is called its *rate*. Fig. 12-4 shows how you can observe the set of the tidal stream; with experience you can estimate its strength.

The tidal stream has its strongest rate half-way between consecutive high and low waters and is *slack* at about high and low water. If the water level at high and low water does not appear to change over a period the tide is said to *stand* for that period. When the tidal stream changes its direction of flow it is said to *turn*. The rate of the tidal stream in both directions reaches a maximum and minimum at spring and neap tides respectively.

Sufficient is known for the times of tides and the rate and direction of tidal streams in certain places to be predicted. These predictions are published in the *Admiralty Tide Tables* for each year.

If you try to cross a stretch of water in a boat you will quickly appreciate that you have to make allowances for both the tide and the tidal stream in order to ensure that you have enough water under the keel to prevent the boat being set off her track by the tidal stream. Similarly, a ship proceeding from one place to another must make such allowances if she is to avoid hazards or grounding and if she is to reach her destination safely.

Wind

There are many contributory causes of wind and a detailed account of how a wind is produced would be too complicated for this book. It is only intended here to tell you some of the ways of describing a wind, some points about it and how it affects the sea and your ship.

A wind is said to blow from a certain direction, and if it changes that direction clockwise it is said to *veer*; if it changes its direction anti-clockwise it is said to *back*. For example, a wind blowing from a northerly direction is called a *north* wind; if it changes its direction to easterly it is veering; if it changes its direction from northerly to westerly it is backing.

The force of the wind is estimated from a scale called the *Beaufort scale* which is tabulated at the beginning of the ship's log book. The wind's force, together with the weather, sea state, etc., is noted in the ship's log at the end of every watch.

The behaviour of a wind can be an indication of a change in the weather. This is important when a change in its behaviour precedes bad weather, for it can give the sailor time to take the necessary precautions against such weather.

The surface of the sea, and consequently anything floating on it, is affected by the wind. If you blow across a bowl of water you will see waves formed; if you stop blowing the waves will take a short while to die down. The wind affects the ocean on a much larger scale, producing two types of wave: the waves caused by the wind blowing at the time form a *sea*, and those caused by the wind at some other place at some previous time form a *swell*.

The direction of the wind can be estimated by looking at right-angles to the line of the waves. If there is a swell running at the same time from a different direction this is not easy to do, but it is an art acquired with practice. Just as a bird flying across an open space has to struggle against, and allow for, a strong wind so a ship at sea has to allow for the effects of the wind. The wave formations caused by the wind will offset her from her intended track and the wind itself will blow her to leeward. This movement to leeward is called *drift*. A ship steaming at sea has therefore to make allowances for the effects of the wind in order to maintain her intended track.

Effect of a sea on a ship

A ship steaming with her bows meeting the seas end on is said to be meeting a *head* sea. If she is steaming with her stern to the sea she is said to be steaming with a *following* sea. In each case her bow and stern will alternatively rise and fall in a *pitching* movement. With the sea abeam she has a *beam* sea and she will *roll*, heeling alternately from side to side. A ship which rolls quickly is known as lively or *stiff*, whereas a ship that is slow to recover is known as *crank* or *tender*.

A ship which deliberately remains stationary or very nearly stationary is said to be *hove to*. In heavy weather a ship heaves to to avoid damage.

When running before a heavy sea it is sometimes very difficult to steer a ship. If steering control is lost, she may bury her bows in the trough of the waves and be turned beam on to the sea. This is called *broaching to* and is dangerous because the following wave may capsize her.

A vessel is said to be 'shipping it green' when unbroken masses of water are coming on board in a heavy sea. A green sea will sweep away anything not properly secured.

When a ship is steaming ahead in conditions other than a flat calm there is normally a tendency to turn into the wind, if it is blowing from the bow or from abeam. Consequently the rating steering the ship (the *helmsman*) has to adjust his steering to counteract this tendency (see page 162).

ELEMENTARY NAVIGATION

When a ship sails out of sight of land her position can be found by calculation, using the sun, the stars and occasionally the moon, or by modern radio aids to navigation. When in coastal waters, if the land and various aids such as lighthouses, light-vessels, landmarks, beacons and buoys are visible, her position can be found by observing the bearings of such objects and plotting them on the chart. Even if they are not visible a ship equipped with modern navigational aids (i.e. Decca, radar, etc.) can still find her position.

Just as the driver of a car will look out for obstructions, turnings, etc. and other road-users, so the captain of a ship will ensure that due care is taken to avoid dangers to his ship and will watch the movements of other ships at sea.

Charts

Charts are the sailor's maps and show coastline, navigational marks and dangers and the depth of water. A ship can be taken safely from one place to another by a planned route on a chart and by making certain that she is, in fact, following the selected route. Plate 6 shows a typical chart of an estuary and approaches to a port. The following paragraphs will tell you something about the things you will see marked on a chart and how you can recognize them as your ship steams at sea.

Buoys

Buoys are used to mark channel edges, obstructions, dangers, edges of shoals, etc., and their positions are marked on the charts (see Plate 7). Three principal types of buoy are used:

    (a) *Starboard-hand buoys* mark the starboard or right-hand side of the channel when going with the main flood stream or entering an estuary, a river or harbour from seaward. These buoys are conical in shape and are painted black or black-and-white chequered, or black-and-yellow chequered for secondary channels.

    (b) *Port-hand buoys* mark the port or left-hand side of a channel under similar circumstances. These buoys are can-shaped and are painted red or red-and-white chequered, or red-and-yellow chequered for secondary channels.

    (c) *Middle-ground buoys* mark the inner and outer ends of a shoal or obstruction and the junction of two or more channels, and they may be passed on either hand. These buoys are spherical in shape and are painted with red-and-white or black-and-white horizontal bars.

There are many kinds of special buoys used to mark specific objects such as *wrecks, outfalls, cables,* etc. Small rivers have their channels marked by spar buoys and posts.

Fittings mounted on buoys. Buoys can be marked with topmarks to indicate the purpose of the buoy, e.g. where a middle-ground buoy marks a shoal separating a main and secondary channel the topmark will indicate which channel is which.

Lights are fitted on important buoys to help to identify them at night. These lights are arranged so that starboard-hand buoys can be distinguished from port-hand buoys, and so that adjacent buoys on the same side of the channel can be distinguished from one another. Fog signals and radar reflectors are fitted to some buoys to help to identify them in fog and low visibility. The fog signals may consist of whistles and bells. Some of these fog signals are operated by wave motion and may not be working on a calm day.

Landmarks

Beacons and other conspicuous landmarks such as factory chimneys and church spires may provide good marks for observing bearings to fix the ship's position. In towns and cities where there may be several church spires, those which stand out against the surrounding buildings are marked 'conspicuous' on the chart. Occasionally certain pairs of objects ashore may, when observed to be in line with one another, provide a good *leading line* or *clearing line* for a ship proceeding along a channel or past a danger.

Lights, lighthouses and light-vessels

Lights and lighthouses are placed to mark salient features of the coast and hidden dangers such as rocks or shoals. They are lit from sunset to sunrise and in times of low visibility. Light-vessels are used to mark shoals or channels for the purpose of navigation and are usually painted red, with their name in large white letters on their sides.

Light characteristics

So that one light can be distinguished from another, different combinations of light and darkness, colour and time cycles are used. The commonest forms of light, with their abbreviations, are:

(a) *Fixed light* (F). This shows a steady beam. There are comparatively few fixed lights, as they may well be confused with shore lights or the lights of a ship.

(b) *Flashing light* (Fl). This shows one or more flashes at regular intervals, the intervening period of darkness being longer than the period of light.

(c) *Occulting light* (Occ). This appears as a fixed light broken at intervals by one or more periods of darkness, the periods of light being longer than the periods of darkness.

(d) *Sectored light.* Certain lights have coloured sectors to indicate dangerous areas to the approaching mariner. The light may be fixed, flashing or occulting. From a certain position only one colour will be seen.

(e) *Alternating light* (Alt). This is a flashing or an occulting light that alternates the colour of the light. From a certain position different colours will be seen.

Compasses

The gyro-compass. This is fundamentally a wheel spinning at high speed and balanced so that its axis points to true North. The compass is normally placed low down in the ship and therefore the directions indicated by it must be transmitted

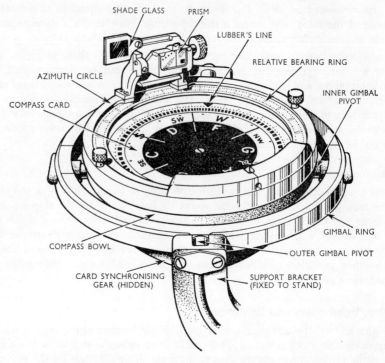

FIG. 12-5. A compass repeater fitted with an azimuth ring

electrically to repeaters (Fig. 12-5) placed in convenient positions such as the bridge and steering position. The principal bridge repeater from which bearings can be taken, using an *azimuth ring*, is called the *pelorus*.

The magnetic compass. A magnet hung horizontally and free to rotate settles with its axis pointing in the direction of magnetic North, which differs from true North in varying amounts from place to place: this difference is called *variation* (Fig. 12-6). The magnetic compass consists essentially of a card marked in degrees from

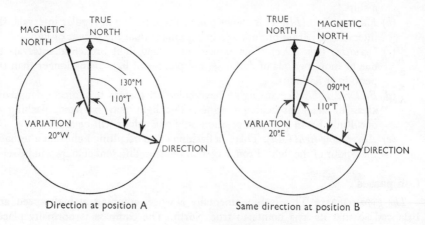

FIG. 12-6. Application of **variation**

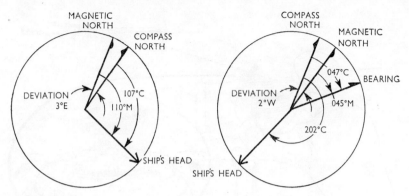

FIG. 12-7. Application of deviation

0 to 360, supported at its centre on a pivot and having several magnets secured underneath it and parallel to the direction of 0 on the card.

Ships are usually made of steel, or have a certain amount of iron or steel in their construction. The iron and steel cause a *deviation* of the compass from the direction of magnetic North (Fig. 12-7). Thus corrections for deviation and variation must be applied to the direction shown on a magnetic compass in order to convert it to true direction.

The magnetic compass must be sited as clear of the ship's structure as is possible (usually on the bridge). It is not possible to operate repeaters from it.

The gyro-magnetic compass. By combining the magnetic North-seeking property of a magnetic compass with the steadying effect of a gyroscope, a gyro-magnetic compass has been developed as the primary compass of small ships and secondary compass of larger ships. Both deviation and variation can be applied mechanically to the compass readings to feed repeaters with true readings.

Fixing the ship's position on a chart

When the Officer of the Watch wishes to obtain the direction or *bearing* of an object from the compass card, he turns the azimuth ring until he can see the object in the sight above the *azimuth mirror* and the reflection of the compass card in the mirror. He is then able to read off the compass bearing. In Fig. 12-8 the bearing of the lighthouse is 045 degrees.

When within sight of land the position of the ship is normally obtained by taking bearings by compass of three or more prominent objects marked on the chart. These bearings are then drawn in pencil on the chart and the point where the lines intersect is the position of the ship.

When out of sight of land the position of the ship may be found by observations of the sun, moon or stars with a sextant, by radar if land is visible on the radar screen, or by radio fixing aids such as 'Decca', 'Loran', 'Consol' or direction-finding from radio stations.

Ship's speed and logs

The ship's speed through the water is found from the number of propeller shaft revolutions per minute and also by the use of *logs*, which are instruments for measuring speed through the water. Her speed over the ground is found by measuring the distance between two fixes on the chart.

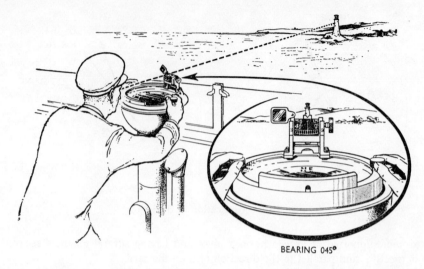

BEARING 045°

FIG. 12-8. Taking a compass bearing

Engine revolutions. A table of speeds at various engine revolutions per minute is prepared by steaming the ship over a measured mile.

Patent logs. The towed log consists of a rotor streamed astern on a *log line* at a set distance. The rotor's blades cause it to rotate a certain number of times every mile, like a speedometer. The line is connected to a dial fixed on the quarter of the ship which shows the distance run. Speed can be calculated by the distance run in a specified time. This type of log is in common use by smaller merchant vessels.

Bottom logs. The following two types are in use in the Service:

   The Pitometer log. This consists of an open tube beneath the hull in which water pressure builds up as the speed increases. It measures the speed of the ship, which is converted into distance electrically.

   The Chernikeeff log. This log consists of a miniature impeller exposed beneath the hull. The impeller revolves as water flows past it and measures the distance, which is converted into speed electrically.

Both types of log show both speed and distance on dials.

Dead reckoning and estimated position (D.R. & E.P.)

The position of the ship is always shown on the chart by plotting the distance run on each course steered. This gives the *dead reckoning position.* When allowances are made for tidal streams, currents and drift caused by the wind the position is called the *estimated position.*

CONNING AND STEERING

Passing of orders

In a warship the Captain, or the Officer of the Watch, or the Navigating Officer cons the ship by passing wheel, engine, and revolution orders from the *compass platform* to the *steering position* (the wheelhouse, in small ships), where the quartermaster sees that they are applied to the wheel and to the engine and revolution

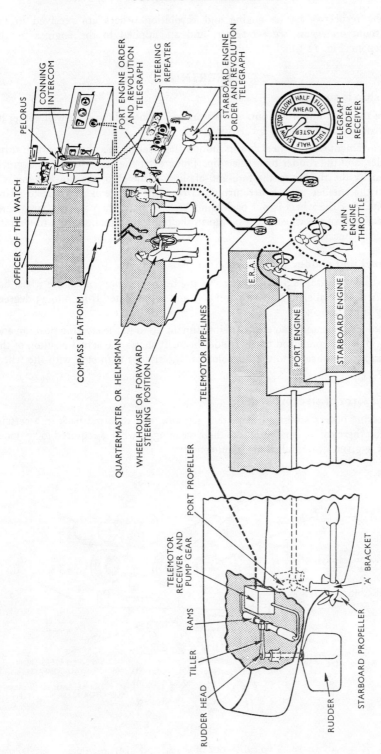

CONNING INTERCOM

PELORUS

PORT ENGINE ORDER AND REVOLUTION TELEGRAPH

STEERING REPEATER

STARBOARD ENGINE ORDER AND REVOLUTION TELEGRAPH

OFFICER OF THE WATCH

SLOW HALF FULL AHEAD
STOP
FULL HALF SLOW ASTERN

TELEGRAPH ORDER RECEIVER

COMPASS PLATFORM

QUARTERMASTER OR HELMSMAN

WHEELHOUSE OR FORWARD STEERING POSITION

TELEMOTOR PIPE-LINES

E.R.A.

MAIN ENGINE THROTTLE

PORT ENGINE

STARBOARD ENGINE

PORT PROPELLER

TELEMOTOR RECEIVER AND PUMP GEAR

RAMS

TILLER

RUDDER HEAD

'A' BRACKET

STARBOARD PROPELLER

RUDDER

FIG. 12-9. How conning orders are passed

telegraphs respectively. The engine and revolution orders are received in the engine room on *engine order repeaters* and are applied to the engines by the watchkeepers (Fig. 12-9).

STEERING

How a ship is steered

One of the most important duties of a seaman is to be able to steer well, either by sight on an object ordered or by compass.

The movement of the wheel sets in motion the steering mechanism, which turns the rudder, and the rudder turns the ship. The greater the angle (up to 35 degrees) presented by the rudder to the fore-and-aft line of the ship, the quicker she will turn and the smaller will be her turning circle. The ship will continue to swing some time after the wheel is put back amidships, so that when she is approaching the desired course the wheel must be put in the opposite direction for a time, until the swing is checked.

The wheel and rudder indicators

The wheel indicator is provided to show the helmsman how much the wheel has been turned. It is labelled *starboard* and *port* and is graduated from 0 to 35 degrees each way (Fig. 12-10).

The rudder indicator is an electrical instrument fitted in the steering position and on the bridge and connected to the rudder head. It shows the actual position of the rudder and also indicates to the helmsman if the rudder is in step with the wheel indicator.

Standard form of steering orders

All steering orders are given, repeated, acted on and reported back in a certain way so that there can be no doubt as to their meaning or what is required to be done. An order is given in the following manner:

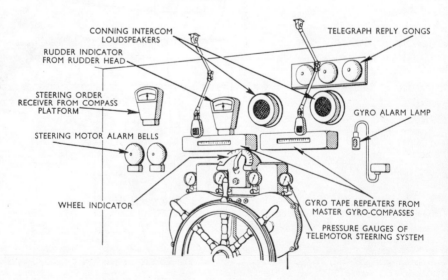

FIG. 12-10. Typical layout of wheel and instruments

first, the *direction*—port, starboard or midships,

second, the *amount*—degrees of rudder angle required if other than 'amidships'.

For example, the Officer of the Watch orders: 'Starboard twenty'. Orders are repeated exactly as they are given, so the helmsman's reply to the above order is, 'Starboard twenty, Sir'. The helmsman acts on the order, puts the wheel over until the indicator reads 20 degrees of starboard wheel, and then reports that he has done so: 'Twenty of starboard wheel on, Sir'.

Thus the sequence for all wheel orders is:

wheel order—by the Officer of the Watch, e.g. '*Starboard twenty*'
order repeated exactly—by the helmsman, e.g. '*Starboard twenty, Sir*'
order obeyed—by the helmsman
order completed—reported by the helmsman, e.g. '*Twenty of starboard wheel on, Sir*'.

Steering by compass

In Fig. 12-10 the compass repeaters in the wheelhouse are shown as tapes moving in long rectangular boxes. In the centre of the window is a line. On the bowl-type repeater as shown in Fig. 12-5 this line takes the form of a pointer level with the edge of the compass card. Both the line and the pointer are fixed in line with the ship's head, and they are both known as the *lubber's line*. The lubber's line is part of the ship and moves with her when she turns, while the compass card and compass tape repeater remain stationary. When steering a course the helmsman keeps the lubber's line constantly in line with the course ordered by moving the wheel to port or starboard and so moving the ship, and hence the lubber's line, round the compass card as necessary to regain the course should she wander off it.

Steering by eye

In ships where the helmsman can see ahead from the steering position, he may be required to steer on a ship ahead or on a distant object. If so, the order to 'Steer on the next (ship) ahead' or 'Steer on the beacon (object) ahead' will be given.

When following a ship ahead the helmsman follows in her wake by keeping her mast and funnels in line dead ahead and turning astern of her as she alters course. When steering on an object (or mast) the helmsman keeps the object (or mast), the jackstaff and the centre of the wheel in line. The helmsman must always be ready to revert to compass steering whenever ordered to do so.

Hints on steering

Remember that if the ship is moving ahead and turning, the ship's head will move in the direction in which the top spokes of the wheel are turned. Likewise when going astern and turning, the stern will go in the direction in which the top spokes are turned.

In large ships, when the wheel is put over the ship does not start swinging immediately. If at the time of putting the wheel over the ship is swinging in the opposite direction it will take even longer to start swinging in the right direction.

The art of steering lies in watching the lubber's line very closely and putting the wheel over as soon as the ship starts to swing off course, and not waiting until she has done so: as soon as the swing is checked, ease the wheel. Avoid over-correcting a swing—the secret of success is to use the wheel as little as possible.

Always turn the wheel steadily by its spokes and do not use undue force and speed. If it jams or gets stiff inform the Officer of the Watch at once.

In a seaway a ship cannot be kept always on exactly the same course, owing to the wind and sea. The helmsman must endeavour to swing the ship back an equal amount on the other side of his course so that the *mean* course steered agrees with the course ordered. To counteract the tendency of a ship to turn into the wind or fall away to leeward the helmsman may have to apply a certain amount of wheel. This is called 'carrying wheel' and the amount is passed on from one helmsman to the next; for example, 'carrying 5 degrees of starboard wheel'.

ENGINES AND ENGINE ORDERS

Engines

A ship's main propulsion machinery may be steam, diesel, gas-turbine or nuclear-powered. Each engine is connected through gearing to a shaft which runs out through a watertight gland to a screw propeller outside the ship.

A ship may have one or more engines and one or more propellers. One shaft may be driven by a pair of engines coupled together. A ship fitted with two or more propellers is usually easier to manoeuvre in narrow waters than a ship fitted with only one.

Engine and revolution orders

Engine and revolution orders are passed, as described on page 158, by a transmitter fitted in the wheelhouse to a repeater fitted in the engine room. Both are shown in Fig. 12-11.

Engine orders

These may be:

SLOW
HALF   } AHEAD or ASTERN   STOP
FULL

Slow (*ahead* or *astern*) means a predetermined number of revolutions per minute as laid down by the Captain in his Standing Orders, usually to give a speed of about 5 knots. Whenever 'Slow ahead (or astern)' is ordered, the engines will be adjusted to give that set number of revolutions. These revolutions will be maintained, even if the revolutions shown on the revolution telegraph repeater differ from them, until the engine orders are changed as indicated by the engine telegraphs (see Fig. 12-11).

Half (*ahead* or *astern*) is used for all speeds between Stop and Full. At this order the engines are adjusted to give the number of revolutions shown on the revolution telegraph.

Full (*ahead* or *astern*) is used only in emergency and is an order to give the maximum number of revolutions in the required direction with the power available.

Engine orders are given to engines individually or collectively, e.g. 'Half ahead, port'—'Stop, starboard'—'Slow astern, both engines'.

In all cases the helmsman repeats the order exactly as it is given, sees that it is applied to the correct telegraphs by the telegraphsman and, when the engine room staff have acknowledged the order by ringing their reply gong, reports that it has been repeated to the Officer of the Watch.

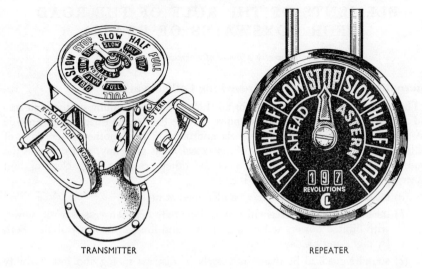

TRANSMITTER   REPEATER

FIG. 12-11. Combined engine and revolution transmitter and repeater

Engine revolutions. A table of the revolutions required to drive the ship at a certain speed is displayed on the bridge. Changes in revolutions are passed to the helmsman thus: 'Revolutions one five zero'.

As before, the helmsman repeats the order exactly as it is given, and sees that the drill (which is the same as that described for passing engine orders) is carried out.

SEA DUTYMEN AND SPECIAL SEA DUTYMEN

Sea dutymen

Apart from the four quartermasters who stand watch in rotation in charge of the steering position, helmsmen and telegraphsmen are detailed as sea dutymen from the watch on deck. They should not carry steel, such as knives or keys, if there is a magnetic compass in the steering position.

The helmsman's duty is to steer the ship under the supervision of the quarter-master and he is relieved at regular intervals. On being relieved he must turn over the following to his relief:

the course to steer
what the engines are doing (half ahead, slow ahead, etc.)
the engine revolutions
the amount of wheel the ship is carrying.

Special sea dutymen

When entering or leaving harbour, during certain evolutions and in action, certain ratings are required to close up in specified positions in the ship. The Chief Quartermaster is in charge of the steering position, some or all of the quartermasters are available at alternate steering positions in case of steering failure; and special sea dutymen, who are selected and experienced seamen, take over the duties of telegraphsmen.

ELEMENTS OF THE RULE OF THE ROAD
(FOR COXSWAINS OF BOATS)

See *Admiralty Manual of Seamanship*, Vol. I

International Regulations for Preventing Collision at Sea

These rules have been compiled for all ships and vessels sailing on the high seas and waterways. They are commonly known as 'The Rule of the Road'. They provide for almost all occasions of two vessels approaching one another where risk of collision exists, and tell a seaman which vessel must give way, and describe the conditions under which he may expect the other vessel to keep clear of him (Steering and Sailing Rules). They include:

(*a*) means whereby vessels may be identified at night;

(*b*) means whereby the seaman may differentiate between vessels with power, with limited power, and with no power and limited manoeuvrability, both by night and by day;

(*c*) sound signals to be made by vessels in distress in fog and low visibility and in other circumstances, and precautions to be taken by all vessels.

Definitions

Vessel. Every kind of water craft other than a seaplane.

Power-driven vessel. Any vessel propelled by machinery.

Sailing vessel. Any vessel propelled only by the wind acting on her sails. If a vessel is propelled by machinery and sails she is to be considered as a power-driven vessel.

Visible. When applied to lights, means 'visible on a dark night with a clear atmosphere'.

Short blast. A blast lasting about one second.

Prolonged blast. A blast lasting between four and six seconds.

Under way. A vessel not at anchor, made fast to the shore or aground. A vessel may be described as 'under way but stopped' or 'under way and making way'.

Not under command. A vessel under way but unable to manoeuvre.

Risk of collision

When two ships are converging, risk of collision exists if the compass bearing of one ship from the other does not alter or alters only slightly. If the bearing draws ahead the other ship should pass ahead. If it draws aft she should pass astern.

If a compass is not available the relative bearing of the other vessel gives an indication of the risk of collision, provided your own vessel stays on a steady course.

THE SAILING RULES

These rules are related to the direction of the wind and are based on the principle that the vessel which would lose least ground by giving way should do so. These rules must be obeyed by all sailing vessels unless they are not under command.

When sailing vessels are approaching one another so as to involve risk of collision one of them shall keep out of the way of the other as follows (Fig. 12-12):

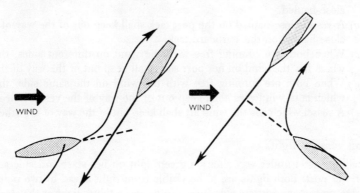

A vessel running free gives way to one close-hauled.

A vessel close-hauled on the port tack gives way to a vessel close-hauled on the starboard tack.

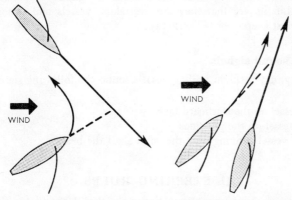

Both vessels running free with the wind on opposite sides, the vessel with the wind on her port side gives way.

Both vessels running free with the wind on the same side, the windward vessel keeps out of the way of the leeward vessel.

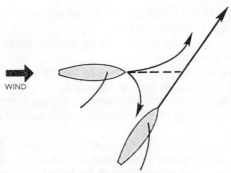

Two vessels running free, the one with the wind right aft gives way.

FIG. 12-12. Sailing rules

(a) A vessel which is running free shall keep out of the way of a vessel which is close-hauled.

(b) A vessel close-hauled on the port tack shall keep out of the way of a vessel close-hauled on the starboard tack.

(c) When both are running free with the wind on different sides, the vessel which has the wind on her port side shall keep out of the way of the other.

(d) When both are running free with the wind on the same side, the vessel which is to windward shall keep out of the way of the vessel to leeward.

(e) A vessel which has the wind aft shall keep out of the way of the other vessel.

Sailing vessels' lights

A sailing vessel under way shows a green light on her starboard side and a red one on her port. Both lights are to be visible from right ahead to two points abaft the beam on the appropriate side. She also carries a white light at the stern visible from two points abaft the beam on one side through right astern to two points abaft the beam on the other. It is called an 'overtaking' light because it indicates to other vessels within its arc that they are overtaking vessels and, where risk of collision exists, must keep clear (Fig. 12-14).

Sailing vessels' sound signals

In low visibility, day or night, sailing vessels sound the following signals on the foghorn:

one blast: vessel on the starboard tack
two blasts: vessel on the port tack
three blasts: vessel running with the wind abaft the beam.

THE STEERING RULES

The rules for power-driven vessels meeting each other depend upon the relative bearing of one vessel from the other. All power-driven vessels must obey these rules unless they are not under command:

(a) Two vessels approaching end on to each other must both give way by altering course to starboard.

(b) In all circumstances where risk of collision exists one vessel holds her course and speed and the other gives way.

(c) The vessel giving way must do so by altering course or reducing speed, stopping or going astern.

(d) The vessel giving way should avoid crossing close ahead of the other vessel.

(e) In a broad sense vessels keep to starboard.

(f) Every vessel, whether power-driven or sailing, overtaking another shall keep out of the way of the overtaken vessel until she has passed and is well clear.

(g) Vessels must keep a good lookout, show the correct daymarks and lights, make the correct sound signals and be handled in a seamanlike manner with due caution and consideration for others, especially in conditions of low visibility.

(h) If a collision appears probable each vessel must take whatever action is possible in order to avoid it, even if such action involves a departure from the normal rules.

Power-driven vessels' lights

A power-driven vessel under way shows the same lights as a sailing vessel over the same arcs. In addition, she also shows one or more steaming lights (usually from her masts), according to her length. When there are two steaming lights, the after one is higher. Each steaming light shows over the combined arc of the two bow lights. (See Fig. 12-15.)

A power-driven vessel's sound signals

In sight of one another. When vessels are in sight of one another, a power-driven vessel under way and acting according to the Steering Rules may make the following signals:

one short blast: 'I am altering course to starboard'
two short blasts: 'I am altering course to port'
three short blasts: 'My engines are going astern'.

In fog, mist, etc. Under these or any other similar conditions of low visibility by day and night, a power-driven vessel makes the following signals at intervals of not more than two minutes:

one prolonged blast: 'I am making way through the water'
two prolonged blasts: 'I am under way but stopped'.

The giving-way vessel

Divide the circle of your horizon into three arcs representing the arcs of visibility of the two bow lights and overtaking light (Fig. 12-13).

Ship A. A is approaching head-on (both bow and steaming light(s) visible at night). Both ships alter course to starboard.

Ship B. If B remains on a steady bearing (red light and steaming light(s) visible at night) own ship gives way by altering course to starboard, reducing speed, stopping or going astern.

Ship C. Provided C holds her course and speed there is no risk of collision.

Ship D. On her present course (green light and steaming light(s) visible at night) there is no risk of collision.

Ship E. If E remains on a steady bearing there is risk of collision. At night you can see her red light and steaming light(s) and she can see your green light and steaming light(s)—own ship must give way.

Ship F. F is an overtaking vessel (she can see only your overtaking light at night) and must keep clear until she is well past and clear ahead of you.

Ship G. G is on a collision course. She can see your red light and steaming light(s), and must give way. You must maintain your course and speed.

Ship H. Provided H maintains her course and speed there is no risk of collision.

Ship J. If you are coming up on J and can see only her overtaking light you must keep clear of her.

Ship L. In this situation there may be some doubt as to who has right of way. You could be considered as the overtaking vessel. At night you would be able to tell at once, because you would see either her overtaking light or her bow and steaming light(s). It is better to assume that you are an overtaking vessel and to make an early and bold alteration of course.

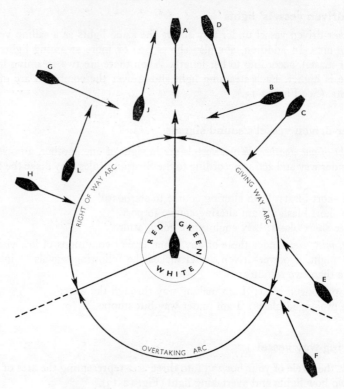

Fig. 12-13. The giving-way vessel

Conduct of power-driven vessels

(a) If you are the giving-way vessel, always give the other vessel as wide a berth as possible. It is bad manners and bad seamanship to pass close aboard another vessel.

(b) If you are giving way to another vessel, your avoiding action must leave no doubt of your intentions in the mind of the other vessel. Therefore:

    (i) Take avoiding action in plenty of time

    (ii) Make the initial alteration large

    (iii) Steady on your new course without undue yawing

    (iv) Make the appropriate sound signal.

(c) On approaching another vessel, keep your course steady and make allowance for her yawing. A vessel approaching nearly end-on, on an opposite course and yawing, must be assumed to be approaching end-on, and you should alter course to starboard, giving her as wide a berth as possible.

(d) In a narrow channel keep to the side which is on your starboard hand.

Power-driven vessels and sailing vessels

Power-driven vessels give way to sailing vessels except when the sailing vessel is overtaking. In a narrow channel where movement is restricted small sailing vessels and small power-driven vessels should not embarrass large power-driven vessels by passing close to them or obstructing them.

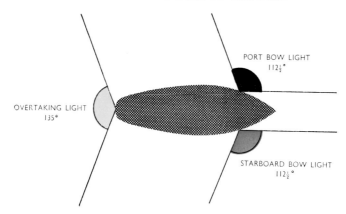

FIG. 12-14. Lights shown by a sailing vessel

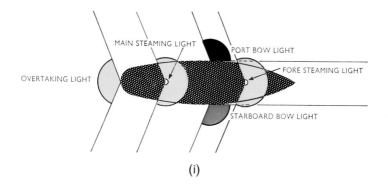

(i)

(ii)

FIG. 12-15. (i) Lights shown by a power-driven vessel over 150 ft in length; (ii) the same vessel seen from her starboard bow

CHAPTER 13

Anchoring, Securing to a Buoy, Berthing

See *Admiralty Manual of Seamanship*, Vol. I

ANCHORS AND CABLES

A ship can be secured to the sea bottom by means of her anchors and cables, with either a single anchor or with two anchors down. In the latter case she is said to be *moored*. In most ports and harbours a ship can also be secured to the bottom by unshackling one of her cables from its anchor and shackling the cable to a *mooring buoy*, which in turn is secured to the bottom by its own permanently laid ground-work of mooring anchors and mooring chain. A modern naval anchor is shown in Fig. 13-1.

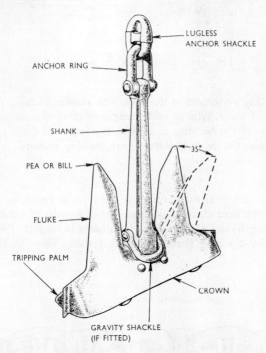

FIG. 13-1. Bower anchor A.C. (Admiralty Cast) 14 Type

How an anchor holds

Fig. 13-2 shows how an anchor embeds itself in the bottom after it has been let go and the strain has come on the cable. The anchor lies flat along the bottom until the strain on the cable pulls it along: the tripping palms tilt the flukes and they dig in. After further dragging, the anchor embeds itself until it holds. The pull of the cable must always be horizontal if the anchor is to maintain its maximum hold.

The cable must be long enough to ensure that a part of it near the anchor always remains in the sea bed. The rest of the cable acts as a spring, preventing the anchor

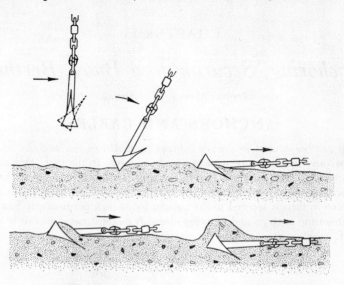

FIG. 13-2. How a modern anchor holds

being jerked by any movement of the ship. The amount of cable put out depends upon the depth of water, type of cable, length of stay, weather, and, to a certain extent, the nature of the bottom; in general, the length of cable put out is almost always several times the depth of water where the ship anchors.

Cables

Anchor cables vary in size according to the type of vessel for which they are provided. Warships have chain cable made up of lengths of cable called *shackles* (15 fathoms in length) and *half-shackles* ($7\frac{1}{2}$ fathoms in length). These shackles are joined together by a joining shackle. Fig. 13-3 shows how shackles of cable are joined together.

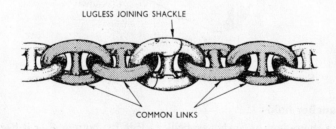

LUGLESS JOINING SHACKLE

COMMON LINKS

FIG. 13-3. Two shackles of cable joined by a joining shackle

The lead of the cable. When a ship is anchored the cable of the anchor comes inboard on to the forecastle through the *hawsepipe*, round a *cable holder*, and down through the *navel pipe* to the *cable locker* (Fig. 13-4).

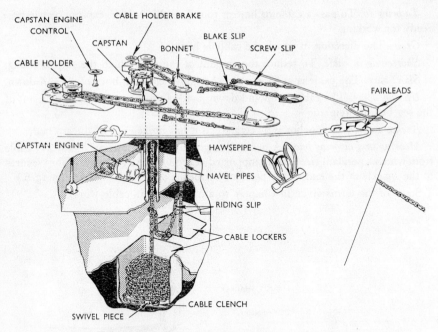

FIG. 13-4. Lead of the anchor cable

Cable gear and fittings

Slips. These are used to hold the cable and are:

the *Blake slip* (Fig. 13-5), in which the tongue fits across a link of cable;

FIG. 13-5. A Blake slip

the *screw slip*, which is a Blake slip incorporating a bottlescrew, and is used primarily to haul the anchor close up into the hawsepipe;

the *riding slip*, which is a Blake slip on deck between the navel pipe and cable holder or in the cable locker. It is put on the cable as a preventer when the ship is riding to her cable.

Cable holders, windlasses and capstans. These are power-driven machines for working cables, and, in the case of windlasses and capstans, for working hawsers as well.

Terms used in anchor-work

Bullring. A ring situated at the top of the stem on the forecastle, through which cable or hawsers can be passed.

Heave in cable. To heave in steadily by turning the cable holder or capstan.

To bring to. To pass a cable or hawser round a cable holder, capstan or windlass ready for working.

Grow. The direction in which the cable is lying.

Shortening in cable. To reduce the amount of cable by which the ship is riding.

Short stay. The cable is at short stay when hove close in, but not up and down.

Up and down. The cable is up and down just before the anchor is broken out of the sea bed on weighing.

Anchor aweigh. An anchor is aweigh when it has broken out of the sea bed.

Mooring and mooring buoy. A permanent groundwork of anchors and heavy cable from which a pendant rises and is supported at the surface by a buoy. A ship secures to the shackle at the end of the pendant by means of her cable. (See Fig. 13-6.)

Some of the terms given in Chapter 10 are also used in cable-work.

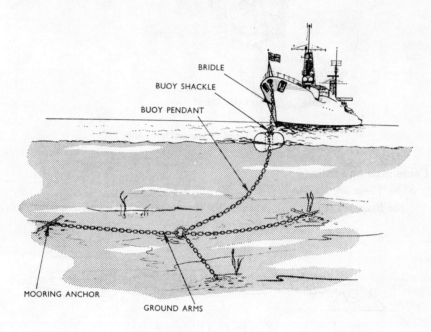

BRIDLE

BUOY SHACKLE

BUOY PENDANT

MOORING ANCHOR

GROUND ARMS

FIG. 13-6. A ship secured at a buoy by a single bridle of cable

Bringing a ship to a single anchor

The Captain first studies the position of the anchor berth on the chart. Having considered such factors as the direction of the wind and the depth of water, he decides which anchor to use and how much cable to lay out. The Navigating Officer prepares a plan for anchoring so that the ship's speed may be reduced and the ship stopped in sufficient time. A warship usually passes through the position of the berth with very slight headway, dropping the anchor in the berth and laying out the cable along the bottom, and finally coming to rest with the correct amount of cable out (Fig. 13-7).

During the approach the anchor is eased down the hawsepipe until its weight is carried only by the Blake slip on the forecastle, and then the brake is put on and

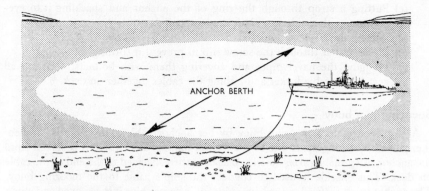

FIG. 13-7. A ship riding at single anchor

the cable holder is disconnected from its spindle. Just before the anchorage position is reached the Captain orders 'Stand by!'. The brake is taken off and the pin is removed from the Blake slip. When the Captain estimates that the ship is passing through her berth, he orders 'Let go!'. A rating on the forecastle knocks off the Blake slip with a hammer, the anchor falls to the bottom, and the cable runs out with it. The Captain now takes the way off the ship by reversing the engine and brings the ship up with the right amount of cable out.

A ship rides at anchor with the weight of the cable held by the brake of the cable holder. The riding slip is put on so that it is not quite taking the weight and the Blake slip is put on slack as an additional preventer.

Weighing anchor

A ship lying at anchor is said to 'shorten in' her cable when she heaves in a part of it; for example, a ship riding to eight shackles might shorten in to three shackles before weighing anchor. The Captain would then order 'Shorten in to three shackles,' whereupon the cable holder is connected up, the brake and slips taken off, and the cable hove in until three shackles remain outboard; the brake is then reapplied.

When the Captain orders the anchor to be weighed, the cable is hove in steadily and washed down with water as it comes in. The Cable Officer will indicate to the bridge how it grows, reporting to the bridge when it is 'Up and down' and 'Anchor is aweigh'. On sighting the anchor he reports whether it is clear or foul ('foul' used in this way means 'being encumbered with hawsers or anything picked up off the sea bed'). If it is clear, he orders the anchor to be hove in. The anchor and cable gear are finally secured when ordered by the Captain.

Securing for sea

After weighing, and when clear of the harbour, the Captain will order the anchors and cables to be secured for sea. The object of this is to put the anchors and cables in such a state that they cannot work loose in a heavy sea. Securing the forecastle and gear for sea includes:

(a) Bringing the anchor hard home in the hawsepipe by screwing up the screw slip.

(b) Putting on the cable holder brake and disconnecting the cable holder.

(c) Putting a strop through the ring of the anchor and shackling it to eye-plates on either side just abaft the hawsepipe.

(d) Putting the Blake slip on.

(e) Placing a bar through the screw slip to prevent it turning.

(f) Plugging the navel pipes and covering them with bonnets; securing all gear in the cable locker and lashing the cables together on deck.

Securing to a buoy

A ship secures to a mooring buoy by her anchor cable. The cable is 'broken' (i.e. parted by taking apart one of the special joining shackles) and removed from the anchor. A special *securing-to-buoy shackle* is then shackled to the end of the cable on deck. This shackle is used to connect the ship's cable to the mooring buoy. The anchor is left secured in the hawsepipe, or in some ships it is removed and slung from a fitting called a *cathead*. Because the cable is heavy and cumbersome a special *picking-up rope* is used to secure the ship to the buoy initially. This is a wire hawser which is fitted with a strop and spring-hook at its outboard end and is secured to the buoy as shown in Fig. 13-8.

FIG. 13-8. A picking-up rope

On approaching the buoy a ship's boat is lowered to take two men, known as *buoy jumpers*, to do the work on the buoy. The ship approaches at slow speed; the boat is lowered and slipped, and makes her way forward under the bows. A heaving line is passed down to the boat from the forecastle, one end of it being bent to the picking-up rope. The boat proceeds to the buoy, and the buoy jumpers haul down the picking-up rope and secure it to the buoy shackle as shown in Fig. 13-8, embarking in the boat on completion. The buoy jumpers should always be taken off the buoy on each occasion of the ship heaving in or veering cable and wires when she secures to and slips from a buoy. The attending boat should lie close to, but at a safe distance from, the buoy whenever this is done.

The ship is now hauled forward by means of the picking-up rope until her stem is over the buoy, and the cable is eased out through the bullring or hawsepipe until it is about 6 ft from the waterline. The buoy jumpers secure the cable (called a *bridle* when used in this way) to the buoy with the securing-to-buoy shackle. The picking-up rope is veered until the bridle has the strain and it is then removed. Two bridles can be secured to a buoy if necessary, but an anchor is left ready for letting go in case of an emergency.

There is more than one method of passing the picking-up rope to a buoy. The commonest method has been described here.

Slipping from a buoy

The bridle is hove in to short stay and the buoy jumpers taken to the buoy to reeve the sliprope. This is a wire hawser fitted with a soft eye. It is rove *out* through a convenient fairlead, *down* through the buoy shackle so that it will be unlikely to foul it when slipped, then in through another fairlead and put on to a slip. The other end is then hauled taut by hand and belayed. The sliprope must be rove so that it will not jam, or be jammed by, the bridles. (See Fig. 13-9.)

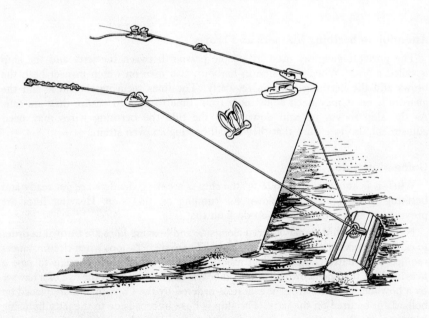

FIG. 13-9. A slip rope rove ready for slipping

When the Captain is ready he orders the bridle to be removed. The bridle is veered until the sliprope takes the weight of the ship. The buoy jumpers unshackle the bridle and return inboard. When the Captain orders 'Slip!' the turns on the bollards are eased off, the slip holding the other end of the sliprope is knocked off, and the sliprope run inboard. The forecastle and cable locker are secured for sea in the normal way.

BERTHING ALONGSIDE A JETTY

Berthing hawsers

Fig. 13-10 shows how berthing hawsers are used to secure a ship alongside a wall or jetty. It will be seen that she has two *breast ropes* (marked 2 and 5) which are known as *fore* and *after* breast ropes. They are used to breast the ship bodily towards the wall or jetty when coming alongside, and when belayed they limit her distance from the jetty. The hawsers marked 3 and 4 are known respectively as the *fore* and *after spring*. Any spring which is tending to prevent a ship from moving back (aft) is called a *back spring*, and from moving forward (ahead) a *head spring*. The springs prevent the ship from surging ahead or astern in her berth. The hawsers marked 1 and 6 are known respectively as the *head rope* and the *stern rope*.

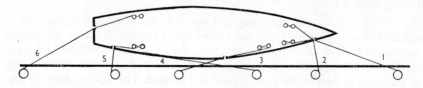

FIG. 13-10. Berthing hawsers

Attention to berthing hawsers and brows

The portable gangway used by people passing between the jetty and the ship is called a *brow*. When alongside in harbour, two men on watch inspect both the brows and the berthing hawsers regularly. The lines securing the brow and the guardrails on it may need adjustment from time to time to ensure they are safe. As the ship moves up and down with the tide the berthing wires may need adjustment also to ensure that they are all bearing an even strain.

Going alongside

When it is known which 'side to' the ship is securing, fenders are got ready and berthing hawsers are faked down for running on that side. Heaving lines are provided at appropriate points on deck on that side.

Normally the ship is manoeuvred alongside and heaving lines are thrown in order to carry the eyes of berthing hawsers ashore. There are occasions when circumstances require these hawsers to be taken ashore by boat. When close enough to pass a heaving line, the line is thrown and its inboard end is secured to the eye of a hawser by a bowline. Hawsers are sent ashore as ordered by the Captain and are placed on bollards or secured on the jetty. The ship is hove in broadside to the jetty by using her hawsers. When the ship is in the right position and the required number of hawsers are put out, the Captain orders all hawsers to be secured and belayed. Each hawser may be doubled if necessary to ensure safety (see 'To place two hawsers on one bollard', page 120).

Leaving a jetty

Before leaving, the Captain specifies which hawsers he wishes to be left to hold the ship and assist her departure. The evolution of removing all the other hawsers is called 'singling up'. The hands muster on deck for leaving harbour and stand by the remaining wires.

The Captain may use certain hawsers for springing the ship away from the jetty: for example, he may use a head spring (hawser No. 3 in Fig. 13-10) which, when the engines are put to 'ahead', will tauten and cause the ship's stern to swing out. In any case he always specifies which hawsers he wishes to be let go and the order in which he wants them let go; for example:

> *Let go head rope*—from the Captain
> *Let go head rope, Sir*—repeated by the forecastle officer
> *Head rope gone, Sir*—reported by the forecastle officer
> *Head rope clear, Sir*—reported by the forecastle officer.

These reports are most essential when letting hawsers go aft, for the Captain wants to use the engines and needs to know when it is safe to do so without risk of fouling propellers. To show the bridge the situation aft, indicator boards or flags (called *screw flags*) are used (red for foul, white for clear). They are shown from positions on both sides of the ship as ordered by the officer in charge of the quarterdeck.

Once clear of the jetty, all fenders and hawsers are recovered and the hands fallen in. One anchor is always kept ready for letting go in case of emergencies. When well clear of harbour, gear is returned to its stowage and secured for sea.

Fendering

A ship going alongside another ship or jetty requires a soft fender to absorb any initial impact, then a fender of more solid construction to provide protection and to allow sufficient separation for any overhanging structure, proud propellers, etc.

For boats and other small craft whose sides are strong in comparison with the weight of the vessel, fendering presents no difficulties and any soft fender is adequate. For larger vessels fendering must be sufficiently robust to withstand the crushing of the weight of the ship and sufficiently resilient to spread and absorb the shock over a large area of comparatively weak hull plating.

Fendering can be divided into three categories:

> *Portable fenders.* These are of various types and are made of rubber, cane or coir. They are hung from inboard over the ship's side and tended as the ship comes alongside, so that they can be moved quickly to take the rub at the point of impact.
> *Port fenders.* These are usually *catamarans*, i.e., rafts of rectangular plan that lie in the water between the jetty and the ship.
> *Fixed fendering.* This consists usually of wooden battens or planks fixed to the structure of a stone or metal jetty to take the rub of a ship coming alongside.

CHAPTER 14

NBCD

FIRE PRECAUTIONS

See B.R. 1257, *Ship Firefighting Manual*

It is essential to the safety of his ship that every sailor should know the causes of accidental fires and how to prevent and control them. For a fire to burn it needs:

Flammable material—gasoline, paper, wood, etc.

Heat

Oxygen—which, with heat, ignites the fuel.

These three ingredients may be represented by the three sides of a triangle, which is only complete when all three are present (Fig. 14-1).

FIG. 14-1. Ingredients for a fire

Fire prevention

Fire prevention consists of keeping these three ingredients separated by paying careful attention to the stowage of flammable materials and their protection from sparks, and by observing the precautions for the disposal of matches, cigarette ends, etc. With the exception of those caused by enemy action, most fires on board ship can be prevented by keeping things in their proper places, and by cleanliness, tidiness and obeying relevant instructions.

Firefighting

This consists of eliminating one or more of the ingredients required for a fire to burn: a firefighter must attempt to:

Starve the fire—by removing the flammable material and preventing more from igniting;

Cool the fire—by cooling the material and the air round it to below ignition point;

Smother the fire—by preventing oxygen from reaching the fire by smothering it or shutting off the ventilation in the vicinity.

Flammable material

Most of this has been eliminated from H.M. ships, but they may have to carry some liquids and materials which will burn. The following precautions must be observed:

Gasoline. This is one of the greatest fire risks on board ship, so as little as possible is carried. It is used only in ships carrying certain aircraft and helicopters and in gasoline-driven small craft, and it must be carried in an authorized stowage. No unauthorized stocks, such as lighter fuel, are allowed on board. When embarking gasoline the following rules must be observed:

(i) No smoking or burning of naked lights in the vicinity.
(ii) Fires, such as galley and incinerator fires, must be extinguished.
(iii) Radio transmission must cease because of the danger of sparking.
(iv) Ship's side scuttles adjacent to gasoline tanks must be closed.
(v) Sentries must be posted.
(vi) Ships must fly the appropriate danger signal.

Avpin. This is a helicopter starter fuel which is subject to the same regulations as gasoline.

Furnace fuel, diesel oil, kerosene and avcat. Stowage and transport arrangements of these fuels on board are designed to ensure minimum leakage, but there is always the possibility of some leakage, especially after damage. Any man discovering a leak must report it at once. The cause must be dealt with and the leakage mopped up without delay. Rags used for mopping up must not be left lying about.

Wood. Wherever possible wood has been replaced by metal in H.M. ships. Timber should not be stowed near hot surfaces or where it can become saturated with flammable liquids.

Paint. Paint, pots and brushes should be stowed in the paint locker; to keep them anywhere else is a highly dangerous fire risk. Paint stores in ships are fitted with spraying arrangements.

Clothing and bedding. These must be stowed in their correct places. Kit lockers must be shut to prevent gear from falling out in the event of damage.

Cooking fat. This must be stowed in a cool place, and when in use in the galley it must never be left unattended in case it boils over.

Paper. This must be properly stowed so that it cannot be spread about the ship by an explosion. Scrap paper must be collected and disposed of and books and papers stowed away—not tucked overhead near sleeping billets.

Cotton rags. When supplied for cleaning purposes they must not be left lying about, but must be placed in metal bins and disposed of regularly. These materials are particularly dangerous when soaked with oil or gasoline and may well be a source of spontaneous combustion.

Explosives and fireworks. These are obviously a grave risk. The regulations concerning their handling and stowage are contained in the *Naval Magazine and Explosives Regulations.* Further regulations may be found on posters and in the ship's standing orders.

Heat

Hot surfaces and compartments. Combustible materials must not be stowed near hot surfaces. Hot compartments (galleys, boiler rooms, etc.) must be kept clean and free from accumulations of grease and rubbish. Galley hoods are particularly susceptible to such accumulations, and may well catch alight from sparks from the galley range or from boiled-over cooking fat.

Spontaneous combustion. Chemical action between oil and the fibres of rags can easily generate sufficient heat to cause a fire.

Smoking has been the cause of numerous fires. Failure to observe the smoking regulations, or to see that cigarette ends, pipes and matches are properly extinguished, may cause a very serious fire. Never throw cigarette ends out of scuttles or over the side: they may be sucked inboard or fall into a boat alongside and start a fire.

Sparks from incinerator and galley funnels can start fires, and these funnels must be cleaned regularly.

Sparking of electrical apparatus and *short circuits* can cause a dangerous generation of heat, which can be avoided by good maintenance and care of wandering leads and temporary connections.

Oxygen

Wherever there is air there is oxygen, and it is impossible to eliminate it. Keeping watertight doors and hatches closed when not in use prevents the spreading of fire as well as flooding, but in fire it is as important to close the doors and hatches above the waterline as below it. The control of ventilation in the vicinity of a fire is most important.

PRINCIPLES OF FIREFIGHTING

A fire will spread rapidly if unchecked, so it must be tackled with the best means at hand immediately it is discovered. Many a potentially dangerous fire has been extinguished at its start by the resolute initiative of one man. It must be remembered that a fire can quickly get beyond the control of those in the vicinity. Therefore, on discovering a fire:
  1. Attempt to deal with it;
  2. Shout 'Fire'!
  3. Inform the Officer of the Watch.
This will not only ensure speedy assistance, but also that the necessary precautions are taken to prevent the fire from spreading.

Starving

Starving is effected by removing flammable material from the vicinity of the fire or cutting all liquid fuel supplies to the area, e.g. where a fire is being fed by oil from a fractured pipe the shutting of the appropriate valve is essential.

Cooling

The finest cooling agent is water, but it must be used with discretion. In ships it is generally used in the form of spray and the firefighting nozzles are designed to ensure that the smallest quantity of water will achieve the greatest cooling effect. The spray should be directed at the burning material and not at the flames.

Excessive use of water in firefighting may:
  (a) cause the ship to heel or even to capsize;

(b) entail much more pumping than would otherwise be necessary;

(c) if used on a fuel tank, cause burning fuel on its surface to overflow from it and spread the fire;

(d) cause damage to non-watertight electrical equipment;

(e) cause electric shock if played on live electrical apparatus—dangerous in the case of high-voltage apparatus.

Although water may prevent explosives from catching fire, it will not necessarily extinguish them, since they contain their own oxygen. If water comes into contact with some substances, e.g. the contents of smoke floats, it will produce highly flammable gas. Water will also cause certain metals to decompose when heated, and accelerate their burning, e.g. magnesium alloy, used in aircraft construction.

When a fire is extinguished, the material and its surroundings must be thoroughly cooled to prevent reignition. Likewise, it is very important to cool all the structure adjacent to the compartment in which a fire is burning, to prevent it from spreading. This, which is done by spraying water on all surrounding bulkheads and decks, is known as 'boundary cooling'.

Smothering

This is done to prevent oxygen from reaching a fire. Smothering alone may extinguish a fire, but other methods will often have to be used. Smothering includes the use of steam, C.B.Freon, or carbon dioxide, all of which displace oxygen; and of foam, which floats on a burning liquid and blankets the surface, separating the fuel from the air.

Wherever possible the ventilation in the vicinity of a fire should be shut down, but where there is a large amount of smoke it may be necessary to have an outlet for its escape.

It is possible to extinguish a fire of burning flammable liquids by sealing the compartment in which it is situated. Even if the seal is incomplete, as long as there are no openings low down through which air can reach the seat of the fire, this method is quite successful. It is essential, however, to keep adjacent compartments and structure cool.

Reignition. There is always a danger of a fire reigniting after being extinguished, particularly after it has been smothered.

Smoke

Unless a fire is attacked in its very early stages, smoke will fill the compartment and hide the seat of the fire. A firefighter should approach by crawling or crouching, using the clear air near the deck to breathe. This will also help him to see the fire. The air is always cooler near the deck than it is higher up.

Smoke can be driven off *towards an outlet* by using a jet spray nozzle. By keeping the face close behind the nozzle the firefighter can breathe fresh air. As a fire uses oxygen rapidly and often gives off poisonous gases a breathing apparatus must be worn if smoke and fumes are dense.

Protective clothing

The firefighter must be completely clothed and his face and hands must be covered for protection against heat. If the clothes are damped they provide additional protection, but wet clothing must not be worn too long.

Fearnought suits and anti-flash hoods and gauntlets are supplied for fire-parties, and the manning of branch pipes at the fire should be taken over as soon as possible by men fully clothed with this gear.

The anti-gas respirator. The service anti-gas respirator must not be worn for firefighting, except as a means of *escape in extreme emergency.* Although it gives limited protection against most poisonous gases, it does not provide the wearer with oxygen, of which there is often a lack in the fire area, particularly near a fire which intermittently gives off dense volumes of smoke; neither does it protect the wearer against carbon monoxide or carbon dioxide, both of which are likely to be present.

Cover

Attacking a fire from low down is a relief from exposure to the heat, and for further protection advantage should also be taken of any bulkheads or lockers.

PORTABLE FIREFIGHTING APPLIANCES

2-gallon water extinguisher (red)

This consists of a container holding fresh water into which is placed a steel cylinder containing carbon dioxide (CO_2). It is shown in Fig. 14-2.

To operate. Press down on the knob at the top and direct the water from the nozzle as required. The nozzle can be switched from jet to spray or vice versa by means of the two knobs on its end.

FIG. 14-2. Two-gallon water extinguisher

2-gallon foam extinguisher (cream)

This consists of an outer cylinder containing a solution of bicarbonate of soda and a stabilizing substance, and an inner cylinder containing solution of aluminium sulphate. They are kept apart by the seal of two rubber valves coupled together. This extinguisher is shown in Fig. 14-3.

To operate. Turn the T handle at the top and allow it to spring up. Place the thumb firmly over the nozzle, turn the extinguisher upside down, shake it to mix the chemicals up, release the thumb and direct the foam against some suitable obstruction so that the foam runs down and over the surface of the burning fuel. The extinguisher can be used as a partial shield for the face against heat whilst in use.

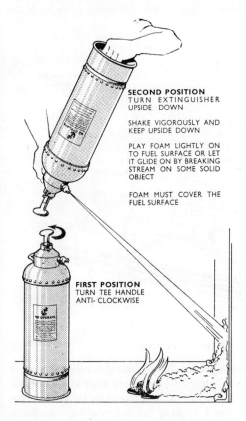

SECOND POSITION
TURN EXTINGUISHER
UPSIDE DOWN

SHAKE VIGOROUSLY AND
KEEP UPSIDE DOWN

PLAY FOAM LIGHTLY ON
TO FUEL SURFACE OR LET
IT GLIDE ON BY BREAKING
STREAM ON SOME SOLID
OBJECT

FOAM MUST COVER THE
FUEL SURFACE

FIRST POSITION
TURN TEE HANDLE
ANTI-CLOCKWISE

FIG. 14-3. Two-gallon foam extinguisher   FIG. 14-4. 2½-lb CO_2 extinguisher

2½-lb CO_2 extinguisher (black)

This is a small gas container, filled with CO_2 under pressure. (See Fig. 14-4.)

To operate. Remove the pin from the trigger mechanism at the top of the extinguisher, turn the hose towards the base of the fire, and, *holding it by the trigger mechanism only*, squeeze the trigger. This releases CO_2, which will smother the fire. Do not touch the hose while the apparatus is in use—it will freeze your hand.

Dry chemical powder extinguisher P12

This is used in the vicinity of aircraft and helicopters. It consists of a container holding a dry chemical powder which is discharged by the use of a small CO_2 cylinder fitted externally to it.

FIREFIGHTING INSTALLATIONS

The salt water main

Sea-water under pressure is supplied to all parts of a ship through a system of piping, which is painted bright red throughout. This system of piping is called a *salt water main* (Fig. 14-5). Pumps between decks supply sea-water to the main, which is divided into sections by stop valves. Each section has its own pump, so that if one section is damaged it can be isolated from the rest. Modern aircraft carriers have also a completely independent flight deck salt water main with its own pumps.

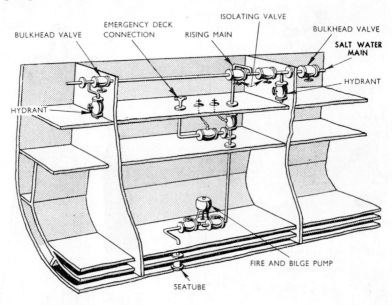

FIG. 14-5. Section of a salt water main

To prevent too great a loss of pressure in a section, only a limited number of nozzles should be used at any one time—as a rough guide, not more than three nozzles to one section. If more are required, the supply to a section can be boosted by starting extra pumps in another section and opening the isolating valve between sections.

Hydrants. These branches from the salt water main, fitted with valve and hose connections, will be found around the weather decks and in almost every main compartment of a ship. By shutting stop valves on either side of a damaged section and cross-connecting hydrants on either side of it with hoses, a temporary supply of water can be maintained (Fig. 14-6).

Hoses

These are supplied for every hydrant on board and should be kept connected ready for instant use. In order to avoid damage the brass couplings at each end (one female and one male) should not be dragged, dropped or knocked about.

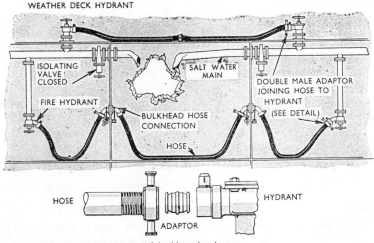

WEATHER DECK HYDRANT

ISOLATING VALVE CLOSED

SALT WATER MAIN

DOUBLE MALE ADAPTOR JOINING HOSE TO HYDRANT (SEE DETAIL)

FIRE HYDRANT

BULKHEAD HOSE CONNECTION

HOSE

HOSE   HYDRANT

ADAPTOR

Detail showing use of double male adaptor

FIG. 14-6. How a damaged section of a salt water main is isolated

The male end is taken to the hydrant and the female end to the fire, or next male connection if more than one hose is needed.

Care of hoses

Do not paint hoses or couplings.

Do not wash hoses with strong soda.

Do not leave hoses faked down too long without opening them for inspection.

Do not spill oil or grease on them.

Do not use fire hoses for washing decks: special wash-deck hoses are provided for this purpose.

Do not expel water from hoses by walking on them; under-run them at shoulder height.

Dry out hoses before stowage to avoid rotting.

Fake down hoses in their correct stowage.

Nozzles

The commonest types of detachable hose nozzles used in the Service are:

Spray-jet. For general purposes; gives an adjustable spray, from a wide cone to a hollow jet.

Jet-spray. At fire posts and certain other positions; gives a jet or spray of more water than the spray-jet and can be shut off completely.

Oilfyre. Supplied chiefly to spaces such as boiler rooms or where oil fires are likely to occur. It produces a spray only.

Types of fire and extinguishers used

Oil fuel. 2-gallon foam, major foam, steam. Under some circumstances water spray, but *never* when foam is being used.

Diesel oil. Foam.

Electrical. CO_2, water spray.

Gasoline. Foam, dry powder.

Paintwork, bedding, wood, etc. Water, preferably spray.

Immediate action

In its initial stage a fire requires immediate action by the man on the spot. Therefore know your ship, where the equipment is kept, and its correct use.

SHIP SAFETY

See B.R. 2170 and 2171, *Ship NBCD Manual,* Vols. 1 and 2

Ship safety

This term is used to describe the normal precautions taken in a warship to guard against and minimize the effects of fire, flooding and general damage and casualties, whether caused by accident or by the enemy.

FIG. 14-7. A ship saved

Every member of the ship's company is a potential link in the organization and the action taken by him, whether as a matter of routine or in emergency, may prove decisive to the safety of the ship. Everyone on board must have some understanding of:

(*a*) the effects of damage and how they can be minimized;

(*b*) the layout of the ship and of the positioning of equipment for firefighting, emergency repair, NBC monitoring, and decontamination and how to use it;

(*c*) the function of NBCD control positions;

(*d*) the method of passing quick and accurate reports;

(*e*) the necessity for watertight and gastight integrity and the meaning of risk and control markings;

(*f*) the care and use of personal equipment for his own protection, and a knowledge of first aid;

(*g*) the necessity for seaman-like precautions in the stowage of storerooms, offices and personal belongings.

ORGANIZATION

The nucleus

Every ship has one officer responsible for directing the ship's NBCD organization and for co-ordinating NBCD training. The organization has a small team of officers and men from each department as its nucleus. The NBCD organization will vary according to the size of the ship. A coastal minesweeper's organization will be extremely simple, whereas that of an aircraft carrier will be very complex. It is framed so that the required degree of control can be exercised under all the different circumstances of peace and war, and can be transferred from one set of conditions to another.

Headquarters and sections

Every ship larger than a destroyer is divided into NBCD sections, each of which extends from the keel to the weather deck between certain transverse bulkheads. Incidents in these sections are controlled from a *section base*, which in turn controls two outposts known as *fire and repair party positions*. Destroyers and below, although theoretically one-section ships, do not have a section base, but have their men and material divided between two fire and repair positions, one forward and one aft. Overall assessment and control is exercised from NBCD Headquarters.

In larger ships there are a main and secondary NBCD Headquarters (H.Q.1 and H.Q.2). In some new-construction ships the H.Q.2 may be combined with a section base. In smaller ships there is only one H.Q., which is situated in a compartment normally used for some other purpose in peacetime, e.g. Combined Technical Office.

Communications

Large ships. The fire and repair party within a section are connected to the section base by telephone. Certain other positions are connected directly to the NBCD Headquarters, e.g. the principal electrical control positions and rapid flooding positions.

Small ships. The NBCD telephone is centred on NBCD Headquarters, with connections to all important positions in the ship.

There are three types of telephone system in use:

Red for fire and general damage,
Green for electrical equipment and circuits,
Yellow for pumping and flooding.

Control and manning

Large ships. The organization is controlled from H.Q.1 except in harbour in peacetime, when it may be controlled by the Officer of the Watch.

Small ships. The organization is only controlled from H.Q.1 when action is imminent or highly probable. Under normal conditions it is controlled by the Officer of the Watch.

The extent to which positions (stations) are manned depends upon the probability of action or the risk of damage (by mines, etc.). When action is imminent or highly probable, stations are fully manned.

The teams in H.Q.s 1 and 2 and section bases consist of officers and men trained to judge the results, and organize the repair, of any damage that may occur, and to take such safety measures as may be necessary. There are teams of fire and repair parties, pumping and flooding, first aid and electrical repair parties and W.T. integrity patrols under the control of an officer at each section base. These teams work within their section limits, but H.Q.1 may back up the teams of one section with teams from another. When action is less probable stations are only manned by skeleton teams on a watchkeeping basis.

When action is unlikely, stations may not be manned at all and any damage control requirements would then be met by the 'part of the watch' or emergency party.

WATERTIGHTNESS AND GASTIGHTNESS

Watertightness (watertight integrity)

Ships are divided by watertight decks and bulkheads (see Chapter 3), so that if flooding occurs it can be confined within a watertight unit. However, no compartment can be kept continuously watertight, because doors and hatches have to be opened to give access to it and it has to be provided with ventilation. To preserve the watertight integrity of a ship as far as possible, rules are made for the opening and closing of all openings within a ship. These rules are adapted to the use of a compartment and to the liability of flooding in its vicinity: also blast and fire can be prevented from spreading by keeping openings shut. ('Openings', as used in this chapter, includes all doors, hatches, scuttles, flaps, valves and any hole in the ship's structure which affects her watertight and gastight integrity.)

Gastightness (gastight integrity)

A ship must be gastight as well as watertight: radioactive materials and chemical and biological agents (known collectively as 'gases') must be kept out. Most of the outside of a ship can be made gastight: where interconnecting compartments can be grouped together within unbroken gastight boundaries they form a *citadel*. Spaces which can be made gastight, but which for certain reasons cannot be included in the citadel, are *gas-free spaces*.

Openings in the boundaries of citadels and gas-free spaces must be controlled in a similar way to watertight openings. Some openings fulfil both functions and with them watertightness has prior claims on certain occasions, gastightness on others.

Ventilation systems

Ventilation is required to provide fresh air for general habitability, for machinery and to remove foul air, etc. It may be natural, or forced by means of fans and trunkings.*

To meet NBCD requirements in a ship her ventilation is designed and arranged so that:

(a) Ventilation systems are grouped to minimize the number of weather deck openings.

(b) Weather deck openings are fitted with watertight or gastight covers.

(c) Gas flaps are fitted in certain places to allow air to be recirculated within citadels.

(d) When closed down, air can be drawn into a ship through filtration units to augment the air within citadels. This allows a positive pressure to be built up within a citadel to help exclude gas.

Unventilated compartments. There are compartments, such as double-bottom spaces, which have no fitted ventilation systems. They sometimes contain poisonous, flammable and explosive gases, and certain precautions must be observed before entering or working in them.

CONTROL OF OPENINGS

Watertight and gastight integrity are maintained by the use of *risk and control markings.*

Risk markings

Risk markings are coloured markings on doors, hatches and other openings which denote the risk to the watertight and gastight integrity of the ship if they are left open, as shown below.

(a) *Red zone.* When a ship is damaged at or below the waterline, compartments in the vicinity will flood immediately and, because of heel or trim after damage, the zone in which this can happen may extend above the waterline, especially at the ends of a ship and the sides of a big ship. Openings to all compartments within this zone are deemed to be, when open, an immediate risk to watertight integrity. All such openings are marked with a red disc or flash and are known as *red openings.* In an emergency (after damage, or if collision is imminent) these can be shut by the order 'Close all red openings'. *This order overrides any permission which may be in force for a red opening to be open.*

(b) *Blue zone.* After damage or under adverse weather conditions, etc. it may be necessary to exercise rigid control over the openings to compartments adjacent to the red zone, overriding normal control rules. These openings are given a blue marking, which denotes this lesser risk; but this marking is not an emergency marking in the same way as is the red.

(c) *Orange.* Openings in the citadel and gas-free space boundaries constitute a risk to the gastight integrity and are marked in orange.

---

* *Trunkings.* The main athwartships bulkheads are pierced by ventilation trunkings only where absolutely necessary, and then as high in the ship as possible; where they pierce bulkheads, slide-valves are fitted to prevent interflooding. Slide-valves are also fitted in vertical trunks which go down below a certain level.

The zone limits for red, blue and orange risk markings are decided when a ship is designed.

Conditions and control markings

Watertight and gastight conditions are grades of control necessary to maintain watertight and gastight integrity under varying circumstances while allowing maintenance, habitability and reasonable access and traffic flow. An opening is opened or closed in the different conditions according to the control letter which it bears and which corresponds to the condition in force at the time, e.g. a door marked X is closed in condition XRAY.

Watertight conditions

The following watertight conditions are used in a ship:

(a) Condition *XRAY*, which is reached when all openings marked with the control letter X are shut. In peacetime it is used in harbour and when cruising at sea: in wartime it is used in defended harbours, when refitting, etc.

(b) Condition *YANKEE*, which is reached when all openings marked with the control letters X and Y are shut. In peacetime it is used under dangerous circumstances (i.e. navigational hazards, passing through waters still dangerous because of mines, etc.); in wartime it is used when in undefended harbours and cruising at sea.

(c) Condition *ZULU* is reached when all openings marked with the control letters X, Y and Z are shut. In wartime it is used in action or when at action but relaxed.

Gastight conditions

The following gastight conditions are superimposed on watertight conditions as required:

(a) Condition *BRAVO*, which is reached when all openings marked with the control letter B are shut. In wartime this is the normal condition of preparedness for NBC attack and is that condition from which ALFA can be reached in 5 minutes.

(b) Condition *ALFA*, which is reached when all openings marked with the control letters A and B are shut. It is used in wartime when NBC attack is imminent.

A ship can be in any one of the following conditions: X, Y, YB, Z, ZB, ZA. These conditions can be ordered as required for exercises in peacetime.

Basic rules for control of watertight and gastight openings

Control letter	Rule
X	Watertight control. Opened only by permission from NBCD Headquarters. If required to be kept open, a sentry must be posted or arrangements made for immediate closing: to be reported when closed. Red zone only.
Y	Watertight control. Closed in condition Y and Z, open in X. When closed, it may be opened for access and then closed again. If required to be left open, X rules apply. Red zone only (see Note 1).
Z	Watertight control. Closed in Z, open in X and Y. When closed, Y rules apply. Used above the red zone (see Note 1).

B   Gastight control. Closed in B. When closed, not to be opened without permission. Openings which affect gastight efficiency except doors and hatches.

A   Gastight control. Closed in A, open in B. Rules and uses as for B (see Note 2).

M   Gastight conditions only—under control of the 'user' department. At all other times controlled by a watertight marking if so marked. On some openings to machinery spaces and air filtration units.

R   Gastight control. On fans and openings essential for recirculation. Fans and openings marked 'R' must continue to run and remain open respectively.

NOTES

1. In condition ALFA, any Y or Z openings with an orange risk mark must not be opened without permission (except as in Note 2).

2. In condition ALFA, doors or hatches for 'Citadel in' or 'Citadel out' and 'Shelter' may be opened only for the purpose designated, and are to be shut and fully clipped on completion. Before contamination 'Citadel in/out' can be used, but after contamination entrance must only be through a *cleansing station*, whose outer door or hatch is marked CLEANSING STATION.

3. The letters X, Y and Z are coloured black; A, B, M and R are coloured orange.

4. There are certain other modifying symbols, but they are mainly self-explanatory.

STATES OF READINESS

States of readiness are required in order to ensure that a ship is always ready to combat damage, flooding and fire, no matter how caused. There is *always* some risk present. States of readiness govern the requirements of NBCD personnel and equipment, and the state adopted depends on the calculated risk existing at the time, the warning time expected and the speed at which the highest state can be assumed.

Watertight and gastight conditions are not tied to states of readiness, but can be related.

Comparison with 'degrees of readiness'

States of NBCD readiness and the degrees of readiness of the armament do not necessarily coincide. For example, if a ship is steaming in mine-infested waters, but where air or surface attack is improbable, the armament may well be in the third or fourth degree while the NBCD state of readiness may be 2 or 1 relaxed. Also, degrees of readiness can be changed in a few minutes, but NBCD states of readiness may take half an hour to change, owing to the changing of machinery states.

States of NBCD readiness used

STATE 1	Attack imminent	Highest state of NBCD preparedness. All positions fully manned.
STATE 1 relaxed	Attack likely but not imminent	All positions manned, but up to 50 per cent of personnel may be relaxed for meals, etc.
STATE 2	Attack possible or dangerous waters	War seagoing state. Watch system. In peace for navigational hazards, etc.
STATE 3	Attack unlikely without adequate warning	Defended harbour in war. Normal cruising in peace.
STATE 4		Normal peace routine in harbour.

Relations between states and conditions

Condition	When used	State of NBCD readiness
X	Peace—in harbour or when cruising	4 in harbour 3 when cruising
	War—in a defended harbour or when refitting, etc.	3
Y	Peace—under dangerous circumstances, fog, etc.	3 or 2 depending upon circumstances
	War—in an undefended harbour, normal cruising at sea	2
YB	Peace—as required for exercises	2
	War—as for Y, but prepared for NBC attack	2
Z	Peace—as required for exercises	1 or 1 relaxed
	War—at action or relaxed during a pause in action	1 or 1 relaxed
ZB	Peace—exercises	1 or 1 relaxed
	War—as for Z, but prepared for NBC attack	1 or 1 relaxed
ZA	Peace—exercises	1
	War—as for Z, but NBC attack imminent.	1

NOTES

1. A gas condition cannot be used alone.

2. The ordering of a state or condition is by pipe or broadcast. They can be assumed or changed independently of one another or together as required, e.g. 'Assume state 3, condition BRAVO'.

PRECAUTIONS AGAINST GENERAL DAMAGE

Dispersal of machinery and alternative power supplies

Where possible, main machinery is divided into units, each unit (boilers, engines and ancillary equipment) driving one shaft. In this way, damage to one unit will not affect the remainder. When damage is unlikely, units can be linked together to save watchkeepers.

Important items of auxiliary machinery, such as electrical generators and pumps, are dispersed through the ship so that any single hit will cause the least possible loss of their services and, in general, capacity is greater than requirements to allow for some damage. Electrical or other power for important equipment can be supplied from two or more widely separated sources, any of which can be brought into use if another fails—for example, steering gear and some armament. Pipe systems, such as the salt water main, can be divided by isolating valves into self-contained sections.

These principles apply to all ships, but the arrangements in a big ship are necessarily more elaborate than those in a small ship, because there is more sub-division.

Provision of damage control equipment

Equipment for firefighting and damage repair and such items as battery-operated floodlights are kept in stowages at focal points throughout the ship. Emergency electric cables are kept either in reels or on brackets and are also dispersed at focal positions in the same way. All equipment must be properly maintained and readily available for use.

Duplication and dispersal of stores

Important stores are distributed in widely separated storerooms, so that in the event of damage a certain proportion of them is still available. Also, emergency ration dumps are made in certain sections of the ship before going into action.

PRECAUTIONS AGAINST CASUALTIES IN ACTION

Flash from explosion

This spreads farther than splinters and can travel along ventilation trunking. It is of short duration and even thin clothing affords protection. In action, or when action is imminent, everyone should be fully clothed and wear the anti-flash gear provided.

Shock from violent explosion

Shock from the explosion of a mine or a torpedo may be severe enough to throw men about, breaking their necks or limbs. In action, or when sweeping known minefields in peacetime, for example, every man not actually employed should lie down on his back with his hands behind his head.

Nuclear air-burst

An air-burst nuclear explosion emits light, heat, blast and nuclear radiations. The first indication may be a flash of light, and everyone exposed should *instantly* take advantage of any convenient structure (bulkhead, turret, screen, etc.) between himself and the explosion. But speed is vital and no time should be wasted in trying to seek better shelter. Men caught in the open away from protecting structures must throw themselves to the deck, face down, eyes shut, arms round the back of the neck, and stay in this position until the blast wave has passed. Do not look at the flash or follow the course of a falling object.

Poisonous fumes

Anti-gas respirators, although they provide a certain degree of protection against poisonous fumes, are only filters and do not provide oxygen. When attacking a fire a special breathing apparatus must be used. In war the respirator must always be at hand for protection against N, B or C agents.

RULES FOR SHIP SAFETY

General rules

(a) Report flooding, fire or any dangerous incident immediately to NBCD headquarters, if manned, and to the Officer of the Watch.

(b) Tackle flooding at once by closing all watertight openings. Tackle fires immediately by closing ventilation and using first aid firefighting equipment.

(*c*) Observe the rules for opening and closing watertight openings.

(*d*) Ensure that flammable articles are returned to their proper stowages after use.

(*e*) Know your ship thoroughly; you should be able to find your way about her in the dark.

(*f*) Keep your personal gear tidy, your locker correctly stowed and its door shut. Do not hang gear on valves or rod gearing, or leave it where it blocks a gangway. Loose gear is a fire risk and can block suction hoses.

(*g*) See that stores and equipment are stowed securely and correctly. Before leaving any compartment observe the security rules given on page 210.

(*h*) Ensure that all lifelines, ladders, etc. are correctly rigged.

(*i*) Never allow any NBCD equipment to be put to other than its correct use. Keep it in good order and learn the maintenance routines and rules.

(*j*) In war, observe the rules about unauthorized lights during hours of darkness.

(*k*) At sea, in wartime, observe the rules concerning throwing gear over the side. A ship's position can be given away by a 'gash' trail.

(*l*) Learn to swim. At sea, in wartime, wear your lifejacket and test it daily.

(*m*) At sea, in wartime, sleep in your clothes, or have them at hand so that you can be ready for action at a moment's notice.

Rules for maintenance of fittings and equipment

(*a*) Report defects at once.

(*b*) Keep the bearing surfaces of watertight and gastight fittings and their rubber sealings clean and free from paint; likewise moving parts of hinges, clips and rod gearing, which should also be properly greased.

(*c*) Lower hatch covers and close doors *gently* to avoid damage and distortion. Never hammer clips into place.

(*d*) Do not remove door clips and tallies for cleaning. Tallies must always be readable. Keep markings clear and properly painted.

(*e*) Keep fire hoses ready for running out. Ensure that hydrant connection rubbers are in place and inspect hoses regularly for wear and defects. Handle hoses, connections, nozzles and branch pipes carefully.

(*f*) Never put a fire extinguisher away in its stowage empty. See that it is refilled first.

EMERGENCY STATIONS

Generally the pipe 'Hands to emergency stations. Close all red openings' is used to 'clear between decks' of all hands not employed on damage control duties. This is to ensure watertight integrity and to give the D.C. parties room to work. At this order all hands close all red openings, and those not on watch or in D.C. parties should inflate their lifejackets and fall in, in silence, at their emergency stations on the upper deck. They are then available to assist below if and when required.

Before vacating a compartment all watertight openings should be closed, fires and lights switched off, lockers, cupboards, etc. shut. After leaving, shut the hatch or door and clip it properly, reporting the fact that you have done so to NBCD headquarters, and go up to the upper deck.

BASIC NBC

See B.R. 2170 and 2171, *Ship NBCD Manual*, Vols. I and II

THE THREAT

Nuclear weapons

A nuclear explosion produces on a large scale the effects of a conventional explosion (extremes of light, heat and blast) and, in addition, the radiation of alpha and beta particles, neutrons and gamma rays. Alpha particles are only harmful if taken into the body, for example, by breathing or swallowing. Beta particles are harmful if taken into the body and also inflict burns if they come into contact with the skin. Gamma rays and neutrons can deliver a dose of radiation which may cause injury to health.

Radioactive contamination. A nuclear explosion produces a quantity of vaporised radioactive material. In an air-burst (Fig. 14-8) this condenses on the extremely fine dust particles in the upper atmosphere and does not fall back to earth. A burst just above, at, or just below the surface of land or water (Fig. 14-9) sucks up vast

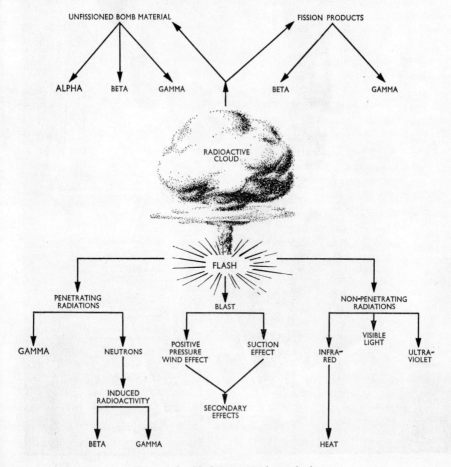

FIG. 14-8. Air-burst atomic explosion

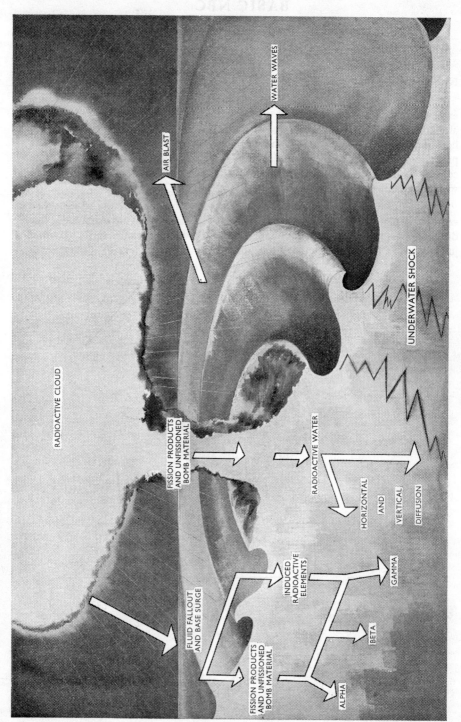

FIG. 14-9. Underwater atomic explosion

quantities of quite large particles of earth or drops of water. The radioactive material condenses on these and they return to earth as fall-out—sooner or later, according to size. Any surface on which they fall and remain is said to be 'contaminated'.

Chemical and biological weapons

A chemical warfare agent is a substance used to reduce an enemy's efficiency by its poisonous, irritant or blistering effect. It can be a gas or volatile liquid (non-persistent agent) or a liquid that evaporates slowly (persistent). Either may be lethal or have a disabling or harassing effect.

Biological warfare is the use of living organisms or their products to cause injury, disease or death to man, animals or plants. Some agents act directly, others can spread by multiplication or infection causing epidemics. Effects can be temporary or permanent, and vary widely in intensity.

Chemical and biological agents destroy or incapacitate men while leaving material intact.

PROTECTION

The precautions taken in a hospital operating theatre against infection, and the methods used to dispel it, are somewhat similar to those used in the Royal Navy against NBC warfare agents; but the latter pose one extra problem—penetrating radiations. The measures taken in ships to deal with these agents come under two headings—collective protection and personal protection.

Collective protection

Prewetting. Water running over the exposed surfaces of a ship helps to prevent radioactive material, liquid gas, etc. from settling, and washes it away. The process of washing down exposed surfaces is called 'prewetting' and is done with a spray of sea water supplied by the ship's salt water system. The system is turned on when warning of an attack is received. In the latest ships the system is a permanent arrangement of fixed nozzles, but in older ships hoses are arranged in the best positions around the ship to give spray coverage over the whole of the exposed surface.

Closing down. This implies closing the Citadel after withdrawing inside it all men not particularly required in exposed positions. Depending on the type of ship and the operational requirements, this may include most or all of the ship's company. The boundary of the Citadel is sealed from the atmosphere and air is recirculated within it, replenished by means of air filtration units which filter out N, B or C agents. All within the Citadel are protected from biological and chemical agents and from *contamination* by radioactive materials. Reliefs must be arranged for any who are in exposed positions.

Taking shelter. Gamma radiations can penetrate solid materials just as light can penetrate paper—the thicker and the denser the screen the less radiation will pass through it. If, in spite of prewetting, enough radioactive material remains on the exposed surfaces of the ship to be hazardous to men within the Citadel, then they must be sent lower in the ship to gain the greater shielding of extra structure. These 'shelter stations' vary with the type of ship—an aircraft carrier can provide better protection than a coastal minesweeper.

FIG. 14-10. Gas sentry dressed in protective clothing

Personal protection

This includes:

Precautions against casualties in action (see page 195)

Taking cover. Ship's structure, besides shielding from radiation, also gives some protection from flash, blast and splinters. All men not operationally required to be exposed should be under cover, or preferably between decks.

Clothing. The Service action working dress and anti-flash gear give protection against flash and heat. Protective clothing is provided which, with the anti-gas respirator, will give limited protection against beta radiations and liquid chemical agents, and complete protection against chemical warfare vapours (Fig. 14-10).

Anti-gas respirator. If it makes a good fit with the face, the respirator will give complete protection to the eyes, nose and mouth against the vapours of all known war gases, and probably against any biological agent likely to be used. It will *not* protect the wearer from some of the accidental gases such as carbon monoxide, nor is it of any use in concentrations of smoke.

PERSONAL PROTECTION AGAINST CHEMICAL AGENTS

(a) *Personal equipment*

Anti-gas respirator—effective against all known war gases in vapour form
Anti-gas ointment—for use *after* contact with blister gases
Absorbent pads or swabs—for dabbing off liquid gas from the skin.

In war the following may be issued:
BAL ointment—specially for treating Lewisite in the eyes
Atropine ampoules—for self-injection as an antidote to nerve gas poisoning.

(b) *Immediate action.* Once chemical warfare has started, if you observe:

SMOKE, SMELLS, SPLASHES, SYMPTOMS (see (c))

or are subject to bombardment, take the following action:

WIPE FACE quickly, while holding your breath

PUT ON RESPIRATOR, keeping your face shielded and taking care not to allow contamination of the inside of the facepiece

PASS ON THE WARNING

CLEANSE THE EXPOSED SKIN. Mop off any liquid and wash skin. This should be done at a cleansing post.

(c) *Symptoms of nerve gas poisoning.* Early symptoms are:
Sudden intense headache
Difficulty in breathing (tight chest, choking)
Running eyes and nose
Dimness of vision: difficulty in focusing (pupils become pin-pointed).

(d) *If you observe these symptoms*, in addition to action in (b):
INJECT ATROPINE

Later, when ordered to do so at a cleansing station:

REMOVE CONTAMINATED CLOTHING

WASH BODY THOROUGHLY

DECONTAMINATE RESPIRATOR

CHANGE CLOTHING.

CLEANSING

Cleansing of personnel

This should not be confused with treatment. Contaminated personnel must remove their clothing, then shower and wash well. Their clothing must be washed, boiled or destroyed according to its texture. Men exposed to contamination during or after attack, including monitoring and decontamination teams, must all be cleansed. This is done at *cleansing stations*, which are always sited at Citadel entrances and of which there may be one or more. After the ship has been contaminated everybody entering the Citadel must go through a cleansing station.

CHAPTER 15

Electrical Installations

Equipment

Electrical power is as important to a modern warship as the main machinery, and the correct functioning of the electrical equipment is essential for the fighting efficiency and safety of the ship and the comfort of all on board.

All electrical equipment is marked by tallies, which are either secured to the equipment or adjacent to it. *These tallies are essential for the proper maintenance of the equipment. They must not be painted over or removed for cleaning.*

Responsibilities

The *Marine Engineer Officer* is responsible for:
    maintenance of domestic equipment,
    the electrically-driven auxiliaries in, and associated with, the machinery compartments,
    internal, engineering and NBCD communications.

The *Weapons and Radio Engineer Officer* is responsible for:
    generation and distribution of electrical power,
    maintenance of weapon electrics,
    maintenance of weapon control systems,
    maintenance of radio and radar equipment,
    communications associated with weapons and weapon control systems,
    maintenance of all ASW equipment,
    lighting and heating.

DISTRIBUTION OF ELECTRICAL POWER

The 'tree' system

This is fitted in destroyers and frigates with 220 volt d.c. electrical supply and in later-construction ships with 440 volt a.c. supply. The electrical power is fed from generators by cables to two switchboards, one forward and one aft. The switchboards have hand-operated switches which either supply or cut off power to outlying electrical services. In 440 volt a.c. supply ships there may be more than two switchboards, depending upon the size of ship.

The 'ring main' system

Cruisers and aircraft carriers with 220 volt d.c. supply employ a *ring main* system. The power is fed from generators to heavy armoured cables which run round the ship in the form of a ring, and which lie within the armoured section of the ship. The ring main can be divided into sections by either electrically- or hand-operated switches. Power is supplied directly from the ring main by electrically-operated switches, which are operated remotely from a central position known as the *main switchboard*.

Emergency supplies

All ships have emergency supply cables which may be rigged to by-pass a broken main supply cable and restore power to electrical services cut off by damage. When not in use the cables are stowed on reels or brackets fitted in mess decks, gangways and compartments throughout the ship.

Emergency lanterns

These are battery-operated lights which come on automatically if the normal lighting fails. They are fitted throughout the ship to provide partial illumination to gangways, ladders, hatches and doorways. They should be moved or adjusted only by electrical ratings.

COMMUNICATIONS

Internal—broadcast and telephone systems installed within a ship.

External—radio, lamp and flag systems of signalling between ships and shore stations.

Telephones

There are two types of telephone normally used in the Service—*power-assisted* and *sound-powered* telephones. Power-assisted telephones are used in domestic systems, control rooms and offices and have amplifier systems fitted into their circuits. Sound-powered telephones are employed in NBCD and armament control systems. They are actuated by the power of the speaker's voice and are therefore ineffective if he whispers or speaks softly.

A ship's telephone systems may be broadly of three kinds: *direct* telephones, *grouped* telephones, and *exchange system*.

Direct telephones. These are two telephones wired together so that one may call the other. They are the normal means of communication in small ships.

Grouped telephones. In some cases a number of telephones are connected together to enable a controlling telephone to pass orders simultaneously to the outlying telephones. These telephones may or may not be fitted with calling arrangements.

Exchange system. This consists of a number of outlying telephones connected to an exchange, either automatic or manual, by which one telephone is connected to another when required.

Automatic exchange system. This is similar to the telephone system fitted on shore by which a person dials the number required. It is fitted for convenience of domestic communication between offices, messes, etc. This system can be connected to the shore telephone system when alongside, and is fitted in all larger ships.

Manually-controlled exchange system. This system consists of a number of telephones connected to a switchbox, which is manned. The operator can connect one outstation to another or several stations in a group by means of switches on the box. This type of exchange is used mainly for NBCD purposes.

Talkback system

This is a system of communication by which messages are broadcast over a loudspeaker to a number of persons in one compartment who are expected to reply.

Before speaking into his microphone the operator makes a switch. Releasing this switch enables the loudspeaker to be used in turn as a microphone for the recipients to make their reply.

Broadcast system

This is a system employing large amplifiers which operate loudspeakers distributed all round the ship, in order to pass messages and commands which affect the general running of the ship. The messages are passed over a microphone from control positions. It is possible to sound action and warning alarms over main broadcast systems.

Smaller broadcast systems are used to pass messages and instructions from control positions, etc. to action positions when replies are not required. They are used mainly in weapon control positions.

Radio

The modern warship carries various types of radio equipment, including wireless telegraphy, radio telephony and radar sets. As far as possible they are fitted in compartments where they are protected from the weather and rough handling, but certain parts of the equipment have to be in exposed positions. Unless care is used these parts can be very easily damaged, with the possibility of the most serious results. Such items of radio equipment which ratings must recognize and treat with care are:

aerials, their feeders and wave guides,
radar displays (on the bridge, in gun directors, target indicator rooms, etc.),
radio telephone microphones and small transmitters (in spaces such as aircraft direction rooms).

Maintenance of radio equipment

The three greatest enemies of all radio equipment are water (especially salt water), dirt and rough treatment.

Water. Most radio sets use high voltages (400 to 20,000 volts). Insulators are used to keep these high voltages in the right channels. Water (especially salt water) conducts electricity, and if water reaches radio gear the insulators will be useless and high voltages will 'flash over', causing burning and serious damage throughout the equipment. Even when the salt water has dried out, the troubles are not over, as the salt itself remains and gets damp again and the damage will recur. So remember:

(*a*) Do not use hoses near radio equipment or near ventilation to radio rooms.
(*b*) When scrubbing decks near radio equipment use as little water as possible and do not splash it about. The deck should be wiped dry with a cloth that has been well wrung out.
(*c*) Ventilation fans should normally be kept running, and radiators switched on as necessary, to keep the air warm and dry.

Dirt. This is harmful for the same reasons and in the same way as is water. Dust consists of tiny particles of metal, carbon and other conductors of electricity; a film of dust over insulators allows high voltages to discharge through it. Therefore:

(*a*) In the vicinity of radio gear put your cigarette ash and ends in a tin (a good sailor never throws them on the deck, anyway).
(*b*) Use a moist cloth for dusting; a dry duster only scatters the dust into the air—and so into the radio equipment.

Rough treatment. Radio gear is extremely delicate and will not stand being knocked about. Serious damage can be done to it by inexperienced persons. For this reason no unauthorized person is allowed to touch any radio equipment.

Care must be taken not to break, crush, bend or chafe the cables connected to aerials, as they are very delicate. Never paint any part of an aerial unless expressly ordered to do so. Ordinary paint contains metal, and the high voltages of many aerials will cause leakages over insulators if they are painted.

ELECTRICAL DANGERS

All electrical devices depend upon power supplies which are carried along the conductors inside the wires and cables that run through every compartment in the ship. To prevent power leaks, all conductors must be insulated from the ship's structure. The conductors are therefore wrapped in layers of insulant and run inside the protective watertight cover of the cable. Water or damp in any form is harmful to electrical apparatus: therefore the utmost care must be taken to prevent damage to cables and to replace the caps on plug sockets (power points) where they are fitted.

Care of electrical cables

Before painting any electric cables contact the Technical Office.

Never paint rubber-covered cable, because the oil in the paint would ruin the rubber.

Do not chip or scrape electric cables.

Do not hang anything from electric cables or from the channel plating overhead.

Portable cables and portable leads

Just as hoses are more likely to leak than the salt water main, so flexible electric cables on portable apparatus are more likely to leak than the ship's permanent wiring, and a leak of electricity can be lethal. An inexperienced person should never attempt to repair electric irons, drills, wandering leads, etc., because incompetently executed repairs may lead to serious injury or loss of life.

All portable equipment must be properly 'earthed' by connecting the earth pin of the plug via the earth lead to the metal body of the piece of equipment. Portable equipment should be tested by an electrical rating every six months to ensure that it is in a safe condition for use.

Aerials—'man aloft'

There is a danger of shock from aerials, and with radar aerials an additional risk that they might revolve without warning. (See also page 120.)

Before going aloft, report to the wireless office to draw the 'safe to transmit' boards. These are either fuses or connecting links of transmitters. Then report to the technical office to draw the 'safe to rotate' keys for the various radar aerials affected. Then take them to the Officer of the Watch and request permission to proceed aloft.

Whilst aloft, avoid damaging insulators and wave guides, and do not touch anything connected with them. Although low-powered transmitters may not be considered dangerous electrically, even a slight 'tingle' is enough to make a man let go, and if the hand affected is the only one by which a man is holding on, the results may be serious.

On returning from aloft, report immediately to the Officer of the Watch, draw the boards and keys from him and return them to the wireless office and technical office. This prevents a wireless transmitter or aerial from being out of action for an unnecessarily long period.

Electrical fires

These are usually caused by the heat generated by short circuits. A short circuit will occur when bare current-carrying conductors make contact with other conductors or with the metal of the ship. They differ from ordinary fires in that if the current is not switched off the heat source remains and may start another fire, even if the original one has been dealt with. If a solid jet of water is used anywhere in the vicinity of a live electric circuit it will act as a conductor and the holder of the metal end of the hose may receive a lethal electrical shock. Whenever possible switch off the current before tackling a fire involving electrical apparatus. Where high voltage may be present (e.g. in a radar office) use only a CO_2 fire extinguisher.

CHAPTER 16

National Security, Safety of Property and Handling of Small Arms

NATIONAL SECURITY

Until such time as wars and the threats of wars are abolished nations will try to steal each other's secrets. This is particularly so in matters of international policy and defence. In order to safeguard documents, information and equipment from coming into the possession of unauthorized persons, or being seen by them, the following security classifications are applied to them:

TOP SECRET. Information and material the unauthorized disclosure of which would cause *exceptionally grave damage* to the nation.

SECRET. Information and material the unauthorized disclosure of which would cause *serious injury* to the interests of the nation.

CONFIDENTIAL. Information and material the unauthorized disclosure of which would be *prejudicial* to the interests of the nation.

RESTRICTED. Information and material which require security protection other than that determined to be TOP SECRET, SECRET or CONFIDENTIAL.

All classified material must be carefully guarded and must be handled in accordance with special regulations issued to all ships and establishments by the Ministry of Defence (Royal Navy).

The 'need to know'

It is the duty of anyone who is in possession of classified information not to pass it on to any other person unless he is satisfied that that person has a *need to know* such information to enable him to perform his duties.

Careless talk

In the course of normal Service life every rating will gather information about ships and establishments and the equipment in them. Often pieces of information, no matter how insignificant they may appear in themselves, can be put together into a pattern which could be of value to a possible enemy. Service matters, therefore, must never be discussed in public places. Telephones are particularly vulnerable to eavesdropping, even if fitted with scrambling devices, and conversations involving Service matters should be guarded if they have to be made at all.

Contacts with members of subversive organizations

Communists of any nationality and members of subversive organizations such as a Fascist movement are liable to try to make contact with Service ratings. Any rating who is approached by any person, or is asked to get information or spread a subversive influence, is to report the facts immediately to his Divisional Officer or Security Officer.

Breaches and irregularities

It is the responsibility of everyone to keep his eyes and ears open for possible breaches of security or irregularities which might lead to such breaches and to report them without delay to the Officer of the Watch or to the Security Officer.

Naval Security organization

The Director of Naval Security (D.N.S.Y.) is the Head of the Naval Security Department and is responsible for security policy and procedures throughout the naval Service. Full-time staff officers (Security) are appointed to all the major naval commands, and all ships and establishments are required to designate one officer for part-time security duties. The constant application of strict practical security is, of course, a function and responsibility of command.

SAFETY OF PROPERTY

This subject covers a very wide field, from custody of private property to the safety of establishments, and it obviously includes certain aspects of national security. Most of the rules and principles are common sense, but it is surprising how easily they can be forgotten or ignored. The stores, equipment and food purchased out of public money all have to be accounted for and looked after in order to avoid wastage and unnecessary expenditure.

Valuable and personal effects

All valuable items should be kept under lock and key when not in use and their transfer and issue should be accounted for accordingly. Personal effects and private money should also be carefully looked after. In a ship, where men live close together, the temptations for thieving are great. All clothing must be marked, and, where possible, so should valuable items such as razors, cameras, etc. A record of all bank note numbers should also be kept. Never leave a locker or cupboard door open, and never leave valuables lying about. Avoid putting temptation in other people's way.

Custody of stores

Naval stores and mess gear may be permanent or consumable, the difference being that permanent stores are expensive and/or are worth repairing when they become unserviceable, whereas consumable stores are either inexpensive (for example, nuts, split pins), easily broken (crockery), or are consumed or worn out in use (metal polish). Loan clothing is treated as being in the permanent category.

The Supply Officer has to account for all the items in his storerooms and therefore requires a signature for everything that is issued. Thereafter all subsequent movements of permanent items must be signed for, and the recipient becomes responsible for the item until he obtains someone else's signature. There is no formal accounting action for consumable stores after issue.

Loss of, or damage to, permanent stores must be reported at once so that the circumstances can be investigated while the facts are still clear in people's minds. If there has been misconduct or negligence the person(s) responsible may be required to repay some or all of the loss to the Crown; disciplinary action may also be taken. Concealment of loss or damage is usually evidence of a consciousness of guilt.

While there is not the same necessity to investigate every occasion of loss of, or damage to, consumable stores, nevertheless money charges or disciplinary action can be taken against men who waste the taxpayer's money deliberately or by negligence.

Be careful how you handle and use stores; put them away properly after use. Never throw anything away until you are sure that someone else has not got to account for it. Remember that you have helped to pay for the stores in the first place through the taxes you pay, and you may be required to find the money from your pay to replace anything you waste or lose.

Public money, non-public funds, accounts

For very obvious reasons, all public money and non-public funds must be accounted for. All funds are audited and checked and money is counted at regular intervals to prevent theft, irregularities and errors. All personnel looking after sums of money must keep good and accurate accounts and should welcome periodical checks by outsiders. Even mess caterers, who handle small sums such as cinema subscriptions, have to record their collections and account for them properly.

Dutiable goods

The regulations regarding tobacco have been mentioned on page 108. The regulations regarding the handling of dutiable goods must be strictly observed, as the penalty for infringement is severe. This covers the handling, transferring and accounting of all stocks of dutiable goods and stores.

Documents

Apart from documents affecting national security, there are many other documents and books which require careful handling. They should be stowed correctly and, where necessary, locked away when not in use. Any scrap of paper may be of importance, and it may be very difficult to trace it once it has been mislaid. It is easy enough to tear up, throw away or burn a piece of paper, but before doing so you should satisfy yourself that it is of no value or importance to anybody.

Offices, rooms and stores

All storerooms are fitted with both padlocks and rim locks. Usually racks and cupboards within them have separate locking devices. They must be kept stowed neatly and correctly and their contents checked regularly. Storeroom scuttles, windows and openings are strengthened, and measures are taken to prevent illegal entry.

Offices and rooms which are not in continuous use do not lend themselves to security, and particular care must be taken when leaving them unoccupied for any time.

Checks to be made before leaving a compartment. All compartments are vulnerable to fire, and measures must be taken to reduce risks to a minimum. Before leaving a compartment unoccupied:

Stow away all valuables and lock them up.
Stow away all valuable documents and lock them up.
Secure all scuttles, hatches and windows, etc.
Switch off fires and electrical fittings.

See that any gear, paper, etc. which might be near electrical fittings or sources
of heat are put away.

Check that cigarettes are not left smouldering in ashtrays or other receptacles.

Switch off all *unnecessary* lighting. (In some compartments the lighting is
deliberately left on so that personnel doing rounds can see inside.)

Check all locks.

Shut the door, lock it and check that it is locked.

Keys and keyboards

In order to keep a check on the opening and closing of important compartments,
stores, etc. a ship has a keyboard organization. Basically there are two central
keyboards and separate departmental keyboards. The central keyboards are:

> The *Important and Magazine keyboard*, which contains the original set of keys
> to such compartments as magazines, wine stores and naval stores. The dupli-
> cate keys are held by the Captain. The original keys may only be drawn by
> specially authorized officers and ratings.

> The *Main keyboard*, which contains keys to such compartments as offices
> and bathrooms.

All keys must be signed for on drawing and on returning. The Important and
Magazine keybook is inspected by the officer doing rounds at night.

CUSTODY AND SAFETY OF SHIPS

Custody of establishments. The following paragraphs on the custody and safety
of ships apply equally to establishments, where additional measures have to be
taken, such as the placing of sentries. The rules that apply when leaving a compartment also apply when leaving a building; and, in addition, a thorough check of the
exterior of the building and of all means of access to it should be made.

Rounds and NBCD patrols

In all ships and establishments rounds are carried out during the 24 hours of the
day, and especially at night, in order to:

> Check and discourage irregularities
> Check on the internal security of compartments, offices, stores and rooms
> Act as fire and flooding patrols
> Ensure that no one is in an unauthorized place
> See that the NBCD conditions in force are observed
> Check the security and safety of boats, awnings, covers, berthing wires
> and, if at anchor, the cable.

In larger ships, NBCD patrols are instituted primarily to carry out the aspects
of the above duties which are applicable to the NBCD organization of ships.
They must, however, observe the normal rules for 'rounds'.

Flooding

In a ship there is always the danger of flooding. If a hatch or door is incorrectly
clipped and the compartment to which it gives access is subsequently flooded, water
will pass freely through it and cause an extension of the flooding which might be
dangerous and do unnecessary damage. It is therefore essential to check that
openings are correctly clipped when closed and that control orders in force are
correctly observed.

Gangway staff

In small ships the initial responsibility for the general security and safety of the ship and of boats, tenders, etc. secured alongside out of working hours falls on the gangway staff. This is particularly so during the silent hours, when they must be alive to the first sign of any irregularity. Prompt action is essential, and if any doubt exists in the mind of any rating doing rounds he should act at once to prevent the security or safety of the ship generally being endangered. In most cases this means calling for assistance at the same time as trying to deal with the situation.

Apart from normal duties on the gangway, the gangway staff must keep the whole of the upper deck under surveillance. The gangway should never be left unattended, and it must be at least under supervision if one member of the staff is away on rounds and the other is attending to other duties on the upper deck.

Operation 'Awkward'

Ships in harbour are particularly vulnerable to underwater attack by swimmers and small submersible craft. To counter this threat, ships institute measures known collectively as 'Operation Awkward'. Their object is to ensure that the ship's bottom is kept clear, to prevent underwater attack and generally to prepare both the ship and her company to deal with any action that might result from this threat.

Sentries

As well as detailing personnel to carry out rounds, it may be necessary to place sentries on gangways, gates, jetties, stores, etc. A sentry should be posted by a Petty Officer or Leading Rate, who is to ensure that he understands his task and his orders. Sentries may be 'static' or they may be roving patrols.

There are two main kinds of sentry—ceremonial and operational; they are described below.

An operational sentry should be concealed, if possible, and a roving patrol should keep to the shadows.

Ceremonial sentries. Although primarily for ceremonial purposes, for which they must pay attention to dress, manner, bearing and saluting, ceremonial sentries may well have to fulfil an operational role while still at their posts.

Operational sentries. These may be placed so as to:

Give immediate protection to a group of men, vital point or equipment,

Give early warning of an attack,

Detect the presence of any undesirable person near an establishment or vital place.

SENTRIES' ORDERS

A sentry must know:

The reason for his being posted

The limit of his post and his task

Where and when he may use force

How to raise the alarm

What to do if anyone approaches his post

How to challenge and identify a person

Any special orders.

CHALLENGING AND IDENTIFYING A PERSON

On being approached by, or on approaching, a person, the sentry:

1. Orders 'Halt! Who goes there?'
2. Calls one person forward for identification (if more than one person is present).
3. Halts him a good pace clear.
4. Exchanges the challenge and reply, if in force.
5. Identifies the remainder, calling them forward one by one.

A sentry should never permit an unidentified person to approach within striking distance, and should avoid having two people close by at the same time.

ESCORTING SUSPECTS

If a sentry is not satisfied with a challenged person's identity or presence, he should:

1. Summon assistance.
2. Escort the suspect to the control room, making him lead the way.

Searching suspected persons and vehicles

If a rating is ordered to search a suspect, he should carry out the following drill:

Persons. He should make them stand facing a wall, with their hands pressed flat on it and their feet wide apart. He should then start searching at the cap and work down towards the toes.

Vehicles. If anything needs moving make the occupants do it. Never move anything in the vehicle unless the driver is in it—there may be a booby trap in it. If a vehicle is suspect, turn it over to the experts for stripping.

Alarms

Fire alarms. These are usually distributed throughout an establishment and have instructions listed close by. Some of the alarms will act automatically if a fire breaks out in their vicinity. In some ships telephones throughout the ship are connected to NBCD H.Q. and the Officer of the Watch's position, so that a '999' call will ring a fire alarm.

Security alarms. Operational sentries are issued with whistles for raising an alarm. A sentry raising an alarm should contact his control position to inform it of the nature of the alarm. In some establishments certain buildings are fitted with alarm systems, working on the same principle as burglar alarms, which not only sound an alarm bell or siren in the vicinity but also make a warning signal in a control position.

Alertness

A determined person who is in search of information in order to commit a theft or sabotage, or who wishes to penetrate security arrangements, will study the problem thoroughly. He will look for weaknesses and will exploit them fully if he finds them. Therefore in matters affecting security and safety Service personnel must be at all times alert and prepared for the unexpected.

HANDLING OF SMALL ARMS

Accidents

The greatest single cause of accidents is the issue of loaded pistols to sentries in circumstances where a truncheon would be more appropriate. Sentries should be correctly posted and relieved by a responsible rating. If this is not done under supervision, an accident will occur sooner or later.

The mishandling of fire-arms is another cause of accidents, and no one should have any small arms or ammunition in his possession unless required to have them in the course of his duty.

SAFETY RULES FOR HANDLING WEAPONS

General precautions

The rules given below are really only elementary common sense.

(*a*) Never point a gun at a friend.

(*b*) Do not stand in front of the muzzle.

(*c*) Always assume a gun is loaded until you have had a chance to check the magazine and the barrel.

(*d*) Never leave a loaded gun lying about.

(*e*) Never meddle with a gun you do not understand.

(*f*) Always keep a gun pointed in a safe direction.

(*g*) Never skylark with arms or ammunition.

(*h*) Remember that more accidents are caused with pistols than with any other weapon.

(*i*) Never load a weapon until it is actually required for firing.

(*j*) Never give or receive a weapon without ensuring that it is unloaded.

Pistols

In addition to the general precautions enumerated above, the following special rules should be observed when handling a pistol:

(*a*) Never trust a loaded pistol in the hands of an untrained man. In the hands of a careless or ignorant person the pistol is the most dangerous weapon in the Service.

(*b*) Never take a pistol out of its holster unnecessarily.

(*c*) A loaded pistol should have an empty chamber in line with the firing pin and barrel. This loading will prevent the pistol firing from an accidental blow on the hammer, but it will not prevent it from firing if the trigger is squeezed.

(*d*) Wear a lanyard attached to the pistol. If it is dropped butt first, it may go off and kill or injure someone.

Rifles

In addition, when handling a rifle observe the following precautions:

(*a*) After loading, always apply the safety catch.

(*b*) If a rifle is fitted with a cut-off, close it over the rounds in the magazine until you need to use the rifle. If a cut-off is not fitted, make sure that a round is not loaded when the bolt is closed.

(c) A rifle loaded with blank ammunition can kill or wound up to at least 10 yards range. Treat it as a loaded rifle.

(d) Keep your finger away from the trigger until you require to fire the rifle.

(e) Do not lean on a rifle, and be careful not to get mud in the barrel.

Automatic weapons

In addition, when handling an automatic weapon:

(a) Do not drop it on its base when loaded. If the bolt is forward it may go off.

(b) When clearing the mechanism of a jammed gun, always keep it pointing in a safe direction.

Ammunition

The following points must be borne in mind in connection with ammunition:

(a) Unused ammunition must always be returned.

(b) Ammunition must be accounted for. Clear orders should be in force to ensure that this is done.

(c) Blank ammunition is dangerous up to a range of at least 10 yards.

CHAPTER 17

Aid to Civil Power

DISASTER RELIEF

In peacetime the Royal Navy is frequently required to render assistance to areas which have suffered some form of natural disaster such as an earthquake, typhoon, flood or famine. Typical examples of these disasters in recent years are the volcanic eruption at Tristan da Cunha and the famine in Kenya, both of which occurred in 1961.

The task

The claims on your attention and sympathy will be numerous and, although you will naturally do all you can to help, you must understand the aims of landing a disaster relief party. The task, which will vary with the circumstances, may include some or all of the following:

(a) Re-establishment of power supplies, communications and domestic services.

(b) Rescue and feeding of survivors.

(c) Provision of medical aid, setting up of first aid posts, re-establishment of medical services in the area and improvisation of hospitals.

(d) Inoculation of the local populace against disease and testing of water and local food supplies.

(e) Fighting fires, probably using the ship's portable firefighting equipment.

FIG. 17-1. Disaster relief party landing at Tristan da Cunha

FIG. 17-2. Stores being landed by helicopter for famine relief in Kenya

(f) Demolition of unsafe buildings, building temporary dykes, etc.
(g) Preparation of helicopter landing-fields and repair of temporary jetties.
(h) Restoration of port facilities, operating dockside equipment and clearing channels and waterways.
(i) Improvisation of shelters for the homeless.
(j) Transport and landing of food, bedding and stores.
(k) Provision of anti-looting patrols and sentries.
(l) Burying the dead, including animals.
(m) Encouraging the survivors to help themselves, both by example and by talking to them.

Organization and communications

Your ship will be used primarily as a base and will berth alongside, if possible. However, the approach channels may well be blocked or filled in, in which case she will have to anchor off shore. The direction of operations will be carried out from shore. The ship's company will be divided into several parties, each with its particular task to perform. A typical example of the composition of disaster relief parties in a frigate is shown on page 218.

Control will be exercised from a shore headquarters (which may be a temporary hut) or from the local town hall, if it has survived the disaster. The public must feel they have confidence in those who have come to help, and the conviction that the local authorities and the relief parties are working closely together.

Transport. At first transport will have to be supplied by the ship. However, every local boat, lorry and handcart will be required to help complete the task.

Communications. Here again, depending upon the type of disaster, a great part of the local communications system may not be in working order. If this is so, most of the communications will, to start with, have to be provided by the ship. The sooner local facilities can be made to work the better. The shore H.Q. must be kept informed of what is going on, especially if you find something new which you cannot deal with without help. During the early stages full use will be made of messengers. If you are detailed as a messenger try to find a bicycle (or even a reliable donkey), as this will help you to speed up the circulation of messages during that period.

Public reaction in a disaster area

You will find that many of the general public will be suffering from shock and despair. They will appear apathetic and may take offence at what is intended to be help. You should firmly encourage their co-operation to put things right. This will require a great deal of patience and tact, and you must try to avoid doing anything which is liable to create public resentment, no matter how illogical the latter may seem.

Avoid being diverted from the original task allotted to you. In some cases this will be obvious, i.e. you would not go chasing after a dog with a broken leg if you were sent out to bring in an injured person; but there may be occasions when you will be unwittingly sidetracked. In any case, if you find that you cannot do your particular task or are held up, inform your section leader.

Summary

Always remember you are there to provide help. Firmness, fairness and a high standard of conduct are required from the landing party. Any breaches of law and order should, if possible, be dealt with by the local police.

COMPOSITION OF DISASTER RELIEF PARTIES IN A FRIGATE

Personnel	Equipment	Task
Reconnaissance Party 2 Officers E.A. E.R.A. Shipwright 2 A.B.s/Ordinary Seamen Interpreter (if carried)	Portable radio Maps First Aid kit	Reconnoitre area Establish contact with local government Report situation Select site for H.Q.

Headquarters Party
1st Lieut.
L. Writer
Interpreters
Communication ratings
Photographers
3 A.B.s/Ordinary Seamen
  (messengers)
	Radio
	Flags
	Log books
	Large map
	Tables
	Chairs
	Field telephone
		Establish H.Q.
		Determine task
		  (*The determination of task must
		  be done after consultation
		  with local authorities.*)

Demolition Party
T.A.S. Officer
6 T.A.S. ratings
	Explosives
	Red flags
	Whistles
		Demolition of dangerous structures
		  (*Adequate warning must be
		  given before demolition.*)

Medical Party
M.O.
L.S.B.A.
8 Stretcher - bearers/
  orderlies
	First Aid equipment
	Blankets
	Stretchers
		Set up casualty-clearing station
		  (*If possible, adjacent to any
		  local hospital. Full use to be
		  made of local medical staffs.*)

Personnel	Equipment	Task
Pioneer Party 1 Officer 1 P.O. 1 L. Seamen 24 A.B.s/Ordinary Seamen	Spades Pickaxes Shovels Sheerlegs Awnings, tackles, etc.	Clearance of debris and tidying up. Rigging of shelters, kitchens, etc. *(Party should be split into 3 sections and should be capable of almost any job.)*
Firefighting Party E.O. 2 P.O. M.(E)s 8 M.(E)s	Portable diesel pump Hand extinguishers Fearnought suits Hoses	
Electrical Party P.O. E. 6 E.M.s	Field telephones Portable generators D.C. floodlights Electric cables	Lighting for H.Q., shelters etc. Restore shore power, if possible.
Cooking Party Supply Officer P.O. Cook (S) 3 Cooks (S) S.A. (V)	Field cooking pots Day's ration Soap Towels Messtraps	Provision of hot meals for all *(A hot meal per day per head of the population should be aimed at. The population should be encouraged to feed themselves as soon as possible.)*
Police Party 1 Officer 1 P.O. 10 A.B.s/Ordinary Seamen	Gaiters, belts Steel helmets Whistles Entrenching tools, helves	*(To be used only when requested by the Civil Authorities.)*
Helicopter Control Party 1 Officer (marshaller) 1 Communication rating 2 M/E1 (firefighters) 4 A.B.s/Ordinary Seamen (Stores)	Firefighting gear Paint Canvas straps Handflags	Unloading and transport of stores.

CIVIL DISORDERS

See *Keeping the Peace* (W.O. Publication 9455)

Both at home and overseas British armed forces must be prepared to assist the civil authorities to maintain the peace and to restore law and order once all other methods have failed. This task is normally performed by the Army, but certain factors, such as time and accessibility of the area, may necessitate action by Royal Naval personnel. Since the end of the Second World War naval personnel have assisted the civil authorities in several trouble-spots—for example, Malta and Singapore. When you are part of a unit employed in this role you must understand the principles and aims involved, as you may be part of a relatively small force and the success of the operation may depend largely on the bearing and presence of mind of each individual rating.

The law and procedure for aiding the civil power may differ in detail in different places. It is for the civil authority (usually a magistrate or higher police authorities) to decide whether or not to call in military or naval assistance. Once that decision is made, it is for the military or naval commander to decide what form that action should take, though he should, of course, take into account the advice of the civil authorities and police. The planning of the detailed operation—bearing in mind the legal aspects—will be the serious concern of the officers and senior ratings in charge. You must therefore appreciate what your officers and senior ratings are trying to achieve.

Guiding principles

Whatever you do it must be within the law, not only the law you live by but also the law of the land in which the incident is taking place. You must be impartial and firm: the ultimate aim is to prevent trouble, not to punish it. Not only must your seniors co-operate fully with the local authorities, but you must do the same with the local policemen. Disorders may take many forms, ranging from local troubles and industrial unrest, when you may be required to run essential services, to large-scale violence. In enforcing law and order no one is permitted to use more force than is necessary. Use of excessive force, without full justification, may make a soldier or sailor liable to legal action.

Command

In an operation of this kind it may be necessary for your unit to work with British or other armed forces. Also, separate parties may be detailed to guard vulnerable points, such as buildings, bridges and communications centres. It is therefore necessary for the question of overall command to be settled before any action is taken. You come directly under the command of your officer-in-charge, but you must know who is in command of your part of any operation and what the overall plan of action is.

Dispersal of a crowd without conflict

Every attempt will be made to persuade the crowd to disperse quietly—for example, by using loud-hailers and placards. Failing this, a notice prohibiting unlawful assemblies will normally be read by an official of the civil authorities. By United Kingdom law an assembly which threatens to constitute a riot may be called on to disperse by a magistrate reading out a proclamation under the Riot Act—hence the common expression 'to read the Riot Act'.

While this is going on, you should try to identify the ringleaders and agitators, who, once they have worked up a crowd, will try to make themselves inconspicuous, usually at the back and sides of the crowd. They know that if they are caught they will be the first persons against whom legal action will be taken. If they can be separated from the crowd at a very early stage the disorder may quickly collapse through lack of leadership.

If an advance has to be made you will be ordered to do it in a steady line, so avoid individual contact with the rioters. If hand-to-hand fighting breaks out the situation may rapidly get out of control.

The armed forces in a police role

This role involves conflict with rioters or members of an unlawful assembly. The best force is a combined one, in which you will find yourself working alongside the local police, using batons and shields. Any action taken must be a combined action, and any attempt by the rioters to exploit the sympathy of either the Service or the police force must be defeated.

Equipment

The equipment required for suppressing a riot varies, but is likely to include at least the following:

> *Anti-riot irritant.* This is a double-edged weapon, as when using it our own forces have to wear respirators.
>
> *Batons and shields.* Secure the shield to the forearm and use the baton primarily against the arms of the rioter and not the head.
>
> *Hoses.* The shock of getting wet is often quite sufficient to deter an angry crowd and damp their enthusiasm. Water can also be a weapon in itself: a well-directed jet of water is quite sufficient to knock a man down at a few yards' range.

Conclusion

In all attempts to break up unlawful assemblies and riots it is essential to use the minimum force necessary to achieve the aim, to work closely with the civil authorities, and to ensure that the armed forces behave well throughout the whole operation. The four main points which you must bear in mind are *firmness, politeness, impartiality, minimum use of force.*

CHAPTER 18

Communications and Messengers' Duties

EXTERNAL COMMUNICATIONS

Although external communications are the responsibility of the Communications Branch, there are certain aspects of the subject which are of general application in the Service.

The phonetic alphabet and Morse symbols

ALPHABET

A	Alfa	· —	J	Juliett	· — — —	S	Sierra	· · ·
B	Bravo	— · · ·	K	Kilo	— · —	T	Tango	—
C	Charlie	— · — ·	L	Lima	· — · ·	U	Uniform	· · —
D	Delta	— · ·	M	Mike	— —	V	Victor	· · · —
E	Echo	·	N	November	— ·	W	Whiskey	· — —
F	Foxtrot	· · — ·	O	Oscar	— — —	X	Xray	— · · —
G	Golf	— — ·	P	Papa	· — — ·	Y	Yankee	— · — —
H	Hotel	· · · ·	Q	Quebec	— — · —	Z	Zulu	— — · ·
I	India	· ·	R	Romeo	· — ·			

NUMERALS

Ø	Zero	— — — — —	3	Thuh-ree	· · · — —	6	Six	— · · · ·
1	Wun	· — — — —	4	Fo-wer	· · · · —	7	Se-ven	— — · · ·
2	Too	· · — — —	5	Fi-yiv	· · · · ·	8	Ate	— — — · ·
						9	Ni-ner	— — — — ·

SPECIAL CHARACTERS

The bar over two or more letters indicates that they are to be transmitted as a single character.

$\overline{AA}$	· — · —	Unknown station call.
$\overline{AR}$	· — · — ·	End of transmission sign, used when no receipt is required.
$\overline{BT}$	— · · · —	Long break. Precedes and follows the text portion of a message.
EEEEEEEE	· · · · · · · ·	Error. A succession of eight or more Es means 'Erase the portion of the message just transmitted; the corrected portion will follow': or, if followed by $\overline{AR}$, means 'Cancel this message'.
$\overline{IMI}$	· · — — · ·	Repeat. Made by the recipient, to the originator. If made alone it means 'Repeat all of your last transmission'. If the sign is followed by the letters AA (all after), AB (all before), WA (word after) or WB (word before) followed by a word, then it means 'Repeat only that portion of the message so indicated'. It is used by the originator to precede the second transmission of the whole, or a portion, of the message.

222

K	− · −	'Invitation to transmit' or 'This is the end of my transmission to you and a response is necessary'.
R	· − ·	Received; means 'I have received your last transmission'.
AAA	· − · − · −	Period (in plain language, a full stop).

These are only some of the special signs used when transmitting in the Morse code; others are given in Communication publications.

Voice communications

It is most important that all voice communications should be clear and concise and that they should be passed quickly. When you are using any kind of voice communication system, external or internal:

(a) Speak up. Your voice should be pitched at a rather higher level than for normal conversation.

(b) Do not drop your voice at the end of a word or phrase.

(c) Speak clearly and deliberately.

(d) Make up your mind what you are going to say before you say it.

(e) Read a written message to yourself before you repeat it in speech.

(f) Spell out proper names, using the phonetic alphabet.

(g) Transmit groups of numbers singly and phonetically, e.g. 5243—Fi-yiv, Too, Fo-wer, Thuh-ree.

(h) Always make your message brief.

Typical voice nets

The radio telephone (voice net) is the commonest form of communication between ships which you will meet in the Service. The main types of nets used are:

Surface tactical nets—for manoeuvring ships and units of ships.

Co-ordination nets—used between operations rooms to exchange plot information and for gunfire co-ordination messages.

Air control nets—for controlling aircraft.

Flag hoisting

The alphabetical flags and their international single meanings are shown in Plate 4, while some other flags and pennants used in naval signalling are shown in Plate 5.

A signal passed by flags (a flag hoist) is answered by the 'answer' pennant or by repeating the hoist if it is understood. If a flag hoist is not understood, the 'answer' pennant or repeated hoist is flown 'at the dip' i.e. two-thirds of the way up.

Although flag hoisting is not practised to such a large extent as it was at one time, certain elements of it are likely to remain—for example, the use of 'Preparative' to indicate five minutes to Colours and Sunset and during replenishment at sea—and the important signals should be known by all ratings. All seamen should be able to recognize their own ship's visual callsign when made by morse or flags, and they may on occasions be employed hoisting flags on the flag-deck.

Points to remember about flag hoisting

(*a*) There is a right and a wrong way to hoist a flag or pennant; the lanyard or 'tack' on one end of a flag indicates the lower end of the hoist.

(*b*) Never let go of either end of a halyard until the hoist is properly bent on.

(*c*) Stow flags away in their lockers correctly.

(*d*) Keep halyards taut and avoid fouling aerials, guys, etc. when hoisting or lowering flags.

(*e*) Make sure that the signal flies out clearly.

(*f*) If a halyard has been let go and it has run right through its block as far as the clip, do not go aloft without permission (see page 120).

INTERNAL COMMUNICATIONS

The principal means of internal communication are:

Telephone, either sound-powered or power-assisted (see also page 204)
Voice pipe
Broadcast systems (see page 205).

How to use a telephone

The telephone is a delicate instrument, and it should always be handled with care. When you are using a telephone remember the following points:

(*a*) Speak directly into it.

(*b*) Speak close to the mouthpiece.

(*c*) Do not shout.

(*d*) Speak slowly and clearly, separating your words.

(*e*) With a sound-powered telephone speak louder than with a power-assisted one.

(*f*) When calling an exchange, ask for the number required and not the person.

(*g*) When connected, state who you are and with whom you wish to speak; do not say 'Hello'.

(*h*) When replying, state who you are and from where you are speaking; again, do not say 'Hello'.

(*i*) Always identify a caller.

(*j*) When using a telephone, make sure that it is connected to the right person before you discuss Service matters, and remember that a telephone conversation can be 'eavesdropped'.

(*k*) If the telephone is disconnected in the middle of a conversation it is the caller's responsibility to re-establish communication: the person called should wait at least half a minute before abandoning the call.

(*l*) Wait at least fifteen seconds before making a fresh call.

(*m*) When taking a message, make a note not only of its contents but also the name of the caller and the time of the call.

Use of group and direct telephones

Group telephones. When using group telephones, state the position called and then the calling position, e.g.:

'Bridge—(This is) Engineroom'.
The answer is either:
'(This is) Bridge', or
'Engineroom—(This is) Bridge'.

Direct telephones. The caller lifts the receiver and turns the handle. The procedure for calling and answering is similar to that for Group telephones except that the person answering need only state his position, e.g.:

'Quarter-deck—(This is) Bridge', **or**
'(This is) Bridge'.

The words in brackets may be omitted.

How to use a voice pipe

When using a voice pipe:

(a) Press the call-up push (if fitted).
(b) Speak loudly and directly into the mouthpiece.
(c) Use the same procedure as for Group telephones.
(d) Make your conversation as brief as possible.

The main broadcast system

This is the normal method of relaying general orders throughout the ship. Should this system fail, 'pipes' have to be relayed by the boatswain's mates. The system is also used to provide alarm signals such as 'Fire' and 'Action Stations'.

When speaking into a microphone, the same rules apply as for a telephone except that the speaker should speak across the microphone and not into it. It should be held three to four inches from the mouth and not close to it.

Repeating orders and messages

If you are given an order or a message over any kind of communications system, e.g. telephone or talk-back system, always repeat the order or message and, if necessary, write it down and make sure that it is correct before leaving to carry it out or deliver it.

MESSENGERS' DUTIES

A messenger should know all the officers and senior ratings in the ship and the Departments in which they work. He should also know his way about the ship. He should always carry a signal pad and pencil. Messengers will in the course of their duties handle messages which are of a confidential nature. They must never discuss any information so gathered with an unauthorized person or persons.

Contents of a message

When given an important verbal message the messenger may be ordered to repeat it back as a means of checking that he will deliver it correctly. If a messenger does not clearly understand the message he is to deliver he must at once ask for it to be repeated. A smart 'get-away' will in no way redound to a messenger's credit when he is reported for delivering a message incorrectly, and incorrect messages may have serious effects in naval life. If a message is a long one, the messenger would be well advised to write it out before leaving the originator.

Handling written messages

On receiving a written message, the messenger must make sure that he understands to whom it is to be delivered and if he is to bring back a reply.

Delivering a message

Messages must be delivered quickly and by the shortest possible route. When delivering a message, the messenger has the right of way anywhere and should not hesitate to enter a Senior Officer's quarters, a conference room, Wardroom, etc. when he has a message to deliver. He should:

1. Enquire if the person sought is inside, and if anyone is with him.
2. Knock, enter, remove his cap.
3. Approach the Senior Officer present to ask permission to deliver the message.
4. Approach the person concerned, addressing him by his official title, or by his rank and name, e.g. 'Commander, Sir', or 'Lieutenant Jones, Sir'.
5. He should wait until the officer is ready to receive the message.
6. Deliver the message.
7. Wait for a reply, acknowledgment or dismissal.
8. Carry on and, if necessary, report back to the originator as soon as possible.

CHAPTER 19

Rescue from Drowning; Resuscitation

See The Royal Life-Saving Society's *Handbook of Instruction*

RESCUE FROM DROWNING

It is the duty of every sailor to learn to swim, not only so that he can save himself should he fall overboard, should his boat capsize or his ship be sunk, but also to save others in danger of drowning. Ideally, he should also know how to dive, float, tread water and carry out one of the recognized methods of resuscitation.

A drowning man will really clutch at a straw, and his grip is frenzied and abnormally strong. If you, as a would-be rescuer, have not learnt to release yourself when grasped you will endanger your own life as well. A drowning man will not, of course, follow any predictable method when he grasps you, so it is important for you to appreciate how he has grasped you (e.g. round one arm and perhaps a leg, or round the throat) in order that you may use every means available to get free.

Hints on rescue

Remove as much clothing as time permits, particularly such items as boots and heavy garments.

Take a deep breath before diving in.

If the depth of water is unknown jump in feet first, keeping the legs together.

Avoid prolonged periods under water.

Where possible approach the drowning person from behind.

Do not grasp a drowning person on first approach if he is struggling violently.

Always grasp a drowning person firmly and tow him on his back.

If clutched by a drowning person free yourself as quickly as possible and remain uppermost.

METHODS OF RESCUE

The rescuer must have control of the situation. Most methods involve the drowning man being turned on his back and his head being held as high as possible out of the water.

If the drowning man is not struggling

Tow him from behind, with your hands on either side of his face, covering his ears (Fig. 19-1(i)). Keep his head as high as possible on your chest. Swim back-stroke with the legs.

If the drowning man is struggling

Tread water out of his reach until exhaustion lessens his energy, then grasp him as opportunity permits. You can then tow him, using one of the following two methods:

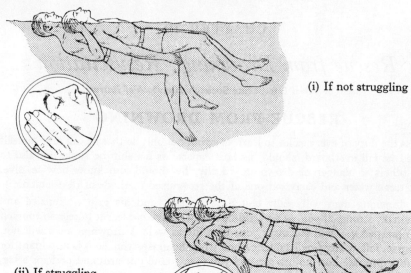

(i) If not struggling

(ii) If struggling

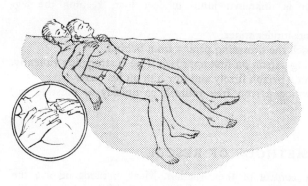

(iii) Arms difficult to hold

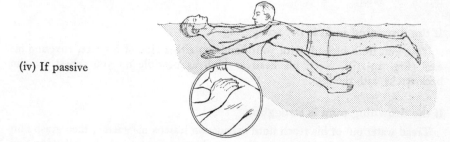

(iv) If passive

FIG. 19-1. Rescue from drowning

(a) *The arm grip*. Grip the man firmly just above the elbows, your hands passing underneath them. Hold his arms out at right-angles to his body: then swim back-stroke with the legs (Fig. 19-1(ii)).

(b) *Arms difficult to hold*. Place your arms under his armpits, with your hands on his chest (fingers wide apart, thumbs on the collar-bone): now raise your upper-arms sideways to bring his arms out at right-angles to his body (Fig. 19-1(iii)). Keep him hard-up on your chest and swim back-stroke with the legs.

Help when the drowning man is passive

This method is for use when the swimmer is exhausted but is capable of helping. Tell the man to turn on his back and to place his hands on your shoulders, arms straight and with his head held back (Fig. 19-1(iv)). Now swim breast-stroke. This is the easiest way of rescuing someone who is obedient, and a man can be conveyed a much greater distance by this method than by any other.

Rescue by side-stroke

This method is also used with a passive subject. Turn him on his back, place one arm over his shoulder, reach as far as possible towards the opposite side of his body and grasp his clothing: alternatively, grasp him under the opposite armpit (Fig. 19-2). Now swim side-stroke.

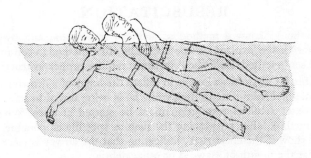

Fig. 19-2. Rescue by side-stroke

McGregor Williams method of rescue

Grasp the man from one side: pass one arm over his shoulder, cupping his chin in your hand (Fig. 19-3). Draw him close to your body, with his head against the shoulder of your occupied arm. Use your free arm to aid propulsion. If he struggles, cut off his breathing with your towing hand and at the same time use the free hand to restrain him. This is done by passing your hand under his armpit and pulling his shoulder close to your chest. He will soon tire, and towing can be resumed.

Hints to bathers

If you are not a strong swimmer, do not bathe alone.

Do not bathe where there is a heavy swell, breakers or surf, as there is usually a strong undertow.

FIG. 19-3. McGregor Williams method of rescue

Do not bathe from steeply shelving beaches without finding out whether it is safe to do so.

Avoid places where there is a lot of mud or weed, or a strong current.

If the depth of water is unknown, jump in feet first.

Do not bathe until at least one hour after a meal.

If unaccustomed to cold water, do not stay in long.

If suffering from ear trouble, giddiness or palpitations, do not bathe.

RESUSCITATION

Everyone should know a method of artificial respiration, and by far the best method to learn is the 'expired air' method. The other method in common use is the 'Holger Nielsen' method. Both these methods require proper instruction.

It is possible for a strong swimmer to inflate the lungs of a drowning man by the expired air method from time to time while he is being towed to safety. Once he is out of the water artificial respiration must be started at once. When using the expired air method, after positioning the man as speedily as possible, a few quick breaths will show if the chest rises, indicating that the airway is clear. If it is not, stop and clear the mouth of seaweed or other debris.

The expired air method

1. Lay the patient on his back and, if on a slope, have the abdomen slightly lower than the chest.

2. Make a brief inspection of the mouth and throat to ensure that they are clear of obvious obstruction.

3. Give the patient's head the maximum backward tilt so that the chin is prominent, the mouth closed and the neck stretched to give it a clear airway (Fig. 19-4(i)).

4. Open your mouth wide, make an airtight seal over the nose of the patient and blow. The operator's cheek or hand supporting the chin can be used to seal the patient's lips (Fig. 19-4(ii)).

5. *Or*, if the nose is blocked, open the patient's mouth, using the hand supporting the chin; open your mouth wide and make an airtight seal over his mouth, and blow. This may also be used as an alternative to the mouth-to-nose technique, even when the nose is not blocked, in which case the nostrils must be sealed with the operator's cheek (Fig. 19-4(iii)) or the hand holding the top of the patient's head moved and the fingers used to pinch the nostrils. The wrist must be kept low on the

patient's forehead to ensure that the full tilt of the head is maintained. If the patient's mouth cannot be opened, blow through his parted lips, as the air passing between his teeth may be sufficient to inflate his lungs.

6. After exhaling, turn your head to watch for chest movement. At the same time inhale deeply, ready for blowing again (Fig. 19-4(iv)).

7. If the chest does not rise, check that the patient's mouth and throat are free of obstruction and the head is tilted backwards as far as possible. Blow again.

8. If air enters a patient's stomach as the result of blowing too hard, press the stomach gently, with the patient's head turned to one side.

9. Commence resuscitation with ten quick inflations of the patient's chest to give a rapid build-up of oxygen in the patient's blood. Then slow down to twelve to fifteen respirations per minute or blow again each time the patient's chest is deflated. With small children and babies, inflation at the rate of twenty a minute is achieved by a series of puffs, each one ceasing as the chest starts to rise. *UNDER NO CIRCUMSTANCES BLOW VIOLENTLY INTO A BABY'S LUNGS.*

10. Whilst preparing to start resuscitation, breathe deeply with the mouth open to build up your oxygen content.

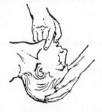

(i) Head tilted fully backwards   (ii) Mouth sealed round nose of patient

(iii) Mouth sealed round mouth of patient, cheek sealing nose (or nostrils may be pinched)

(iv) Watching for chest movement whilst taking a deep breath

FIG. 19-4. The 'expired air' method of resuscitation

CHAPTER 20

First Aid and Personal Hygiene

FIRST AID

A knowledge of First Aid is extremely valuable, and the application of this knowledge will frequently save life, relieve pain and prevent injuries from getting worse. It therefore behoves all ratings to obtain an intelligent knowledge of, and training in, First Aid. B.R. 25, *First Aid in the Royal Navy*, should be studied carefully.

Points for general guidance

First Aid means treatment before the doctor arrives. If therefore you are the first person to discover an accident in which someone has been injured:

Keep calm, use common sense, and act.

Take charge from the start; send one person for a doctor, another for a bandage, and so on.

Improvise splints and bandages, etc.

Do not forget the injured man. Make him comfortable, cheer him up and talk to him.

Shock

Shock, which may be caused by injury to the body, can by itself kill a person. A person suffering from shock will show the following symptoms:

He will be pale, with cold, clammy skin.

He will at first have a slow pulse, which becomes increasingly feeble and rapid.

He will look frightened and may be shivering.

He will be giddy and feel faint and may feel sick and vomit.

Treatment. Where possible:

1. Remove the injured person from danger.
2. Rest him. Lay him down. Put something under his head.
3. Reassure him.
4. Keep him comfortable, but do not give him spirits or use hot water bottles; and only give him fluids if he is suffering from burns or crush injuries, or if there is a delay in getting him to hospital.
5. Treat his injuries.
6. Get him off to hospital.

Electric shock. With electric shock do the following:

1. First of all, switch off the current (having insulated yourself first).
2. Remove patient from source of shock by pulling him away or pushing him away with a wooden stick.
3. Once clear, start artificial respiration until patient comes round.
4. Then treat for shock as above.

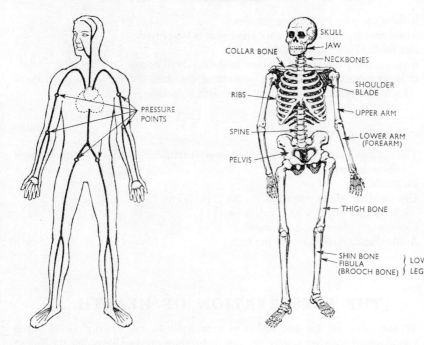

FIG. 20-1. The circulation of the blood   FIG. 20-2. The human skeleton

Bleeding

Internal bleeding. A person suffering from severe bleeding always suffers from shock, and it is difficult to stop internal bleeding. The important thing is to treat for shock.

External bleeding. Grazes and minor cuts can be treated by applying a dressing.

Deep cuts. Raise the affected part to slow down the rate of flow. Apply a dressing and press it firmly. If bleeding continues press on a pressure point (Fig. 20-1), and if this fails apply a tourniquet. A tourniquet is a last desperate effort and should be applied with care.

Burns

Treatment. Burns always cause shock, which must be treated. Cover the burn with a clean, dry dressing. Never use ointments, oils or lotions. Do not prick blisters. Get medical aid. Treat scalds in the same way.

Electric burns. Treat as for a burn, but remember to give artificial respiration first if the patient is not breathing.

Broken bones

Recognizing a break. Usually the patient cannot move the affected part, and he suffers from shock. The limb may be crooked and swollen and the site of the break painful to the touch.

Treatment for broken bones depends upon the site of the break, but, as a general guide for treatment:

Relieve the pain by treating for shock.

Avoid moving the patient until the break is supported.

Get medical assistance quickly.

Avoid moving the broken limb or broken ends of bones.

If broken ends of bones have penetrated the skin, do not try to push them back into place; simply cover them with a dressing.

General points to remember

The various parts of the body need special treatment and knowledge of how to handle them.

Be gentle.

Use padding where necessary.

Tie bandages firmly with a reef knot.

Get the ambulance to drive slowly.

Adjust bandages if they get too tight.

THE PRESERVATION OF HEALTH

Everyone, whatever his job, wishes to keep really fit and healthy. Good health and a good sound body are among the best possessions one can have. But the human body is a most complicated machine which, though it will stand up to hard wear, cannot remain in good condition unless it is intelligently looked after.

Need for personal hygiene

In Great Britain the community has an efficient Public Health system which looks after the purity of water and food, control of disease and many other things which we take for granted. In the Navy matters are not always so simple: ships visit parts of the world where health services hardly exist and the responsibility for co-operating actively in simple and sensible health precautions is largely up to the individual.

At sea you live and work in very close contact with your shipmates. If you keep fit and healthy, you help to contribute to the general fitness of the ship's company. The Royal Navy depends first and foremost on the health, vigour and efficiency of its members. In times of hardship and strain it is the fittest who conquer and survive.

The mind and the body

People tend to forget that an alert, active and interested mind helps to maintain a healthy body. In the Service you have wonderful opportunities for visiting interesting places all over the world. Make an effort to learn something about these places and the people in them.

Take all the chances you can of developing hobbies and of using the educational facilities of the Service. You will keep yourself alive in every sense of the word and will set a good example to others as a result. Boredom and lack of interest have a depressing effect which spreads to others and is not conducive to fitness.

PERSONAL HYGIENE

Cleanliness

Personal cleanliness is the first rule for good health—your own health and that of other people. Lice and other vermin flourish on dirty bodies and dirty clothing, and they can cause and spread disease. A dirty body is offensive to other people, so:

Bath and wash your body thoroughly and regularly.

Keep hair and nails short—this makes it harder for dirt to stick.

Wash thoroughly before meals and at the end of the working day.

Take a bath or shower and rub down well after strenuous work or playing games.

Wash your hands thoroughly after going to the heads.

Teeth

Look after your teeth by brushing them regularly morning and night. It is the brushing, not the toothpaste, that counts. Have your teeth checked regularly, at least once a year. If anything seems wrong get it seen to as soon as possible.

Exercise

Regular exercise will help you to keep fit, with muscles and body in tone. Take advantage of the excellent opportunities afforded by the Navy for playing games. It will help you to appreciate the benefits of being really fit.

Ventilation and fresh air

You are more likely to get coughs and colds in stuffy, badly ventilated rooms with shut windows and doors than you are in spaces with access to fresh air. The more people there are living or working in a room the more fresh air is needed to keep the atmosphere healthy. A draught is far healthier than a really good fug.

Diet

If you take a good mixed diet you need not bother about further diet. The body requires a balanced amount of fats, proteins and starchy foods. Every effort is made to maintain this diet in Service food. Eat fresh vegetables and fruit whenever you can and avoid being faddy about your food.

Bowels

Cultivate a regular habit of having your bowels open early in the day; then forget about them. A few days' constipation does not, in fact, do any harm, but the regular use of aperients is harmful and will encourage constipation. Always report an attack of diarrhoea to the Medical Officer. Once again, remember to wash your hands after using the heads, and avoid dirty towels. Failure to do this often leads to food poisoning.

Food-handling

If you have anything to do with the preparation or handling of food the need for personal cleanliness cannot be over-emphasised. Therefore:

Wash your hands with soap and water after doing any dirty job.

Do not smoke while preparing or handling food.

If you have cuts or abrasions on your hands, go to the Sick Bay and have them covered with a waterproof dressing.

Remember your responsibility when handling other people's food. A little carelessness or negligence on your part may cause unnecessary illness to your messmates and thus loss of time and efficiency to the Service.

Alcohol

There is nothing wrong in the use of alcoholic liquor in moderation. What is important is to know when to STOP. *Never* be persuaded to drink any native or home-made spirits when you are abroad. They often contain dangerous forms of alcohol which, even in small quantities, can cause serious illness, blindness, and even death.

Venereal disease

It is worth making every effort to avoid contracting V.D. If you do not you are sure to regret it when it is too late, and the one sure method of prevention is not to expose yourself to infection. You are most likely to give way to temptation when you have had a few drinks during an evening ashore. However, if you do run the risk and you later think there is something wrong, it is most important for your own and messmates' sake to report to the M.O. at once. Delay makes the cure slower. It is an offence in the Navy to conceal an infectious or contagious disease, of which this is one.

SPECIAL PRECAUTIONS WHEN OVERSEAS

People who live in foreign countries have sometimes different standards of cleanliness in the production and preparation of food from ours; many of them are lower than those in the British Isles. For instance, in the Middle East human dung and urine are used to fertilise the soil, and this may infect the fruit and vegetables grown in it with the germs of food poisoning, cholera and dysentery.

Hints about food abroad

Avoid small shops and cafes which cater mainly for native customers.

Fruit and vegetables. Only thick-skinned fruit which you can peel should be eaten raw. Water melons are particularly dangerous and should not be eaten ashore. Avoid bruised fruit.

Food. Sausages, meat pies and cream buns should not be eaten ashore unless they have come from a source approved by a Medical Officer. Such foods are apt to be left lying about exposed to flies and dirt. They should be kept in a refrigerator or food safe, even when they have been prepared from clean food.

Ice and mineral waters. These are both dangerous unless they come from an authorized source. The danger is that they may have been made from impure water.

Water. The only safe water to drink in foreign countries that do not have Western standards of health preservation is that which has been newly boiled and allowed to cool.

Shellfish. Raw shellfish, such as oysters, are apt to be particularly dangerous, as they may have been contaminated by sewage. Fresh shellfish, such as prawns and lobsters, which have been cooked in boiling water immediately before eating are much safer.

Milk, milk products and ice cream. These products should not be eaten unless they have come from an authorized source.

Vaccinations and inoculations

Everyone in the Service is vaccinated against smallpox and has inoculations against various diseases, particularly before going on foreign draft. These precautions strengthen the body's defences against the particular disease, but they do not necessarily confer complete protection. Therefore do not imagine that the health precautions can be ignored just because you have had all the routine inoculations.

Hot climates

Special precautions are needed in tropical climates, because not only do disease-carrying insects and pests flourish there, but also because the heat imposes an extra strain on the body and skin. There is no reason why one should not remain healthy in the tropics despite the heat and insects, provided reasonable precautions are taken. You will be told fully what these are, and they must be carefully carried out if they are to be effective.

CLEANLINESS

Cleanliness of the skin is important, as a moist, sweating skin is more liable to infection and encourages dirt to stick. Have regular showers and changes of clothing.

FOOT ROT AND DHOBIE ITCH

These diseases are caused by fungus infection of the skin. It is a good thing to use a talc or dusting powder regularly after taking a shower. Keep the skin in the groin, armpits and between the toes as dry as you can.

Never walk about baths and changing-rooms in bare feet, and, when permitted, wear sandals without socks to keep the feet cool and well ventilated.

SUNBATHING

This will help to keep the skin healthy, provided you do not overdo it. Start with a few minutes only and increase the exposure as you become more tanned. In this way you will avoid sunburn. Fair and red-haired people burn far more readily than dark-haired people and must be more careful to start with short exposures.

SEA-BATHING

Provided the water is clean, sea-bathing will help you to keep fit. If possible, follow sea-bathing with a fresh-water shower, ensuring that the ears are dried out thoroughly and gently, preferably with a clean handkerchief. This will help to prevent a painful inflammation of the ear passages which is common in the tropics.

Always wear sandals or gym shoes when walking about beaches, as they protect your feet against cuts from coral. These cuts are painful and slow to heal in tropical climates.

MOSQUITOES

When these insects bite human beings they convey malaria and other diseases. They usually avoid bright sunlight and appear after sundown. In daytime they often lurk in dark corners, such as under tables and beds. They are dealt with by:

(a) attacking their breeding-places,
(b) killing adult mosquitoes with insecticides,

(c) protecting personnel from their bites, especially during the dark hours. Long-sleeved shirts and long trousers should be worn after dark. Use a mosquito net to enclose your bed, making sure that it is in good repair and is well tucked in at the bottom under the mattress.

HOUSEFLIES

These are much more numerous in hot climates, because they breed more freely and quickly. They are dangerous to health, because they carry germs of food poisoning and dysentery and infect food. They are dealt with by destroying their breeding-places and by the use of nets and screens to protect food and galleys. It is always dangerous to leave food uncovered where flies can settle on it.

The fly has filthy habits; when it settles on food it eats a little, having first dripped some saliva on it to soften it. It then vomits to make room for more food, and finally empties its bowels to make itself comfortable. It then moves on to some more food. You, or someone else, may then eat that food. If the fly was as big as an elephant you would naturally take some notice of what it was doing; the fact that it is so small makes the food no less dangerous to eat.

HEAT ILLNESS

This may occur when heavy work is done in a hot, moist climate, particularly if enough table salt is not taken in the food. When in a hot climate make a point of eating much more salt with your meals than you would do in England. The reason is that you lose salt when you sweat, and you must make this up in order to avoid heat illness in conditions of strain. When necessary, special salt tablets will be provided, and your own protection lies in your carrying out the measures that are recommended.

Since you may sweat as much as several pints a day, obviously more fluid must be taken in. Large drinks at one time should be avoided—a little and often is much better, and reduces the risk of prickly heat.

Cold climates

In extreme northern and southern waters it may be necessary to use special clothing to protect the skin against frostbite. The fingers, toes, nose and ears are particularly vulnerable. You will be told what to do and given any special equipment necessary, but make sure that you really understand how to use the special clothing provided and that you carry out the instructions with care. A few minutes' carelessness in a cold region may result in severe but quite unnecessary frostbite.

Conclusion

Man is a very adaptable animal who can endure all sorts of hardships and exist, and even flourish, under extreme climatic conditions; but he has learnt how to do this the hard way, by bitter experience and the survival of the fittest.

The purpose of these health rules is to show you how to profit by the experience of others, rather than by trial and error. No one can make you do these things—it is up to you. Mistakes are expensive and wasteful, both to yourself and to the Service.

APPENDIX

USEFUL TABLES FOR SIMPLE CALCULATIONS

LENGTH

$$12 \text{ inches } (in.) = 1 \text{ foot} (ft)$$
$$3 \text{ ft} = 1 \text{ yard} (yd)$$
$$22 \text{ yd} = 1 \text{ chain} (ch)$$
$$220 \text{ yd} (10 \text{ ch}) = 1 \text{ furlong} (fur)$$
$$1,760 \text{ yd} (8 \text{ fur}) = 1 \text{ mile}$$
$$6 \text{ ft} = 1 \text{ fathom} (fm)$$
$$100 \text{ fm} (200 \text{ yd}) = 1 \text{ cable}$$
$$6,080 \text{ ft (approx. 10 cables)} = 1 \text{ nautical mile}$$
$$1 \text{ knot} = 1 \text{ nautical mile per hour}$$
$$1 \text{ in.} = 2 \cdot 54 \text{ centimetres} (cm)$$
$$1 \text{ kilometre} (km) = \tfrac{5}{8} \text{ mile}$$
$$1 \text{ mile} = 1\tfrac{3}{8} \text{ km}$$
$$5 \text{ miles} = 8 \text{ km or } 8,000 \text{ metres} (m)$$

WEIGHT

$$16 \text{ ounces} (oz) = 1 \text{ pound} (lb)$$
$$14 \text{ lb} = 1 \text{ stone}$$
$$28 \text{ lb} = 1 \text{ quarter} (qr)$$
$$4 \text{ qr} = 1 \text{ hundredweight} (cwt)$$
$$20 \text{ cwt} (2,240 \text{ lb}) = 1 \text{ ton}$$
$$11 \text{ lb} = 5 \text{ kilogrammes} (kg)$$

1 cubic foot (*cu. ft*) of water contains 1,000 oz or $6\tfrac{1}{4}$ gallons (*gal*).
35 cu. ft of sea water (or 36 cu. ft of fresh water) weigh approx. 1 ton.

AREA

$$144 \text{ sq. in.} = 1 \text{ sq. ft}$$
$$9 \text{ sq. ft} = 1 \text{ sq. yd}$$
$$4,840 \text{ sq. yd} = 1 \text{ acre}$$
$$640 \text{ acres} = 1 \text{ sq. mile}$$

VOLUME

$$1,728 \text{ cu. in.} = 1 \text{ cu. ft}$$
$$27 \text{ cu. ft} = 1 \text{ cu. yd}$$

CAPACITY

Liquid Measure
$$4 \text{ gills} = 1 \text{ pint}$$
$$2 \text{ pints} = 1 \text{ quart}$$
$$4 \text{ quarts} = 1 \text{ gallon}$$
$$1 \text{ litre} = \text{approx. } 1\tfrac{3}{4} \text{ pints}$$

Dry Measure
$$2 \text{ pints} = 1 \text{ quart}$$
$$4 \text{ quarts} = 1 \text{ gallon}$$
$$2 \text{ gallons} = 1 \text{ peck}$$
$$4 \text{ pecks} = 1 \text{ bushel}$$
$$8 \text{ bushels} = 1 \text{ quarter}$$

MISCELLANEOUS

(r = radius, d = diameter, h = height, l = length of side)
$$\pi = 3 \cdot 14159 \text{ or approx. } \tfrac{22}{7}$$

$$\text{Area of a circle} = \pi r^2 \text{ or } \frac{\pi d^2}{4}$$
$$\text{Circumference of a circle} = 2\pi r, \text{ or } \pi d$$
$$\text{Area of a triangle} = \tfrac{1}{2} \text{ base} \times h$$
$$\text{Volume of a sphere} = \tfrac{4}{3} \pi r^3$$
$$\text{Area of surface of a sphere} = 4\pi r^2$$
$$\text{Volume of a cone} = \tfrac{1}{3}\pi r^2 h$$
$$\text{Area of a cone} = \pi r l$$
$$\text{Volume of a pyramid} = \tfrac{1}{3} \text{ area of base} \times h$$

239

168882   Dd 898681   20M   10/72   Hw

NOTES

NOTES

CORRESPONDING RANKS

ROYAL NAVY			ARMY		ROYAL AIR FORCE
	SLEEVE	SHOULDER STRAP		SHOULDER BADGE	SLEEVE OR SHOULDER STRAP
Admiral of the Fleet			Field Marshal		Marshal of the Royal Air Force
Admiral			General		Air Chief Marshal
Vice-Admiral			Lieutenant-General		Air Marshal
Rear-Admiral			Major-General		Air Vice-Marshal
Commodore	SLEEVE OR SHOULDER STRAP		Brigadier		Air Commodore
Captain			Colonel		Group Captain

PLATE I *(Cont.)*

ROYAL NAVY		ARMY	ROYAL AIR FORCE	
	SLEEVE OR SHOULDER STRAP	SHOULDER BADGE		SLEEVE OR SHOULDER STRAP
 Commander		* Lieutenant-Colonel	 Wing Commander	
 Lieutenant-Commander		* Major	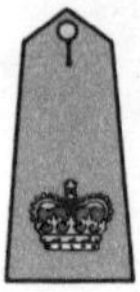 Squadron Leader	
Lieutenant		* Captain	 Flight Lieutenant	
Sub-Lieutenant Acting Sub-Lieutenant (BUT JUNIOR TO MILITARY AND AIR FORCE RANKS)		* Lieutenant	 Flying Officer	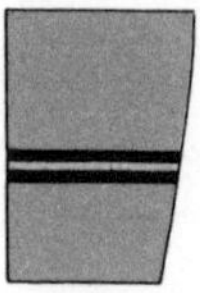
Midshipman (BOTH JUNIOR TO MILITARY AND AIR FORCE RANKS) Naval Cadet	 	* Second Lieutenant	 Pilot Officer Acting Pilot Officer (BUT JUNIOR TO SECOND LIEUTENANT)	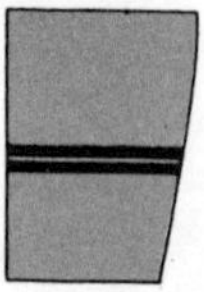

*ROYAL MARINE OFFICERS OF THESE RANKS, WHEN AFLOAT, HAVE A HIGHER EQUIVALENT RANK, E.G. A MAJOR RANKS WITH A COMMANDER

RATINGS' DISTINGUISHING BADGES

PLATE 2

CAP BADGES

Chief Petty Officer

Petty Officer

Other ratings not dressed as seamen

Note: Ratings dressed as seamen wear lettered cap ribbons

RATING BADGES

Chief Petty Officer
Worn on both cuffs

Petty Officer

Worn on the left arm

Leading Rate

BADGES DENOTING SPECIAL DUTIES OR QUALIFICATIONS WITHIN BRANCHES

C.P.O. Coxswain
Worn as a branch badge by C.P.O.
or acting C.P.O. Coxswain

Navigator's Yeoman
Worn on the right cuff in addition to
the Radar Plot Branch badge on
the arm

Master-at-Arms
Worn as a branch badge

PLATE 2 (Cont.)

BRANCH BADGES

Gunnery

Radar Plot

Torpedo and
Anti-Submarine

Coxswain

Surveying Recorder

Boom Defence

Tactical
Communications

Radio
Communications

Engineering Mechanic

Engineering
Mechanician

Regulating

Naval Airman and
Naval Air Mechanic

Weapon
Mechanician

Aircaft Mechanician

Physical Training

Photographer

Electrical

Electrical Mechanician

Supply and
Secretariat

Artisan

Sailmaker

Clearance Diver

Sick Berth

Worn on the right arm except by Chief Petty Officers, who wear the badges in pairs on the
collars of blue uniform, or on the right cuff of white uniform. They are not worn on tropical
shirts. The device on the badge indicates the branch to which the rating belongs. Artificers
do not wear branch badges.

PLATE 2 (Cont.)

ARTIFICER APPRENTICES' AND JUNIORS' BADGES

C.P.O. & P.O. Artificer Apprentice
(worn on left arm by P.O.,
and on both arms by C.P.O.)

First Class Junior
and
Leading Apprentice

Leading Junior

Junior Instructor

Junior Marksman

Junior Coxswain

P.O. Junior

FLYING BADGE FOR AIRCREWS

Rating Aircrew

Worn on Blue uniform (other than working dress) by C.P.O s. on the cuff of the left sleeve $\frac{1}{4}$ inch above the centre button, and by other ratings $1\frac{1}{2}$ inches from the end of the left sleeve, or $1\frac{1}{2}$ inches above the top of the left cuff of jumpers with cuffs. On blue serge working dress this badge is worn above the left breast pocket of the blouse. On white uniform it is worn $1\frac{1}{2}$ inches above the left breast pocket of the tunic, or immediately above the top row of medal ribbons. It is not worn on tropical shirts.

LETTERS INDICATING SPECIALIZATION WITHIN BRANCHES
(But not Qualification)

GUNNERY BRANCH

Quarters Armourer	QA
Gunlayer Armourer	GA
Fire Control Rate	FC
Quarters Rate	QR
Gunlayer	GL

TORPEDO AND ANTI-SUBMARINE BRANCH

Under Water Weapons	W
Under Water Control	C
Under Water Weapons Armourer	WA

WEAPONS AND RADIO BRANCH
(including Mechanics and Mechanicians in each electrical category)

Electrician	L
Electrician (Air)	AL
Radio Electrician	R
Radio Electrician (Air)	AR
Weapon Mechanician	WM

SUPPLY AND SECRETARIAT BRANCH

Writer	W
Stores Accountant	S
Cook	C
Officer's Steward	OS
Officer's Cook	OC
Shorthand Typist	ST
Victualling (Obsolescent)	V
Caterer	CA

NAVAL AIRMAN BRANCH

Aircraft Handler	H
Safety Equipment	SE
Met. Observer	MET
Photographer	P

NAVAL AIR MECHANIC BRANCH

Fitter and Mechanic (AE)	AE
Fitter and Mechanic (O)	O

SICK BERTH BRANCH

State-Registered Male Nurse	N
Radiographer	X
Physiotherapist	M
Hygiene Inspector	H
Medical Laboratory Technician	L
Mental Nurse	P
Operating Room Technician	O
Dental Attendant	D

Colour of badges: Except for cap badges and armlets, badges worn with blue uniforms are red on blue cloth, and badges worn with white uniforms (and also with blue overall suits and blue action working dress shirts) are blue on white cloth. Gold badges have not yet been generally reintroduced.

Note 1: Pilot's mates will wear a badge consisting of a two-bladed propeller on the right cuff in addition to the appropriate branch badge on the right arm.

Note 2: The letters are worn below the branch badge except that for Electrical and Supply and Secretariat branches the letters are included in the centre of the badges.

PLATE 2 *(Cont.)*

QUARTERS RATINGS

Seaman Gunner

Seaman Gunner Star

Q.A. 2nd Class

GUNNERY INSTRUCTOR

C.P.O., P.O.
or confirmed leading rate

Q.A. 1st Class
(P.O. or confirmed leading rate).

C.P.O., Q.A.
2nd Class
or star

C.P.O., Q.A.
1st Class

Stars and crowns are added to branch badges indicating standards of qualifications within the branch, as illustrated by the above group of gunnery branch badges.

MISCELLANEOUS BADGES

Naval Patrol Armlet

These badges are worn on the right cuff. Ship's divers wear a diver's helmet badge (similar to the C D Branch badge) on the right cuff in addition to the appropriate branch or category badge.

Armlet for use by Petty Officers on Watchcoats

Good Shooting Badge

Submarine Badge (Optional)

Bugler's Badge

GOOD CONDUCT BADGES

12 years   8 years

4 years

Worn on the left arm below the rating badge (if any). These badges are not worn by C.P.O s.

R.N.R. GOOD SERVICE BADGES

12 years   8 years

4 years

Worn on the left arm below the rating badge (if any). These badges may be worn in addition to Good Conduct badges, provided that the combined number does not exceed three, and that Good Conduct badges are worn superior to Good Service badges.

PLATE 3

DECORATIONS AND MEDALS

Victoria Cross

George Cross

Order of the Bath

Distinguished
Service Order

Distinguished
Service Cross

Conspicuous Gallantry
Medal

Royal Victorian Medal

1914-15 Star

British War Medal

1939-45 Star

Atlantic Star

Air Crew Europe Star

Italy Star

France and Germany
Star

Defence Medal

King George V
Jubilee Medal 1935

King George VI
Coronation Medal 1937

Queen Elizabeth II
Coronation Medal 1953

Long Service and
Good Conduct Medal

R.F.R. Long Service
and Good Conduct Medal

R.N.R. Long Service and
Good Conduct Medal

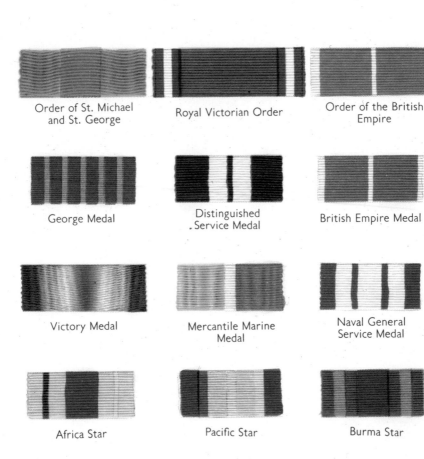

Order of St. Michael and St. George

Royal Victorian Order

Order of the British Empire

George Medal

Distinguished Service Medal

British Empire Medal

Victory Medal

Mercantile Marine Medal

Naval General Service Medal

Africa Star

Pacific Star

Burma Star

1939-45 War Medal

Korea Medal

United Nations Service Medal

General Service Medal 1962

Reserve Decoration

Volunteer Reserve Decoration

R.N.V.R. Long Service and Good Conduct Medal

Reserve Long Service and Good Conduct Medal

Royal Humane Society's Medal
(worn on the right breast)

NAVAL AND INTERNATIONAL FLAG CODES

The meanings given are those of the International Code only

A ALFA	I AM UNDERGOING A SPEED TRIAL	**K** KILO *	YOU SHOULD STOP YOUR VESSEL INSTANTLY	
B BRAVO	I AM TAKING IN OR DISCHARGING EXPLOSIVES	**L** LIMA *	YOU SHOULD STOP— I HAVE SOMETHING IMPORTANT TO COMMUNICATE	
C CHARLIE	YES (AFFIRMATIVE)	**M** MIKE	I HAVE A DOCTOR ON BOARD	
D DELTA	KEEP CLEAR OF ME —I AM MANOEUVRING WITH DIFFICULTY	**N** NOVEMBER	NO (NEGATIVE)	
E ECHO	I AM DIRECTING MY COURSE TO STARBOARD	**O** OSCAR *	MAN OVERBOARD	
F FOXTROT *	I AM DISABLED— COMMUNICATE WITH ME	**P** PAPA	*IN HARBOUR:— ALL PERSONS ARE TO REPAIR ON BOARD AS THE VESSEL IS ABOUT TO PROCEED TO SEA. *AT SEA:— YOUR LIGHTS ARE OUT OR BURNING BADLY	
G GOLF	I REQUIRE A PILOT	**Q** QUEBEC	MY VESSEL IS HEALTHY, AND I REQUIRE FREE PRATIQUE	
H HOTEL	I HAVE A PILOT ON BOARD	**R** ROMEO *	THE WAY IS OFF MY SHIP—YOU MAY FEEL YOUR WAY PAST ME	
I INDIA	I AM DIRECTING MY COURSE TO PORT	**S** SIERRA	MY ENGINES ARE GOING FULL SPEED ASTERN	
J JULIETT	I AM GOING TO SEND A MESSAGE BY SEMAPHORE	**T** TANGO	DO NOT PASS AHEAD OF ME	

NOTE:—ONLY THOSE LETTERS AND MEANINGS MARKED * MAY BE INDICATED BY THE MORSE CODE EITHER BY SOUND OR BY FLASHING

PLATE 4

ALPHABETICAL FLAGS AND SUBSTITUTES			NUMERAL PENNANTS	
U UNIFORM 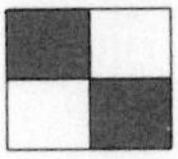	*	YOU ARE STANDING INTO DANGER	ONE 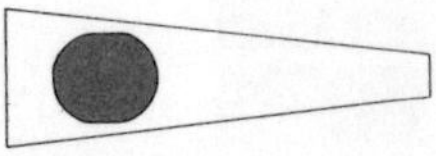	
V VICTOR 	*	I REQUIRE ASSISTANCE	TWO 	USED ON ALL OCCASIONS WHEN IT IS REQUIRED TO REPRESENT NUMBERS IN FLAG SIGNALLING
W WHISKEY 	*	I REQUIRE MEDICAL ASSISTANCE	THREE 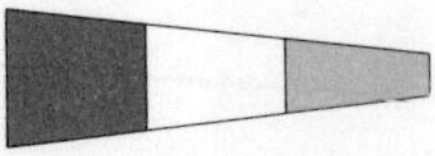	
X XRAY 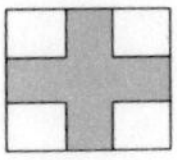		STOP CARRYING OUT INTENTIONS AND WATCH FOR MY SIGNALS	FOUR 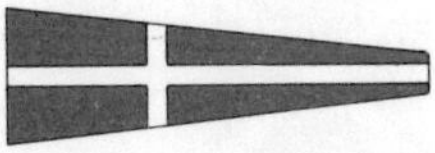	
Y YANKEE 		I AM CARRYING MAILS	FIVE 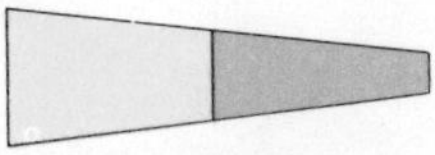	
Z ZULU 	*	TO BE USED TO ADDRESS OR CALL SHORE STATIONS	SIX 	
1st SUBSTITUTE 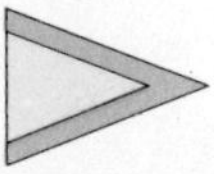		USED TO REPEAT THE FIRST FLAG OR PENNANT IN THE SAME HOIST	SEVEN 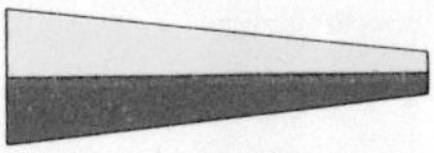	
2nd SUBSTITUTE 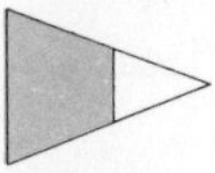		USED TO REPEAT THE SECOND FLAG OR PENNANT IN THE SAME HOIST	EIGHT 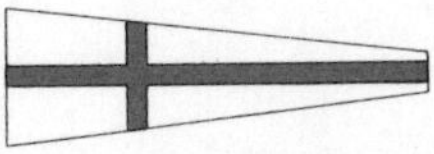	
3rd SUBSTITUTE 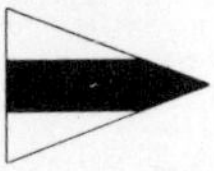		USED TO REPEAT THE THIRD FLAG OR PENNANT IN THE SAME HOIST	NINE 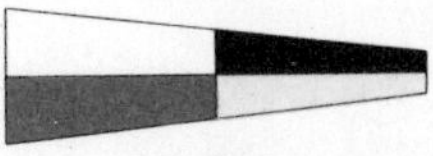	
CODE AND ANSWER 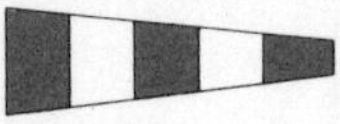		USED TO ACKNOWLEDGE A SIGNAL. ALSO FLOWN BY A WARSHIP WHEN MAKING A FLAG SIGNAL FROM THE INTERNATIONAL CODE TO DISTINGUISH IT FROM THE NAVAL CODE	ZERO 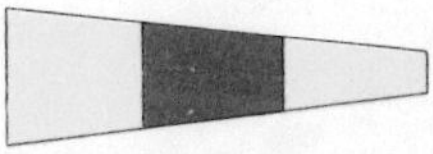	

NOTE:—ONLY THOSE LETTERS AND MEANINGS MARKED * MAY BE INDICATED BY THE MORSE CODE EITHER BY SOUND OR BY FLASHING

OTHER FLAGS AND PENNANTS USED IN NAVAL SIGNALLING

NUMERAL FLAGS		PENNANTS	
ONE		INTERROGATIVE	
TWO		ANSWER AND CODE	
THREE		CORPEN	
FOUR		CHURCH	
FIVE		FORM	
SIX		PREPARATIVE	
SEVEN		DESIG. (ALPHABETICAL/NUMERAL)	
EIGHT		NEGATIVE	
NINE		STARBOARD	
ZERO		TURN	

PLATE 5

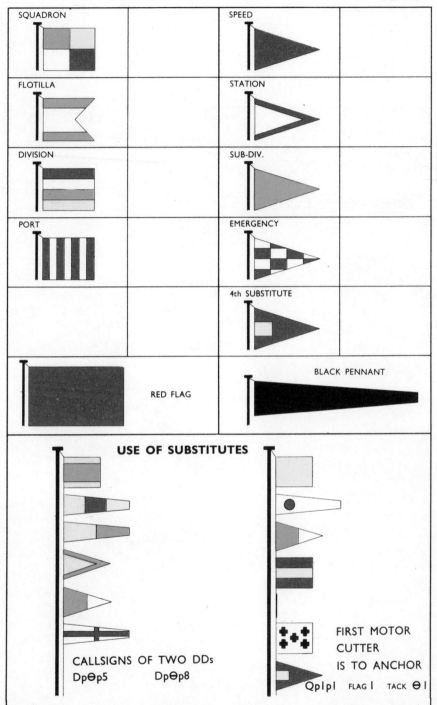

SQUADRON

SPEED

FLOTILLA

STATION

DIVISION

SUB-DIV.

PORT

EMERGENCY

4th SUBSTITUTE

RED FLAG

BLACK PENNANT

USE OF SUBSTITUTES

CALLSIGNS OF TWO DDs
DpΘp5   DpΘp8

FIRST MOTOR
CUTTER
IS TO ANCHOR
Qplpl   FLAG l   TACK Θl

THE FIRST SUBSTITUTE REPEATS THE UPPER FLAG OR PENNANT OF A
HOIST. THE SECOND SUBSTITUTE REPEATS THE SECOND FLAG OR
PENNANT, AND SO ON. TACK LINES ARE NOT COUNTED FOR SUBSTITUTION.

PLATE 6 CHART OF PORT LIBERTY

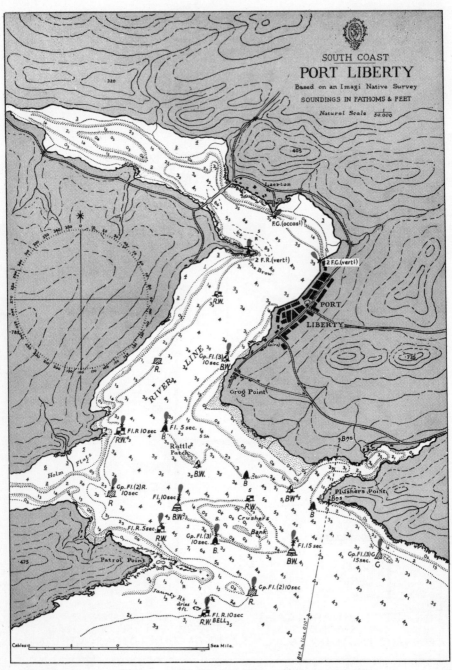

B—black   R—red   G—green   B.W.—black and white   R.W.—red and white

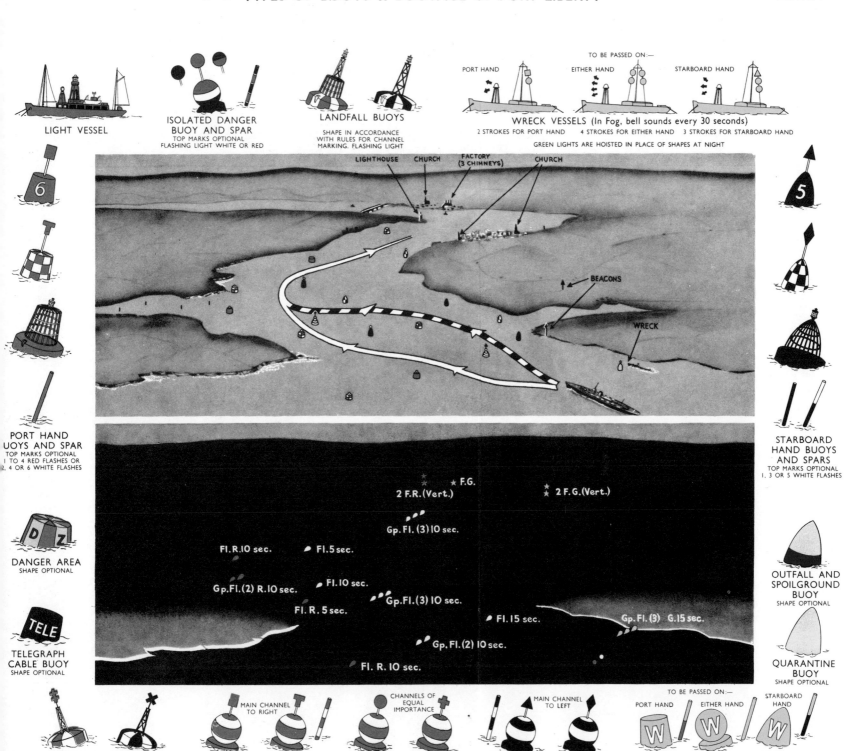

LIGHT VESSEL

ISOLATED DANGER BUOY AND SPAR
TOP MARKS OPTIONAL
FLASHING LIGHT WHITE OR RED

LANDFALL BUOYS
SHAPE IN ACCORDANCE
WITH RULES FOR CHANNEL
MARKING. FLASHING LIGHT

TO BE PASSED ON:—
PORT HAND   EITHER HAND   STARBOARD HAND

WRECK VESSELS (In Fog, bell sounds every 30 seconds)
2 STROKES FOR PORT HAND   4 STROKES FOR EITHER HAND   3 STROKES FOR STARBOARD HAND

GREEN LIGHTS ARE HOISTED IN PLACE OF SHAPES AT NIGHT

LIGHTHOUSE   CHURCH   FACTORY (3 CHIMNEYS)   CHURCH

BEACONS

WRECK

PORT HAND BUOYS AND SPAR
TOP MARKS OPTIONAL
1 TO 4 RED FLASHES OR
2, 4 OR 6 WHITE FLASHES

STARBOARD HAND BUOYS AND SPARS
TOP MARKS OPTIONAL
1, 3 OR 5 WHITE FLASHES

DANGER AREA
SHAPE OPTIONAL

TELEGRAPH CABLE BUOY
SHAPE OPTIONAL

★ F.G.
2 F.R. (Vert.)   ★ 2 F.G. (Vert.)

Gp. Fl. (3) 10 sec.

Fl. R. 10 sec.   Fl. 5 sec.

Gp. Fl. (2) R. 10 sec.   Fl. 10 sec.

Gp. Fl. (3) 10 sec.
Fl. R. 5 sec.

Fl. 15 sec.   Gp. Fl. (3) G. 15 sec.

Gp. Fl. (2) 10 sec.

Fl. R. 10 sec.

OUTFALL AND SPOILGROUND BUOY
SHAPE OPTIONAL

QUARANTINE BUOY
SHAPE OPTIONAL

MID-CHANNEL BUOYS
SHAPE AND TOP MARKS OPTIONAL. BUT DISTINCTIVE
FROM CONE, CAN OR SPHERE LIGHTS
DISTINCTIVE FROM OTHER CHANNEL LIGHTS

MAIN CHANNEL TO RIGHT
OUTER END   INNER END

CHANNELS OF EQUAL IMPORTANCE
OUTER END   INNER END

MAIN CHANNEL TO LEFT
OUTER END   INNER END

MIDDLE GROUND BUOYS AND SPARS
LIGHTS RED OR WHITE AND DISTINCTIVE FROM PORT AND STARBOARD BUOYS

TO BE PASSED ON:—
PORT HAND   EITHER HAND   STARBOARD HAND

WRECK BUOYS AND SPARS
GREEN DOUBLE FLASHING   GREEN SINGLE OCCULTING   GREEN TRIPLE FLASHING

PLATE 7